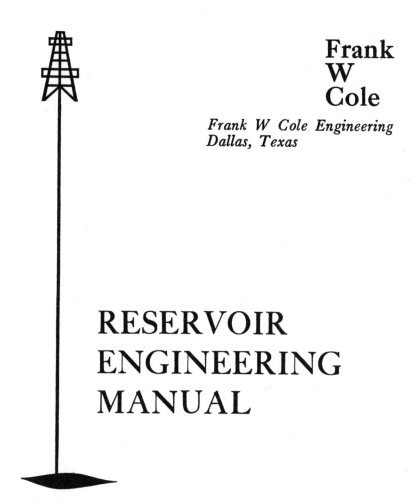

Frank W Cole

Frank W Cole Engineering
Dallas, Texas

RESERVOIR ENGINEERING MANUAL

 Gulf Publishing Company
Houston, Texas

RESERVOIR ENGINEERING MANUAL

Library of Congress Catalog Card Number 60-16853

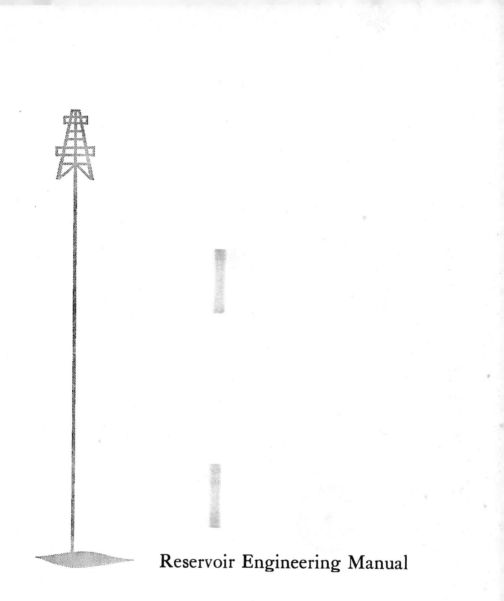

Reservoir Engineering Manual

CONTENTS

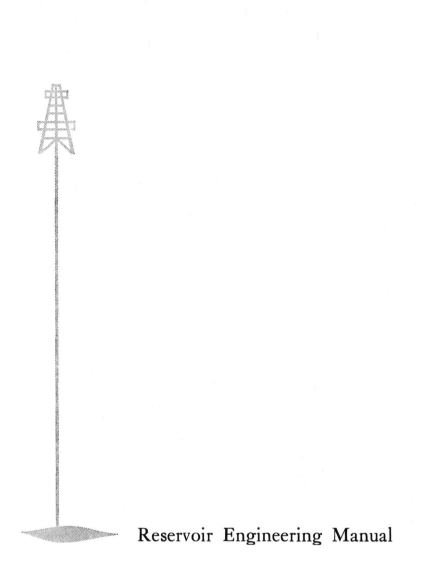

Reservoir Engineering Manual

Chapter 1

INTRODUCTION

Reservoir engineering is that segment of petroleum engineering which is concerned primarily with the reservoirs. Over the years, reservoir engineering evolved gradually as a separate function of petroleum engineering as it became apparent that maximum recovery could be achieved only by controlling reservoir behavior as a whole. As this phase of engineering grew, the individual wells, rather than being the primary consideration, were relegated to a more or less secondary role. In the eyes of the reservoir engineer, they came to be regarded as mechanical devices for controlling reservoir behavior.

During the 1940's, reservoir engineering made remarkable advances as a result of growing demand and because of the relatively large increases in ultimate recovery which could be obtained by utilizing the principles of reservoir engineering.

Reservoir engineering principles are closely related to drilling and production practices, and in order to take maximum advantage of these principles it is necessary to closely coordinate reservoir engineering, drilling engineering, and production engineering practices. As this realization grew, reservoir engineering lost some of its specialized nature. The present state of technology in the petroleum engineering profession demands that *all* petroleum engineers in the industry have a good understanding of the principles governing reservoir behavior. Thus, the production engineer and the drilling engineer must be well grounded in the fundamentals of reservoir engineering, since all of these functions are so closely related.

The principal function of a reservoir engineer is to predict the further behavior of a petroleum reservoir under the various producing mechanisms which are, or may become, available. The economics of various operating plans is an integral part of any reservoir engineering study. A study of the recovery to be expected from various operating plans, along with an economic analysis of these plans, will determine the need for pressure maintenance, secondary

1

recovery, cycling, or other operations. From his studies, the reservoir engineer must recommend an operating plan which will yield the maximum net income, usually expressed in terms of present worth. Since the oil company is in business to make a profit on its investments, the usual objective in oil-producing operations is the realization of the maximum profit, and not necessarily the maximum recovery of oil from a reservoir. Fortunately, maximum recovery of oil from a reservoir will usually result in maximum profit.

This book describes the various forces which result in expulsion of oil from reservoirs and shows, by example problems, the techniques used to predict oil recovery under the various driving forces. Step-by-step solutions are shown for all the problems, making it possible for those unfamiliar with the principles being described to gain an understanding of the problems. Most of the problems in this book are directed toward the solution of the problem of predicting future performance of reservoirs, since this is usually one of the principal problems faced by the reservoir engineer.

Chapter 2

FUNDAMENTAL CONCEPTS
OF RESERVOIR ENGINEERING

A thorough understanding of certain fundamental concepts of reservoir engineering is essential before reliable reservoir engineering studies can be made.

The three most important concepts in reservoir engineering concern certain physical properties of the reservoir rock and the distribution of fluids within the pores of the reservoir rock. These properties are: (1) porosity, (2) permeability, and (3) fluid saturation. Each of these properties will be discussed in this chapter.

Porosity

Porosity is a measure of the space in a reservoir rock which is not occupied by the solid framework of the rock. It is defined as the fraction of the total bulk volume of the rock not occupied by solids. This can be expressed in mathematical form as:

$$\phi_a = \frac{\text{Total Bulk Volume} - \text{Volume Occupied by Solids}}{\text{Total Bulk Volume}} \times 100 \quad (2\text{-}1)$$

where:

ϕ_a = porosity, percent

Porosity is conventionally expressed in percentage form, rather than as a fraction, which is the reason for multiplying Equation (2-1) by 100. Porosity can also be expressed by the following equation:

$$\phi_a = \frac{\text{Total Volume of Void Space}}{\text{Total Bulk Volume}} \times 100 \quad (2\text{-}2)$$

Equations (2-1) and (2-2) must be identical since the volume of the void space must be exactly equal to the total bulk volume minus the volume occupied by solids.

As the sediments accumulated and the rocks were being formed during past geologic time, some of the void spaces which developed became isolated from the other void spaces by excessive cementation. Thus, many of the void spaces will be interconnected, while some of the void spaces, or pore spaces as they are often called, will be completely isolated. This leads to two distinct types of porosity, depending upon which pore spaces are measured in determining the volume of these pore spaces. Absolute porosity refers to the total volume of void space in the reservoir rock, while effective porosity refers only to the interconnected pore spaces in the rock. Equations (2-1) and (2-2) yield the absolute porosity of the rock. An equation for determining effective porosity is:

$$\phi = \frac{\text{Interconnected Pore Volume}}{\text{Total Bulk Volume}} \times 100 \qquad (2\text{-}3)$$

where:

ϕ = effective porosity, percent

In order to recover petroleum from underground reservoirs the petroleum must flow several hundred feet, in many cases, through the pore openings in the reservoir rock before it reaches the producing well bore. If the petroleum occupies isolated pore spaces which are not interconnected then it cannot be recovered and is of little interest to the petroleum engineer. Therefore, effective porosity is the value used in all engineering calculations. All reservoir rocks may contain some of these isolated pore spaces but limestones usually contain the largest percentage of isolated pore spaces.

Since effective porosity is the porosity value of interest to the petroleum engineer, particular attention should be paid to the methods used to determine porosity. For example, if the porosity of a rock sample were determined by saturating the rock sample 100 percent with a fluid of known density and then determining, by weighing, the increased weight due to the saturating fluid, this would yield an effective porosity measurement because the saturating fluids could enter only the interconnected pore spaces. On the other hand, if the rock sample were crushed with a mortar and pestle to determine the actual volume of the solids in the core sample, then an absolute porosity measurement would result because the identity of any isolated pores would be lost in the crushing process.

The porosity of a rock sample is a very important factor to the oil producer as it is a measure of the fluid carrying capacity of a rock. An example will show the effect of porosity on the oil content of a reservoir rock.

Example Problem 2-1

A. Calculate the oil content of one acre-foot of reservoir rock which has a connate water saturation of 25 percent and an effective porosity of 10 percent.

B. Calculate the oil content if the effective porosity is increased to 30 percent.

A. Oil content, bbls/acre-foot $= 7758 \, Ah\phi \, (1 - S_{wi})$

where:

$7758 =$ conversion factor, cubic feet to barrels per acre-foot

$$\left(\frac{43560 \text{ ft}^2/\text{acre}}{5.62 \text{ ft}^3/\text{bbl}} \times 1 \text{ ft.} = 7758 \text{ bbls/acre-foot} \right)$$

$A =$ areal extent of reservoir, acres.
$h =$ average thickness of reservoir, feet.
$\phi =$ effective porosity, fraction.
$S_{wi} =$ connate water saturation, fraction.

Oil content $= 7758 \times 1 \times 1 \times 0.10 \times (1 - .25)$
$= 582$ bbls/acre-foot.

B. Oil content $= 7758 \times 1 \times 1 \times 0.30 \times (1 - 0.25)$
$= 1746$ bbls/acre-foot.

Thus, a three-fold increase in porosity will result in a three-fold increase in the oil content of the reservoir rock.

Fluid Saturation

The previous discussion concerned the pore spaces which the reservoir fluids occupied. More than one fluid is normally present in oil reservoirs. From a history of the formation of petroleum reservoirs it is noted that the pores of the rock were initially filled with water, since most petroleum-bearing formations are believed to be of marine origin. The oil and/or gas then moved into the reservoir, displacing the water to some minimum residual saturation. Thus, when a reservoir is discovered, there may be oil, water, and gas distributed in some manner throughout the reservoir. The term *fluid saturation* is used to define the extent of occupancy of the pore spaces by any particular fluid. Fluid saturation is defined as that fraction, or percent, of the total pore space occupied by a particular fluid. Expressed in equation form for the calculation of oil saturation, this is:

$$S_o = \frac{\text{Oil Volume}}{\text{Total Pore Volume}} \times 100 \qquad (2\text{-}5)$$

where:

S_o = oil saturation, percent

Thus, all saturation values are based on *pore volume,* and not gross reservoir volume.

The fluids in most reservoirs are believed to have reached a state of equilibrium, and therefore will have become separated according to their density; i.e., oil overlain by gas and underlain by water. In addition to the bottom, or edge, water, there will be connate water distributed throughout the oil and gas zones. The water in these zones will have been reduced to some irreducible minimum. The forces retaining the water in the oil and gas zones, are referred to as *capillary* forces because they are important only in pore spaces of capillary size. Laboratory experiments have been developed to simulate the displacing forces in a reservoir in order to determine the magnitude of the capillary forces in a reservoir and thereby determine the connate water saturation in a reservoir. The connate water saturation is a very important factor, as it determines the fraction of the pore space which can be filled with oil. The volumetric equation for calculating oil in place is:

$$N = 7758 \times A \times h \times \phi \times S_{oi}/B_{oi} \qquad (2\text{-}6)$$

where:

N = volume of oil in place initially, stock tank barrels.
B_{oi} = formation volume factor, at initial reservoir pressure, for converting reservoir barrels to stock tank barrels.

Where there are only two fluids present initially, oil and interstitial water, Equation (2-6) can be revised as follows since $S_o + S_{wi} = 1$:

$$N = 7758 \times A \times h \times \phi \times (1 - S_{wi})/B_{oi} \qquad (2\text{-}7)$$

Thus, as shown previously, as the connate water saturation increases, the stock tank oil content of the reservoir decreases.

The restored state capillary pressure technique was developed primarily to determine the magnitude of the connate water saturation. A diagrammatic sketch of this equipment is shown in Figure 2-1. Briefly, this procedure consists of saturating a core 100 percent with the reservoir water and then placing the core on a porous membrane which is saturated 100 percent with water and is permeable to the water only, under the pressure drops imposed during the experiment. Air is then admitted into the core chamber and the pressure is increased until a small amount of water is displaced through the porous, semi-permeable membrane into the graduated cylinder. Pressure is held constant until no more water is displaced, which may require several days or even several weeks, after which the core is removed from the apparatus and the water saturation determined by weighing. The core is then replaced in

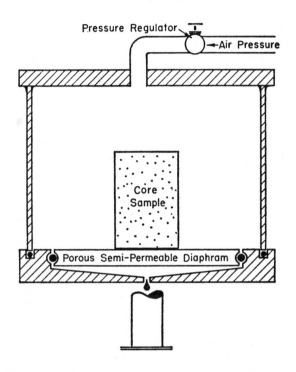

FIGURE 2-1. Restored state capillary pressure equipment.

the apparatus, the pressure is increased, and the procedure is repeated until the water saturation is reduced to a mimimum. The data from such an experiment will plot as shown in Figure 2-2. Since the pressure required to displace the wetting phase from the core is exactly equal to the capillary forces holding the remaining water within the core after equilibrium has been reached, the pressure data can be plotted as capillary pressure data. It can be seen by examining Figure 2-2 that the water saturation reaches some minimum saturation which is equivalent to the connate water saturation.

Using the capillary pressure equation for a single capillary tube:

$$P_c = h \times \Delta\rho \times g = \frac{2\,\gamma\,\text{Cos}\,\theta}{r} \qquad (2\text{-}8)$$

where:

P_c = capillary pressure
h = height above the free liquid surface
$\Delta\rho$ = difference in density of the two fields
g = acceleration due to gravity
γ = interfacial tension between the fluids
θ = contact angle
r = radius of capillary

It is seen that the capillary pressure is related to the height above the free water level. The capillary pressure data can be converted to a plot of h vs. S_w, as shown in Figure 2-2. The transition zone from 100 percent water saturation to minimum water saturation is marked on the graph. The

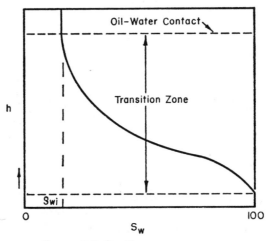

FIGURE 2-2. Capillary pressure curve.

important concept to be gained from Figure 2-2 is that there is no abrupt change from 100 percent water to maximum oil saturation. There is no such thing as an oil-water contact, but there is a gradual transition from 100 percent water to maximum oil saturation. If the oil-water contact is defined as the lowest point in the reservoir which will produce 100 percent oil, then the oil-water contact will be that shown in Figure 2-2, in which case there may be substantial quantities of oil below the oil-water contact, but this oil production would be accompanied by simultaneous water production. The thickness of the transition zone may be only two or three feet in some reservoirs, while it may be several hundred feet in other reservoirs.

Changes in pore size and changes in reservoir fluid densities will alter the shape of the capillary pressure curve and the thickness of the transition zone. Rearrangement of Equation (2-8) to solve for h, the height above the free liquid surface, shows that as $\Delta\rho$, density difference, decreases h increases. From a practical standpoint, this means that in a gas reservoir having a gas-water contact, the thickness of the transition zone will be a minimum, since $\Delta\rho$ will be large. Also, if all other factors remain unchanged, a low API gravity oil reservoir with an oil-water contact will have a longer transition zone than a high API gravity oil reservoir. This concept is illustrated in Figure 2-3.

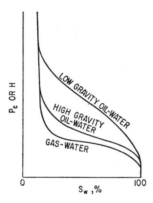

FIGURE 2-3. Variation of P_c with S_w for the same rock system with different fluids.

Inspection of Equation (2-8) will show that as r, radius of the pore, increases the value of h decreases. Therefore, a reservoir rock system with small pore sizes will have a longer transition zone than a reservoir rock system comprised of large pore sizes.

The reservoir pore size can often be related approximately to permeability, and where this applies, it can be stated that high permeability reservoirs will have shorter transition zones than low permeability reservoirs. This latter concept is shown in Figure 2-4.

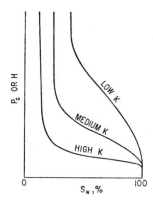

FIGURE 2-4. Variation of P_c with S_w for the same fluid with different rock systems.

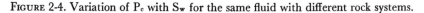

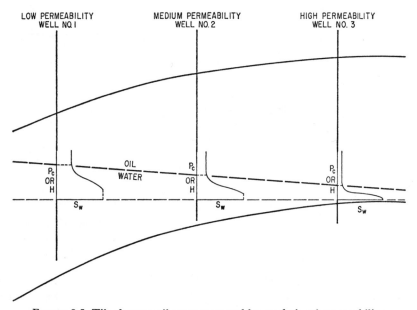

FIGURE 2-5. Tilted water-oil contact caused by gradational permeability.

Figure 2-5 shows how a tilted water-oil contact could be caused by a change in permeability across the reservoir. It should be emphasized that the factor responsible for this change in the location of the water-oil contact is actually a change in the size of the pores in the reservoir rock system.

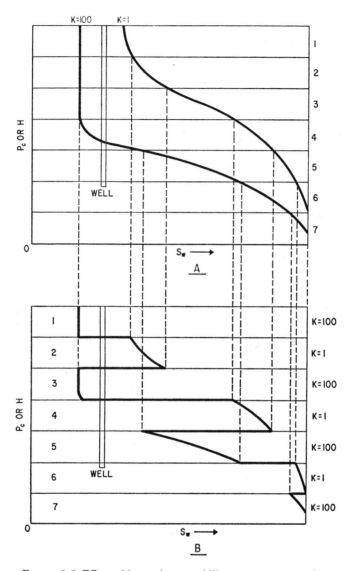

FIGURE 2-6. Effect of layered permeability on water saturation.

The previous discussion of capillary forces in reservoir rocks has assumed that the reservoir pore sizes are essentially uniform. If a reservoir rock system is comprised of several layers of two different pore sizes, and the capillary pressure curves for each set of pore sizes is represented by the curves shown in Figure 2-6A, then the resulting capillary pressure curve for the layered reservoir would resemble that shown in Figure 2-6B. If a well were drilled at the point shown in Figure 2-6B, layers 1 and 3 would not produce water, while layer 2, which is above layer 3, would produce water, since it is located in the transition zone.

The terms connate water saturation or interstitial water saturation are used interchangeably in this book and refer to the irreducible minimum water saturation shown in Figure 2-2. Therefore, using this definition, if an oil reservoir is producing some water, unless water coning is occuring, the completion interval must be in the transition zone, as by definition, the connate water is immobile.

Permeability

Permeability is a measure of the ease of flow of a fluid through a porous medium. The permeability of an oil reservoir is as important as the porosity, for not only is the actual volume of oil in place important, but the rate at which the oil will flow through the reservoir is equally important. For example if a reservoir is located which contains 500 million barrels of oil in place, but the oil cannot flow through the rock to the well bore, then the oil is of no economic value in the light of present-day technology.

The French engineer, Henry Darcy, developed a fluid flow equation which has since become one of the standard mathematical tools of the petroleum engineer. This equation, stated in differential form is:

$$v = -\frac{k}{\mu}\frac{dp}{dL} \qquad (2\text{-}9)$$

where:

v = apparent fluid flowing velocity, cm/sec.
k = proportionality constant, or permeability, darcies.
μ = viscosity of the flowing fluid, centipoises.
$\frac{dp}{dL}$ = pressure drop per unit length, atmospheres/cm.

The velocity, v, in Equation (2-9) is not the actual velocity of the flowing fluid, but is the apparent velocity determined by dividing the flow rate by the cross-sectional area across which fluid is flowing. Substituting the relationship, q/A in place of v in Equation (2-9) and solving for q results in:

$$q = -\frac{kA}{\mu}\frac{dp}{dL} \qquad (2\text{-}10)$$

where:

q = flow rate through the porous medium, cm³/sec.

A = cross-sectional area across which flow occurs, cm².

With a flow rate of one cubic centimeter per second across a cross-sectional area of one square centimeter with a fluid of one centipoise viscosity and a pressure gradient at one atmosphere per centimeter of length, it is obvious that k is unity. For the units above described, k has been arbitrarily assigned a unit called *darcy* in honor of the man responsible for the development of the theory of flow through porous media. Thus when all other parts of Equation 2-10 have values of unity, k has a value of one darcy.

One darcy is a relatively high permeability, as the permeabilities of most reservoir rocks are less than one darcy. In order to avoid the use of fractions in describing permeabilities, the term millidarcy was coined. As the term indicates, one millidarcy is equal to one-thousandth of one darcy or 100 millidarcies are equal to one darcy. The permeability and porosity of various rocks are shown in Table 2-1.

Table 2-1
Permeability and Porosity of Typical Reservoir Rocks

Core Description	Permeability, Mds	Porosity, %
Skinner ss, Hughes Co. Okla.	353	20
Nellie Bly ss, Tulsa Co. Okla.	1288	27
Berea ss, Ohio	90	19
Thurman ss, Seminole Co. Okla.	193	18
Bartlesville ss, Okla.	27	20
Upper Strawn ss, N. Texas	23	17
Bradford ss, Penn.	2	12
Woodbine ss, E. Texas	500	24

The negative sign in Equation (2-10) is necessary as the pressure increases in one direction while the length increases in the opposite direction.

Equation (2-10) can be integrated when the geometry of the system through which fluid flows is known. For the simple linear system shown in Figure 2-7 the integration is performed as follows:

$$q \int_0^L dL = - \frac{kA}{\mu} \int_{p1}^{p2} dp \qquad (2\text{-}11)$$

integrating yields:

$$qL = - \frac{kA}{\mu} (p_2 - p_1) \qquad (2\text{-}12)$$

Since p_1 is greater than p_2, the pressure terms can be rearranged, which will eliminate the negative term in the equation. The resulting equation is:

$$q = \frac{kA\,(p_1 - p_2)}{\mu L} \tag{2-13}$$

Equation (2-13) is the conventional linear flow equation used in fluid flow calculations.

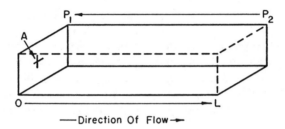

FIGURE 2-7. Linear flow model.

Equation (2-10) can be expanded to describe flow in any porous medium where the geometry of the system is not too complex to integrate. For example, the flow into a well bore is not linear, but is more often radial. Figure 2-8 illustrates the type of flow which is typical of that occuring in the vicinity of a producing well. The limits of Equation (2-11) are now:

$$q\int_{r_w}^{r_e} dr = \frac{kA}{\mu}\int_{p_w}^{p_e} dp \tag{2-14}$$

The term dL has been replaced by dr as the length term has now become a redius term. The minus sign is no longer required for the radial system shown in Figure 2-8 as the radius increases in the same direction as the pressure. In other words, as the radius increases going away from the well bore the pressure also increases. At any point in the reservoir the cross-sectional area across which flow occurs will be the surface area of a cylinder, which is $2\pi rh$. Since the cross-sectional area is related to r, then A must be included within the integral sign as follows:

$$q\int_{r_w}^{r_e} \frac{dr}{2\pi rh} = \frac{k}{\mu}\int_{p_w}^{p_e} dp \tag{2-15}$$

rearranging:

$$\frac{q}{2\pi h} \int_{r_w}^{r_e} \frac{dr}{r} = \frac{k}{\mu} \int_{p_w}^{p_e} dp \qquad (2\text{-}16)$$

and integrating:

$$\frac{q}{2\pi h} (\ln r_e - \ln r_w) = \frac{k}{\mu} (p_e - p_w) \qquad (2\text{-}17)$$

Solving for the flow rate, q, results in:

$$q = \frac{2\pi kh (p_e - p_w)}{\mu \ln r_e/r_w} \qquad (2\text{-}18)$$

Equation (2-10) can be expanded to describe flow in any geometric system which is simple enough to integrate. For example, flow equations for spherical flow or hemispherical flow are derived quite simply.

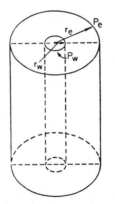

FIGURE 2-8. Radial flow model.

The flow rate q, in Equation (2-18) is the flow rate *through* the porous medium. In the case of a compressible fluid flowing under essentially steady-state conditions, although the *mass* flow rate is unchanging, the *volume* flow rate is different at each place in the medium. The flow rate q, is actually the *mean flow rate*, and is usually designated by q_m. Thus, for compressible flow, equation 2-18 must be modified as follows:

$$q_m = \frac{2\pi k_g h (p_e - p_w)}{\mu \ln r_e/r_w} \qquad (2\text{-}19)$$

where:

> q_m = mean volume flow rate (cc./sec.) measured at the mean flowing pressure
>
> $$\left(p_m = \frac{p_e + p_w}{2} \right)$$

Where an incompressible fluid is flowing, the volume flow rate does not change, and it is not necessary to use q_m. However, Equation (2-19) is a general form of the radial flow equation since for an incompressible fluid $q = q_m$.

Two examples will be used to illustrate typical calculations.

Example Problem 2-2

Calculate the flow rate, in SCF/Day of a gas well, given the following conditions:

> well spacing: 640 acres ($r_e = 2640$ feet)
> sand thickness: 20 feet
> reservoir gas viscosity: 0.025 cp.
> well bore radius: 2.0 feet
> reservoir temperature: 195° F
> reservoir pressure: 2000 psia
> flowing sand face pressure: 1500 psia
> gas deviation factor at p_m: 0.92
> effective gas permeability: 95 mds

Darcy's Law for radial flow can be used to approximate the flow. This equation is:

$$q_m = \frac{2\pi k_g h \ (p_e - p_w)}{\mu_g \ln r_e/r_w} \tag{2-20}$$

Equation (2-20) will yield the flow rate through the reservoir, in cc./sec. Since the flow rate at the surface is desired, the first step in the solution is to convert the flow to standard conditions at the surface, using the gas laws:

$$\frac{p_{sc} \, q_{sc}}{Z_{sc} \, T_{sc}} = \frac{p_m \, q_m}{Z_m \, T_m} \tag{2-21}$$

Where the subscript "sc" refers to standard conditions (14.7 psia and 60° F) and the subscript "m" refers to the mean reservoir conditions. Combining Equations (2-20) and (2-21), and solving for q_{sc}:

$$q_{sc} = \frac{Z_{sc} \times T_{sc} \times p_m \times 2 \times \pi \times h \times k_g \ (p_e - p_w)}{p_{sc} \times Z_m \times T_m \times \mu_g \times \ln r_e/r_w} \tag{2-22}$$

Since $p_m = \dfrac{p_e + p_w}{2}$, Equation (2-22) can be expanded as follows:

$$q_{sc} = \frac{Z_{sc} \times T_{sc} \times \pi \times k_g \times h \times (p_e{}^2 - p_w{}^2)}{p_{sc} \times Z_m \times T_m \times \mu_g \times \ln r_e/r_w} \tag{2-23}$$

The units of q_{sc} are still cc./sec. but have now been converted to standard conditions. Converting from cc./sec. to SCF/Day and using conventional oil field units results in:

$$Q_{sc} = \frac{60 \times 60 \times 24 \times 1 \times 520 \times 3.14 \times k_g \times h \times 2.54 \times 12 \times (p_e{}^2 - p_w{}^2)}{(2.54)^3 \times (12)^3 \times 14.7 \times Z_m \times T_m \times \mu_g \times \ln r_e/r_w \times 14.7} \tag{2-24}$$

$$= \frac{703 \times k_g \times h \times (p_e{}^2 - p_{wf}{}^2)}{Z_m \times T_m \times \mu_g \times \ln r_e/r_w} \tag{2-25}$$

where:

$$\begin{aligned}
Q_{sc} &= \text{SCF/Day} \\
k_g &= \text{Darcies} \\
h &= \text{feet} \\
p_e &= \text{Psi} \\
p_{wf} &= \text{Psi} \\
T_m &= \text{mean temperature (Reservoir temp.), } ^\circ R \\
\mu_g &= \text{viscosity, cp.} \\
r_e &= \text{feet} \\
r_w &= \text{feet}
\end{aligned}$$

Substituting the data from Example 2-2 into Equation (2-25) yields the following solution:

$$Q_{sc} = \frac{703 \times 0.095 \times 20 \times [(2000)^2 - (1500)^2]}{0.92 \times (195 + 460) \times 0.025 \times \ln 2640/2}$$

$$= 21,600,000 \text{ SCF/Day}$$

An equation can also be derived, using conventional oil field units, for calculating flow from oil reservoirs with the radial form of the Darcy flow equation, converting in the same manner as for the gas flow equation:

$$Q_{sr} = \frac{60 \times 60 \times 24 \times 2 \times 3.14 \times k_o \times h \times 2.54 \times 12 \times (p_e - p_w)}{(2.54)^3 \times (12)^3 \times \mu_o \times \ln r_e/r_w \times 5.62 \times 14.7}$$

$$= \frac{7.07 \times k_o \times h \times (p_e - p_w)}{\mu_o \ln r_e/r_w} \tag{2-26}$$

In order to convert from reservoir flow rate to surface flow rate when oil is the flowing fluid, the only conversion factor required is B_o. Thus to calculate the flow rate in stock tank barrels per day the following formula can be used:

$$Q_{st} = \frac{7.07 \times k_o \times h \times (p_e - p_w)}{\mu_o \times \ln r_e/r_w \times B_o} \tag{2-27}$$

where:

Q_{st} = oil flow rate, stock tank barrels per day
k_o = effective oil permeability, darcies.
h = reservoir thickness, feet.
p_e = reservoir pressure, psi.
p_{wf} = sand face pressure, psi.
μ_o = reservoir oil viscosity, cp.
r_e = drainage radius, feet.
r_w = well bore radius, feet.
B_o = oil formation volume factor.

Flow Through Layered Beds

Seldom, if ever, is a homogeneous reservoir encountered in actual practice. In many cases the reservoir will be found to contain sev-

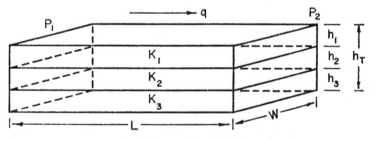

FIGURE 2-9. Flow through layered beds.

eral distinct units, or layers, of varying permeabilities. These layers can often be traced from well to well throughout the reservoir. Where such conditions exist it is necessary to calculate flow through each bed separately, or else to develop an average permeability for the whole sequence. The average permeability can be developed by using the darcy flow equation. Consider the simple linear-flow model shown in Figure 2-9. Flow through each of the beds can be calculated by the following formulas:

Bed 1:

$$q_1 = \frac{k_1 \times W \times h_1 \times \Delta p}{\mu L} \tag{2-28}$$

where:

Wh_1 = cross-sectional area across which flow occurs for bed 1.

Bed 2:

$$q_2 = \frac{k_2 \times W \times h_2 \times \Delta p}{\mu L} \qquad (2\text{-}29)$$

Bed 3:

$$q_3 = \frac{k_3 \times W \times h_3 \times \Delta p}{\mu L} \qquad (2\text{-}30)$$

Flow through the entire model can be calculated by:

$$q_t = \frac{k_{avg} \times W \times h_t \times \Delta p}{\mu \times L} \qquad (2\text{-}31)$$

where:

q_t = total flow rate
k_{avg} = average permeability for the entire model.

The total flow rate through the entire system is equal to the sum of the flow rates through each layer or:

$$q_t = q_1 + q_2 + q_3 \qquad (2\text{-}32)$$

Combining Equations (2-28) through (2-32) results in:

$$\frac{k_{avg} \times W \times h_t \times \Delta p}{\mu \times L} = \frac{k_1 \times W \times h_1 \times \Delta p}{\mu \times L}$$

$$+ \frac{k_2 \times W \times h_2 \times \Delta p}{\mu \times L} + \frac{k_3 \times W \times h_3 \times \Delta p}{\mu \times L} \qquad (2\text{-}33)$$

Cancelling the identical terms W, Δp, μ, and L from Equation (2-33) simplifies the equation to:

$$k_{avg} \times h_t = k_1 h_1 + k_2 h_2 + k_3 h_3 \qquad (2\text{-}34)$$

or:

$$k_{avg} = \frac{k_1 h_1 + k_2 h_2 + k_3 h_3}{h_t} \qquad (2\text{-}35)$$

Equation (2-35) is the equation commonly used to determine the average permeability of a reservoir from core analysis data.

Example Problem 2-3

Given the following permeability data from a core analysis report, calculate the average permeability of the reservoir:

Depth, Feet	Permeability, Mds.
5012-13	500
5013-16	460
5016-17	5
5017-19	235
5019-23	360
5023-24	210
5024-29	3

The permeability of intervals at 5016-17 feet and 5024-29 feet are probably too low in comparison to the other permeability values to yield any substantial quantities of oil, and therefore these intervals will be omitted from the reservoir thickness. The resulting reservoir thickness is called *net* reservoir thickness. Substituting the given data into Equation (2-35) yields:

$$k_{avg} = \frac{(500)(1) + (460)(3) + (235)(2) + (360)(4) + (210)(1)}{11}$$

$$= \frac{3500}{11} = 327 \text{ mds.}$$

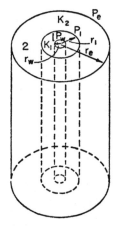

FIGURE 2-10. Flow through series beds.

Flow Through Series Beds

Permeability variations can occur laterally, as well as vertically, in a reservoir. In addition to natural lateral variations in permeability, well bore damage can reduce the permeability in the vicinity of the well bore; also cleaning techniques, such as acidizing can increase the permeability in the vicinity of a well bore. Where lateral variations in permeability occurs, the average permeability of the reservoir must be developed in a different manner than that used for layered beds. Consider the reservoir shown in Figure 2-10. Flow through the beds can be calculated by the following formulas, using Darcy's Law for radial flow:

Bed 1:

$$q_1 = \frac{2 \times \pi \times k_1 \times h \times (p_1 - p_w)}{\mu \times \ln r_1/r_w} \qquad (2\text{-}36)$$

Bed 2:

$$q_2 = \frac{2 \times \pi \times k_2 \times h \times (p_e - p_1)}{\mu \times \ln r_e/r_1} \qquad (2\text{-}37)$$

total flow rate:

$$q_t = \frac{2 \times \pi \times k_{avg} \times h \times (p_e - p_w)}{\mu \times \ln r_e/r_w} \qquad (2\text{-}38)$$

The total pressure drop is equal to the sum of the pressure drops across each bed, or:

$$(P_e - P_w) = (P_e - P_1) + (P_1 - P_w) \qquad (2\text{-}39)$$

Combining Equations (2-36) through (2-39) yields:

$$\frac{q_t \, \mu \ln r_e/r_w}{2\pi \, k_{avg} \, h} = \frac{q_1 \, \mu \ln r_1/r_w}{2\pi \, k_1 \, h} + \frac{q_2 \, \mu \ln r_e/r_1}{2\pi \, k_2 \, h} \qquad (2\text{-}40)$$

Since this is steady-state flow, $q_t = q_1 = q_2$. Cancelling identical terms and simplifying results in the following equation:

$$\frac{\ln r_e/r_w}{k_{avg}} = \frac{\ln r_1/r_w}{k_1} + \frac{\ln r_e/r_1}{k_2}$$

or:

$$k_{avg} = \frac{\ln r_e/r_w}{\dfrac{\ln r_1/r_w}{k_1} + \dfrac{\ln r_e/r_1}{k_2}} \qquad (2\text{-}41)$$

Equation (2-41) can be used to calculate the average permeability of a reservoir where there is a lateral variation in permeability, such as would be caused by acidizing or mud blocks, as previously described.

According to the theory developed by Darcy the permeability coefficient is independent of the type of flowing fluid, the imposed pressure differential, or the geometry of the system. With one exception this has proved to be true in all cases where the porous medium does not react with the flowing fluid. For example, fresh water may react to swell any clays which may be present in a rock sample, causing a reduction in the measured permeability. It may also be possible for certain material to be leached from the rock by the flowing fluid, which could cause an increase in permeability. Therefore, before any permeability measurements are made, care should be taken to insure that the flowing fluid is non-reactive with the porous medium.

Klinkenberg Effect

Klinkenberg[1] discovered that permeability measurements made with air as the flowing fluid showed different results from permeability measurements made with a liquid as the flowing fluid. The permeability of a core sample measured by flowing air is always greater than the permeability obtained when a liquid is the flow-

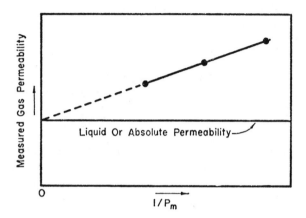

FIGURE 2-11. Klinkenberg effect in gas permeability measurements.

ing fluid. Klinkenberg postulated, on the basis of his laboratory experiments, that liquids had a zero velocity at the sand grain surface, while gases exhibited some finite velocity at the sand grain surface. In other words, the gases exhibited *slippage* at the sand grain surface. This slippage resulted in a higher flow rate for the gas at a given pressure differential. Klinkenberg also found that for a given porous medium as the mean pressure increased the calculated permeability decreased. Mean pressure is defined as upstream flowing plus downstream flowing pressure divided by two, $\left(p_m = \dfrac{p_1 + p_2}{2}\right)$. If a plot of meaured permeability versus $1/p_m$ were extrapolated to the point where $1/p_m = 0$, in other words where $p_m =$ infinity, this permeability would be approximately equal to the liquid permeability. A graph of this nature is shown in Figure 2-11.

Since the permeability measured with an inert liquid is a constant, the liquid permeability is usually referred to as the absolute

---

[1] Klinkenberg, L. J., "The Permeability of Porous Media to Liquids and Gases," *API Drilling and Production Practice*, 1941, p. 200.

permeability. However, it is usually much more convenient to measure the permeability of samples in the laboratory using air as the flowing fluid, since air will seldom react with the rock material. Therefore, most laboratory permeability measurements are made using air. The absolute permeability is determined by extrapolation as shown in Figure 2-11.

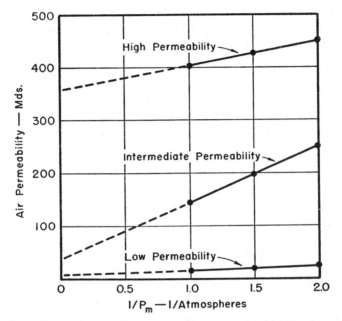

FIGURE 2-12. Effect of permeability on the magnitude of the Klinkenberg effect.

The magnitude of the Klinkenberg effect is greatest in cores with very low permeabilities. The magnitude of the Klinkenberg effect in cores with varying permeabilities is shown in Figure 2-12.

Effective Permeability

All permeability measurements which have been described thus far in this chapter have dealt with the flow of only one fluid. At least two fluids are present in most petroleum reservoirs and in many cases three different fluids may be present and flowing simultaneously. Therefore the concept of absolute permeability must be modified somewhat to satisfactorily describe the flow conditions when more than one fluid is present in the reservoir. If a core is saturated with connate water and oil, for example 25 percent connate water and 75 percent oil, the permeability to oil will be reduced below the permeability which would be measured if the core were 100 percent saturated with oil. As the saturation of a particular phase decreases, the permeability to that phase also decreases. It is difficult to predict the way in which the permeability will change with changes in saturation, and in most cases it is preferable to experimentally determine this variation. "Effective" permeability is defined as the permeability to a fluid when the saturation of that fluid is less than 100 percent. Effective permeability can vary from zero, when the saturation of the measured phase is zero, to the value of the absolute permeability, when the saturation of the measured phase is equal to 100 percent.

One of the phenomena of multiphase effective permeabilities is that the sum of the effective permeabilities is always less than the absolute permeability.

Relative Permeability

Relative permeability is defined as the ratio of effective permeability to absolute permeability, or expressed in equation form:

$$k_r = k_e/k \times 100 \qquad (2\text{-}42)$$

where:

k_r = relative permeability
k_e = effective permeability
k = absolute permeability

Relative permeability is a very useful term since it shows how much the permeability of a particular phase has been reduced by the presence of another phase. For example a relative permeability to oil of 60 percent shows that the oil permeability has been reduced 40 percent as a result of the presence of another phase. The lower limit of relative permeability is zero, when the saturation of the phase is zero and K_e is zero, and the upper limit of relative permeability is 100 percent, when the saturation is 100 percent and K_e equals K.

Relative permeability measurements when made with a compressible fluid, such as gas or air, also require a Klinkenberg correction. However, due to the time-consuming nature of most relative permeability experiments, a short-cut, which yields an approximate answer sufficiently accurate for most calculations, is usually used. This procedure, which is described in more detail in API RP 10 B, consists essentially of obtaining all permeability measurements at the same inlet and outlet pressures, or in other words,

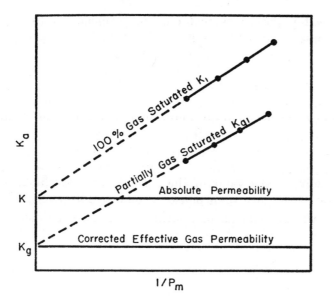

FIGURE 2-13. Klinkenberg correction for relative permeability measurements.

at the same mean pressure. Then relative permeability for the gas phase is calculated by the following formula:

$$k_{rg} = \frac{k_{s_1}}{k_{g100}} \times 100 \qquad (2\text{-}43)$$

where:

k_{s_1} = effective gas permeability at some saturation less than 100 percent.

k_{g100} = gas permeability when core is 100 percent saturated with the gas.

Referring to Figure 2-13, it is apparent that when using Equation (2-43) instead of Equation (2-42) for calculating gas relative permeabilities, the following identies are assumed:

$$\frac{k_{s_1}}{k_1} = \frac{k_g}{k} \qquad (2\text{-}44)$$

Although Equation (2-44) is not completely accurate, if the mean pressure is maintained constant, the error introduced is usually not large.

The wetting properies of a reservoir rock have a marked effect on the relative permeability characteristics of the rock.

The concept of wettability is illustrated by Figure 2-14. Small drops of three liquids, mercury, oil, and water, are placed on a clean glass plate. The three droplets are then observed from one side, as illustrated in the figure. It is noted that the mercury retains a spherical shape, the oil droplet develops an approximately hemispherical shape, but the water tends to spread over the glass surface. The tendency of a liquid to spread over the surface of a solid is an indication of the "wetting" characteristics of the liquid for the solid.

The tendency of a liquid to spread over a solid surface can be expressed more conveniently and in a more precise nature by measuring the angle of contact at the liquid-solid surface. This angle, which is always measured through the liquid to the solid, is called the contact angle, $\ominus$. From Figure 2-14 it can be seen that as the

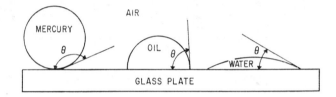

FIGURE 2-14. Illustration of wettability.

contact angle decreases, the wetting characteristics of the liquid increase. Complete wettability would be evidenced by a zero contact angle, and complete non-wetting would be evidenced by a contact angle of 180°. There have been various definitions of "intermediate" wettability but, in much of the published literature, contact angles of 60° to 90° have often been referred to as indicating intermediate wettabilities. However, any contact angle less than 90° will actually tend to wet (or attract the liquid), while any contact angle greater than 90° will tend to repel the liquid.

It should be noted from Figure 2-14 that for a contact angle to be developed, it is necessary to have two immiscible fluids and one solid surface. An interface between the two fluids must be developed, and therefore two fluids which are miscible, for example, oil and liquid propane, will not form an interface, and therefore will not form a contact angle.

The wetting phase fluid will preferentially cover the entire solid surface of the reservoir rock and will be held in the smaller pore spaces of the rock because of the action of capillarity. On the other hand, the non-wetting phase will tend to be expelled from contact with the surface of the rock. Thus, at small saturations, the non-wetting phase will tend to collect in the larger pore openings of the reservoir rock.

The distribution of the reservoir fluids according to their wetting characteristics results in characteristic wetting and non-wetting phase relative permeabilities. Since the wetting phase occupies the smaller pore openings at small saturations, and these pore openings do not contribute materially to flow, it follows that the presence of a small wetting phase saturation will affect the non-wetting phase permeability only to a limited extent. However, since the non-wetting phase occupies the central or larger pore openings, which contribute materially to fluid flow through the reservoir, a small non-wetting phase saturation will drastically reduce the wetting phase permeability. Typical wetting and non-wetting phase relative permeabilities are shown in Figure 2-15.

Figure 2-15 shows four important characteristics of typical wetting and non-wetting phase relative permeabilities. Point 1 on the wetting phase relative permeability shows that a small saturation of the non-wetting phase will drastically reduce the relative permeability of the wetting phase. The reason for this is that the non-wetting phase occupies the larger pore spaces, and it is in these large pore spaces that flow occurs with the least difficulty. Point 2 on the non-wetting phase relative permeability curve shows that the non-wetting phase begins to flow at a relatively low saturation of the non-wetting phase. There may be two reasons for this: (1) the non-wetting phase occupies the larger pore spaces where flow occurs the easiest, and (2) if the non-wetting phase is gas, the viscosity of gas is usually much less than the viscosity of reservoir liquids, and this promotes early gas flow. Where gas is the non-wetting phase, flow may occur at gas saturations as small as three percent.

Point 3 on the wetting phase relative permeability curve shows that the wetting phase will cease to flow at a relatively large saturation. This is because the wetting phase preferentially occupies the smaller pore spaces, where capillary forces are the greatest. Point 4 on the non-wetting phase relative permeability curve shows that, at the lower saturations of the wetting phase, changes in the wetting phase saturation have only a small effect on the magnitude of the non-wetting phase relative permeability curve. Point 4 on the non-wetting phase relative permeability curve is equivalent to Point 1 on the wetting phase relative permeability curve (i.e. the saturations of both phases are high). The differences in the shapes of the two curves is apparent in Figure 2-15. The reason for the phenomenon at Point 4 is that at the low saturations the wetting

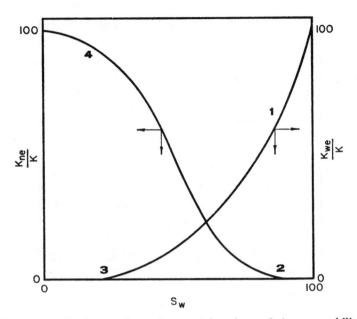

FIGURE 2-15. Typical wetting and non-wetting phase relative permeability.

phase fluid occupies the small pore spaces which do not contribute materially to flow, and therefore changing the saturation in these small pore spaces has a relatively small effect on the flow of the non-wetting phase.

Gas is always considered to be non-wetting; therefore, if gas and oil relative permeability relationships are desired, the gas would be the non-wetting phase and oil would be the wetting phase, since wettability is at best a relative term. Although most petroleum reservoirs are considered to be water wet, when oil and water relative permeability relationships are determined, the distinct and characteristic differences between the wetting and non-wetting phases are often obscured. Typical oil and water relative permeabilities are shown in Figure 2-16. Examination of this figure shows no significant differences in the shapes of the oil and water relative permeability curves. One explanation for the absence of any marked differences in the curves is that neither fluid is either highly wetting or highly non-wetting. In other words, both fluids are intermediate in their wetting characteristics, although the water may be somewhat more wetting to the reservoir rock than the oil as evidenced by the larger decrease in water relative permeabilities at low oil saturation.

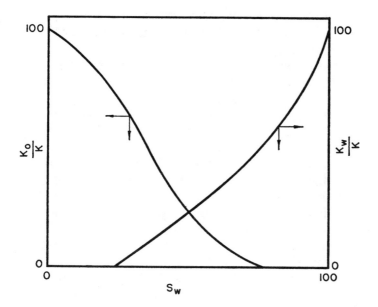

FIGURE 2-16. Typical oil and water relative permeability.

Another important phenomenon associated with fluid flow through porous media is the concept of residual saturations. As discussed previously in the section concerning fluid saturations, when one immiscible fluid is displacing another, it is impossible to reduce the saturation of the displaced fluid to zero. At some small saturation, which is presumed to be the saturation at which the displaced phase ceases to be continuous, flow of the displaced phase will cease. This saturation is often referred to as the *minimum irreducible* saturation. This is an important concept as it determines the maximum recovery from the reservoir. Conversely, a fluid must develop a certain minimum saturation before the phase will begin to flow. This is evident from an examination of the relative permeability curves shown in Figures 2-15 and 2-16. The saturation at which a fluid will just begin to flow is called the *equilibrium* saturation.

Theoretically, the equilibrium saturation and the irreducible minimum saturation should be exactly equal for any fluid; however, they are not identical. Equilibrium saturation is measured in the direction of increasing saturation, while irreducible minimum saturation is measured in the direction of reducing saturation. Thus the saturation histories of the two measurements are different, and result in differing permeability measurements. This is probably due to the different arrangement of the fluids in the pore openings during displacement. This difference in permeability when changing the saturation history is called *hysteresis*. Since relative permeability measurements are subject to hysteresis, it is important to duplicate, in the laboratory, the saturation history of the reservoir. It is generally agreed that the pore spaces of reservoir rocks were originally filled with water, after which oil moved into the reservoir, displacing some of the water, and reducing the water to some residual saturation. When discovered, the reservoir pore spaces are filled with a connate water saturation and an oil saturation. If gas is the displacing agent, then gas moves into the reservoir, displacing the oil. This same history must be duplicated in the laboratory to eliminate the effects of hysteresis. The laboratory procedure is to first saturate the core with water, then displace the water to a residual, or connate, water saturation with oil, after which the oil in the core is displaced by gas. This flow process is called the gas drive or drainage, depletion process. In the gas drive depletion process, the non-wetting phase fluid is continuously increased, and the wetting phase fluid is continuously decreased. The other principal flow process of interest is the water drive, or imbibition process, where water is the wetting phase. The laboratory technique is first to saturate the core with water, then displace the water to a residual, or connate, water saturation with oil. This procedure establishes the fluid saturations which are found when the reservoir is discovered. In the water drive process, water is introduced into the core, and the water (wetting) saturation is continuously increased. Figure 2-17 shows typical drainage and imbibition relative permeability curves and the resulting hysteresis effects.

The actual wettability of reservoir rocks is difficult to determine. However, it is well known that the wettability of reservoir rocks can be affected by drilling fluids, weathering, temperature, and laboratory cleaning procedures. Since the wetting conditions of the reservoir rock have an important effect on the shape of relative permeability curves, it is important that the native wetting conditions be restored prior to obtaining relative permeability data. In the past a large amount of relative permeability data were obtained without taking proper precautions regarding the influence of altering wettability. In these cases the laboratory relative permeability data probably do not reflect the actual flow characteristics in the reservoir.

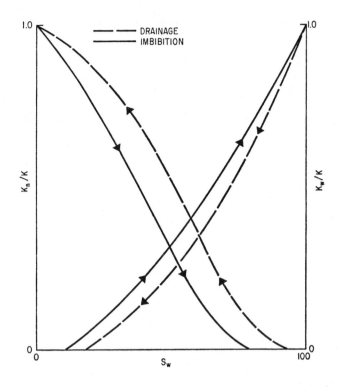

FIGURE 2-17. Hysteresis effects in relative permeability.

Relative permeability measurements for several different formations are shown in Figures 2-18, 2-19 and 2-20. These data may be useful when it is necessary to estimate the relative permeability characteristics of a reservoir where actual laboratory data are unavailable. When available, other pertinent data concerning the character of the formations are presented, in addition to the relative permeability data.

Calculating Relative Permeability Data

In many cases relative permeability data on actual samples from the reservoir under study may not be available, in which case it is necessary to obtain the desired relative permeability data in some other manner. Field relative permeability data can usually be calculated, and the procedure will be discussed more fully in Chapter 3, *Oil Reservoirs*. However, the field data are unavailable for future

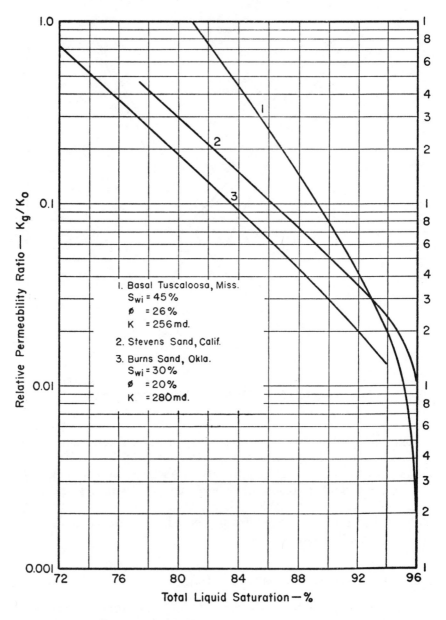

FIGURE 2-18. K_g/K_o curves, sandstone reservoirs.

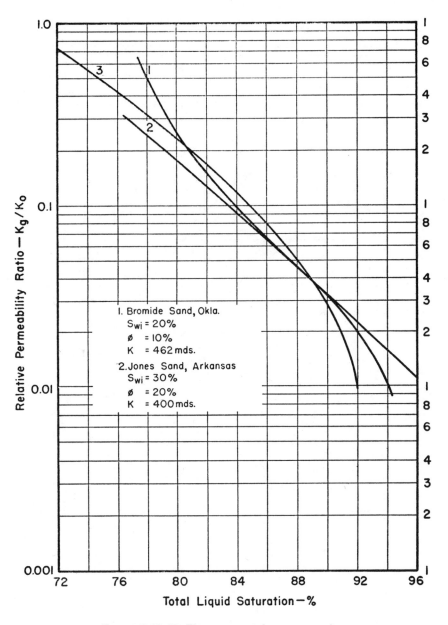

FIGURE 2-19. K_g/K_o curves, sandstone reservoirs.

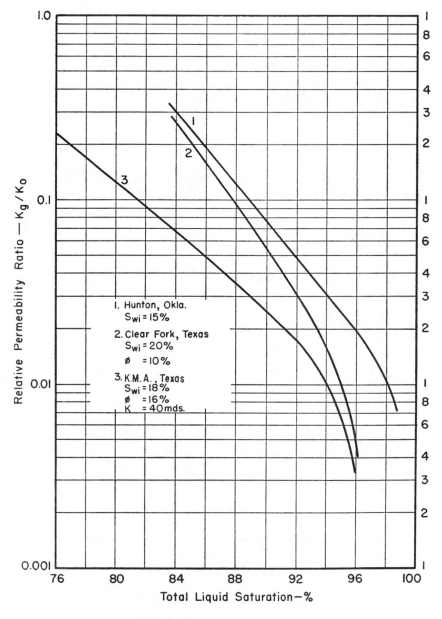

FIGURE 2-20. K_g/K_o curves, limestone reservoirs.

production, and some substitute must be devised. Several methods have been developed for calculating relative permeability relationships. Various parameters have been used to calculate the relative permeability relationships, examples of which are capillary pressure data and residual fluid saturation data. Rose[2] has developed a useful method of calculating relative permeability relationships. The principal disadvantage of this method is that the residual saturation of both fluid phases must be known. If these data are available, then in most cases the entire relative permeability data will be available. However, where the required data are available, or can be estimated fairly accurately, the calculation procedure may be very valuable. The equations developed by Rose for the calculation of wetting and non-wetting relative permeabilities are shown below:

$$k_{rw} = \frac{16\rho_w{}^2 \, (\rho_w - \rho_{wm})^3 \, (1 - \rho_{wm})}{[2\rho_w{}^2 \, (2\text{-}3\rho_{wm}) + 3\rho_w \, \rho_{wm} \, (3\rho_{wm} - 2) + \rho_{wm} \, (4\text{-}5\rho_{wm})]^2} \quad (2\text{-}45)$$

$$k_{rn} = \frac{16\rho_n{}^2 \, (\rho_n - \rho_{nm})^3 \, (1 - \psi_w - \rho_{nm})}{[2\rho_n{}^2 \, (2\text{-}2\psi_w - 3\rho_{nm}) + 3\rho_n \, \rho_{nm} \, (3\rho_{nm} - 2 + 2\psi_w) + \rho_{nm} \, (1 - \psi_w) \, (4\text{-}4\psi_w - 5\rho_{nm})]^2} \quad (2\text{-}46)$$

where:

    k = permeability
    ρ = fluid saturation
    ψ_w = immobile wetting phase saturation

subscripts:

    r = relative
    n = non-wetting phase
    w = wetting phase
    m = minimum saturation value attained under dynamic flow conditions.

Example of the validity of Equations (2-45) and (2-46) are shown in Figures 2-21 and 2-22, where calculated relative permeabilities are compared to measured relative permeabilities on two different core samples selected at random. It can be seen from examination of the figures that, in general, agreement is quite good. In some cases a better match would be obtained by shifting the measured data a constant amount.

---

[2] Rose, Walter, "Theoretical Generalizations Leading to the Evaluation of Relative Permeability," *Trans.* AIME, Vol. 179, 1949, p.

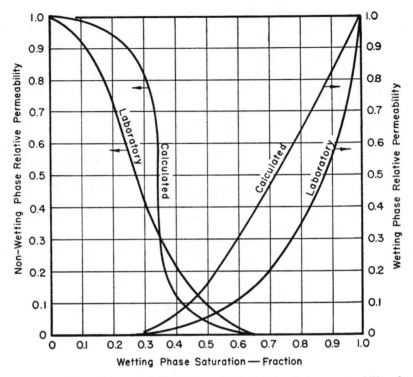

FIGURE 2-21. Comparison of laboratory and calculated relative permeability data, sandstone core.

Torcaso and Wyllie[3] have also published a method of calculating relative permeability ratios which is reported to have been confirmed by laboratory data. Their expression is:

$$k_{rg}/k_{ro} = \frac{(1-S)^2 (1-S^2)}{S^4} \tag{2-47}$$

where:

k_{rg} = relative permeability to gas

k_{ro} = relative permeability to oil

S = effective oil saturation $= \dfrac{S_o}{1-S_{wi}}$

S_o = oil saturation, fraction of total pore space

S_{wi} = interstitial water saturation, fraction

[3] Torcaso, M. A. and Wyllie, M. R. J., "A Comparison of Calculated k_{rg}/k_{ro} Ratios with a Correlation of Field Data," *Journal of Petroleum Technology*, December, 1958, p. 57.

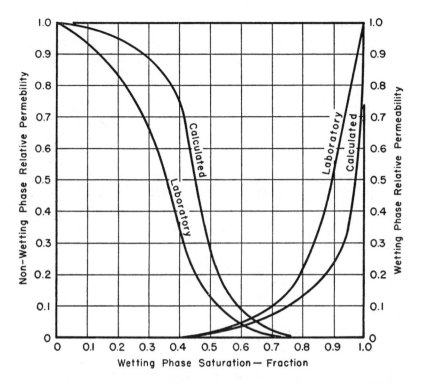

FIGURE 2-22. Comparison of laboratory and calculated relative permeability data, Wasson Limestone.

Since interstitial water saturation is a parameter in Equation (2-47), it is obvious that relative permeability ratios are dependent to a large extent on the determination of correct interstitial water saturation.

Relative permeability data from two sandstone reservoirs having varying interstitial water saturations were randomly selected to test the validity of Equation (2-47). As shown in Figure 2-23, agreement between the calculated data and the experimentally determined Cromwell sand data ($S_{wi} = 20\%$) is very poor, there being a four-fold variation over a portion of the saturation range. The Burns sand relative permeability data ($S_{wi} = 30\%$) shows good agreement with the calculated data over the lower range of saturations, but begins to deviate considerably at the higher saturation values. This limited comparison by no means proves that Equation (2-47) has limited utility, but it does show that there

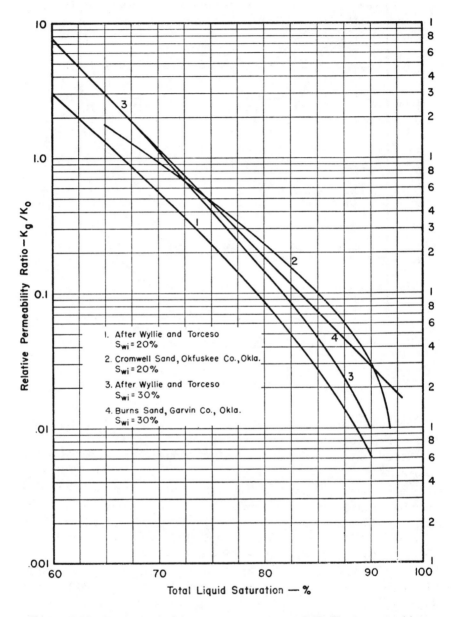

FIGURE 2-23. Comparison of measured and calculated K_g/K_o data. (1. After *Wyllie & Torcaso, $S_{wi} = 20\%$. 2. Cromwell sand, Okofuskee County, Okla., $S_{wi} = 20\%$. 3. After Wyllie & Torcaso, $S_{wi} = 30\%$. 4. Burns sand, Garvin County, Okla., $S_{wi} = 30\%$.)*

can be considerable variation in the answers obtained and the equation should be used with caution.

Knopp[4] has presented some useful correlations for estimating gas-oil relative permeability ratios.

In most cases, some field relative permeability data can be calculated, and this data can then be used to determine the validity of calculated values. This will materially reduce the errors inherent in the calculated data.

Phase Behavior

Although a thorough treatment of phase behavior is beyond the scope of this book, a brief discussion of some fundamental principles will be presented.

Fluids:

Oil and gas are naturally occurring organic materials, composed of varying amounts of hydrogen and carbon. The relative amounts of hydrogen and carbon found in petroleum deposits vary widely. As a result of this wide variation in chemical composition, many types and kinds of hydrocarbon deposits are found. These deposits may occur in the gaseous state, the liquid state, the solid state, or in various combinations of gas, liquid, and solid.

It has been found that hydrogen and carbon exist in many varying fixed compositions. The carbon atom can combine with hydrogen to form very long chains and, as a result, several hundred different hydrocarbon compounds have been identified. Apparently many hundreds of these compounds exist in very small quantities in petroleum.

The various hydrocarbon compounds have been divided into groups according to the structure of the molecule. The principal classes of hydrocarbons are: (1) paraffins, (2) naphthenes, (3) aromatics, (4) olefins, and (5) acetylene. Of these groups, the principal type found in crude oil and gas is the paraffin series. The paraffin series is referred to as being saturated, inasmuch as the carbon atoms contain all the hydrogen possible.

The paraffin series can also be subdivided further into so-called pure components. The principal components in the paraffin series, along with their frequently-used chemical abbreviations, are shown in Table 2-2. Although the paraffin series predominates in most

---

[4]Knopp, C. R., "Gas-Oil Relative Permeability Ratio from Laboratory Data," *Journal of Petroleum Technology*, September 1965, p. 1111.

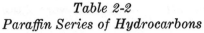

Table 2-2
Paraffin Series of Hydrocarbons

Name	Chemical Formula	Abbreviation
Methane	$C\,H_4$	C_1
Ethane	C_2H_6	C_2
Propane	C_3H_8	C_3
Isobutane	C_4H_{10}	iC_4
n-Butane	C_4H_{10}	nC_4
Isopentane	C_5H_{12}	iC_5
n-Pentane	C_5H_{12}	nC_5
Isohexane	C_6H_{14}	iC_6
n-Hexane	C_6H_{14}	nC_6
Heptane	C_7H_{16}	C_7

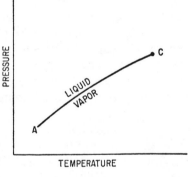

FIGURE 2-24. Phase diagram for a pure component.

petroleum deposits, varying amounts of many of the other types of hydrocarbons are usually found.

If the lower molecular weight (lighter) hydrocarbons—methane and ethane—predominate, then the deposit will usually exist in the gaseous state. If the higher molecular weight (heavier) hydrocarbons predominate, then the deposit will probably exist in the liquid (oil) state.

Changes in pressure and temperature have a pronounced effect on petroleum deposits. Decreasing the pressure on a petroleum de-

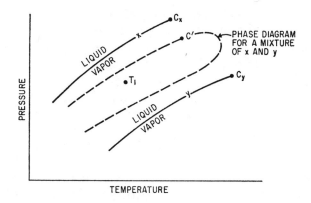

FIGURE 2-25. Phase diagrams for two pure components and a mixture.

posit will permit the individual molecules to move further apart. This is important, since one of the distinctions between a gas and a liquid is that the molecules in a gas are spaced a larger distance apart. Therefore, reducing the pressure on a petroleum deposit will usually tend to gasify the system. By the same reasoning, decreasing the temperature will tend to bring the molecules closer together and tend to liquefy a system.

Both pressure and temperature are subject to change in producing oil and gas and, therefore, the effects of temperature and pressure, or the "phase relationships," are quite important. The phase relationships of hydrocarbons have been extensively studied, and much has been learned about their behavior. Pressure-temperature phase diagrams are very useful for showing the effects of pressure and temperature on the physical state of a hydrocarbon system.

A pressure-temperature phase diagram for a pure component is shown in Figure 2-24. The phase diagram is merely a line which separates the liquid region from the vapor (gas) region. The location of the solid state will not be shown because it is of little interest to those concerned with the study of oil and gas reservoirs. Examination of Figure 2-24 shows that the line A-C represents temperatures and pressures at which both liquid and vapor can exist in equilibrium. Point C on Figure 2-24 is the Critical Point, which is defined as the temperature and pressure above which two phases can no longer exist in equilibrium.

Two different pure components, x and y, might have the phase diagrams shown by the solid lines in Figure 2-25. At some temperature and pressure, T, shown on Figure 2-25, material x will be entirely in the vapor phase, while material y will be entirely in the liquid phase.

If these two materials are mixed in equal proportions, the phase diagram for the resulting mixture will have a shape shown by the dotted line in Figure 2-25. The dotted line separates the two-phase region from the single phase region. The phase diagram for the mixture lies between the phase lines for the two pure components. The reason for this is that along the upper portion of the dotted line the higher molecular weight of material y, which is in the liquid phase will hold the lower molecular weight material x in the liquid state for a longer period. Conversely, along the lower portion of the phase diagram, the lower molecular weight material x will prevent the higher molecular weight material y from being liquified for a longer period of time.

Oil and gas reservoir fluids are comprised of a large number of pure components, and a phase diagram for a typical hydrocarbon reservoir fluid composition is shown in Figure 2-26.

The line ACPTB separates the two-phase region from the single-phase region. Inside the line is the two-phase region, while outside the line all the fluids exist in a single phase. The line AC is called the bubble point line. This line separates the two-phase region from the liquid region. The line CPTB is the dew point line, which separates the two-phase region from the gas region. Point C is the critical point. It should be emphasized that the phase diagram shown in Figure 2-26 is for a specific composition. A different fluid would have a different phase diagram. Although the general configuration of phase diagrams for different fluids are similar, the bubble point and dew point lines will be shifted to different locations.

Figure 2-26 can best be explained by discussing some specific examples. Consider Point li on the figure, which shows the initial pressure and temperature of a certain hydrocarbon fluid. The pressure and temperature conditions are such that the initial state of hydrocarbons is a liquid; i.e., oil. Thus Point li depicts an oil reservoir. Next, consider what happens to the fluids in the reservoir since it is known that reservoir temperature does not change as fluids are produced from the reservoir. Therefore, the production occurs isothermally. Point la shows the abandonment pressure and temperature conditions for this reservoir. As fluids are produced, the pressure in the reservoir decreases, but the temperature remains constant. At the initial pressure and temperature conditions

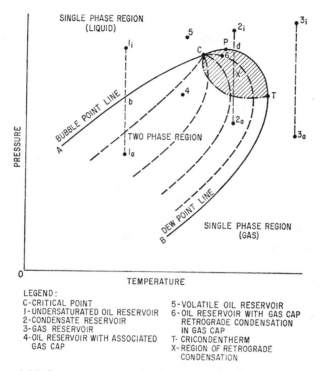

FIGURE 2-26. Pressure-temperature phase diagram constant composition.

the hydrocarbons are 100 percent liquid. As pressure is reduced due to production of oil, no change in the state of the oil occurs until Point "b" on the dashed line is reached. At this pressure, some of the lighter hydrocarbons, principally methane, will be evolved from solution from the oil, and will exist as free gas in the reservoir. The pressure at which gas is first released from solution from the oil is referred to as the saturation pressure, or bubble point pressure. Continued reduction in pressure will result in more and more gas being released from the oil.

The previous discussion was limited to the fluids remaining in the reservoir. It is also of considerable interest to know what happens to the reservoir fluids after they leave the reservoir and move up the well bore to the surface, where they are collected, measured, and sold. As the reservoir fluids move up the well bore and to the surface, both temperature and pressure will be reduced until, at the surface, the remaining oil exists at atmospheric temperature and pressure in the stock tanks. Reducing the pressure to atmospheric will result in the liberation of substantial quantities of free gas. Decreasing the temperature from the reservoir conditions to atmospheric conditions will have the opposite effect on the oil and tend to cause more gas to go into solution.

This latter situation becomes more apparent by studying Figure 2-26. Therefore, in bringing the oil from the reservoir to the surface, pressure and temperature act in opposite directions with respect to their effects on the retention of the lighter components in the liquid phase. Pressure changes have a more pronounced effect than temperature changes. Therefore, the net result is that substantial quantities of free gas will be liberated from the oil during its travel from the reservoir to the surface stock tanks. The actual amount of free gas which will be liberated will depend on the composition of the oil. Oils originally containing large amounts of the lighter hydrocarbons (high API gravity) will release large amounts of gas, while those originally containing only small amounts of the lighter hydrocarbons (low API gravity) will liberate much smaller amounts of gas.

Point 4 is an oil reservoir with an initial gas cap. The gas phase and the oil phase are in equilibrium, and therefore, any reduction in pressure will result in liberation of gas from the oil. This type reservoir is referred to as a saturated oil reservoir. The reservoir oil is said to be saturated with gas, because the slightest reduction in pressure will cause liberation of gas from the oil.

The term *reservoir bubble point pressure* is frequently used. This term is specifically defined as the highest pressure at which a bubble of gas is first liberated from the oil. For the reservoir existing at Point 4, the initial pressure and the bubble point pressure will be identical, because any reduction in pressure will result in gas liberation. For the reservoir existing at Point 1i, the bubble point pressure is at Point b, and the initial pressure is considerably higher than the bubble point pressure. Thus it can be stated if $P_i = P_b$ the reservoir has an initial gas cap. In the previous notations, P_i denotes initial reservoir pressure and P_b denotes reservoir bubble point pressure.

If the initial reservoir conditions exist to the right of the critical point C and outside the phase envelope, then the reservoir fluid will initially be 100 percent gas. Points 3i and 3a on Figure 2-26 depict the initial and abandonment conditions, respectively, of a gas reservoir. It can be noted that at no point in the isothermal depletion cycle is the phase envelope crossed. Therefore, the fluid in the reservoir never changes composition; it is always in the gaseous state. The conditions of pressure and temperature at the surface separation facilities are often such that this point will fall inside the phase envelope, which means that there will be some liquid recovery at the surface.

The reservoir existing at Point 2i on Figure 2-26 is an interesting reservoir. Since the initial conditions of pressure and temperature are to the right of the critical point and outside the phase envelope, this reservoir exists initially in the gaseous state. As production begins from the reservoir and the pressure declines, no change in the state of the reservoir fluids occurs until Point 2d is reached. Point 2d is called the dew point pressure because the dew point line has been crossed. Further reduction in pressure will cause liquid to condense from the gas. This is not considered to be a normal situation, since for most hydrocarbon fluids a pressure reduction will tend to increase the amount of gas. Therefore, this behavior is usually referred to as retrograde condensation. Examination of Figure 2-26 will show that for a reservoir fluid to exhibit the phenomenon of retrograde condensation, the initial conditions of pressure and temperature must exist outside the phase envelope to the right of the critical point C and to the left of T, which is called the cricondentherm, or within the phase envelope in the region marked X. The cricondentherm, point T, is defined as the maximum temperature at which two phases can exist in equilibrium.

Reservoirs having initial temperatures and pressures outside the phase envelope and between the critical point and the cricondentherm, are referred to as condensate reservoirs, or gas-condensate reservoirs.

A reservoir existing initially in the Region X shown on Figure 2-26 is a two-phase reservoir. It initially has an oil zone and a gas

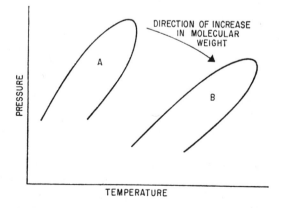

FIGURE 2-27. Influence of molecular weight on the phase diagram.

cap. However, the gas cap exhibits the phenomenon of retrograde condensation, because, as shown in the figure, a decrease in pressure will result in an increase in liquid content of the reservoir, i.e., condensation of a part of the gas phase. This is not an unusual type of reservoir. The Katy Reservoir in South Texas is an example of this type of reservoir. The operation of this type of reservoir is usually very similar to the operation of condensate reservoirs.

The previous discussion of phase diagrams has been limited to fluid of a fixed composition. As previously mentioned if the composition of the reservoir fluids changes, then the phase diagram will also be changed. Figure 2-27 shows that as the molecular weight of the composition increases, the phase diagram will shift down and to the right.

Chapter 3

OIL RESERVOIRS

Oil reservoirs are those reservoirs whose principal product is a reasonably stable hydrocarbon liquid, which normally is brown or green in color.

Reservoir Driving Mechanisms

Oil reservoirs may be classified as either *associated* or *non-associated* reservoirs, depending on whether a free gas cap is present initially with the crude oil. As has been discussed previously, interstitial water is always present within the pore spaces of the reservoir rock. In addition to this interstitial water, there may be bottom water, or edge water, in contact with the oil reservoir. All crude oils contain some constituents which, when the oil is reduced to atmospheric temperature and pressure, will cause the evolution of free gas. Therefore, it can be safely said that all crude oil contains some free gas in solution.

The reservoir engineer is primarily concerned with two problems: (1) the amount of oil and gas which will ultimately be recovered, and (2) the rate at which this oil and gas will be recovered. Both of these factors are directly related to the forces in the reservoir which contribute to the expulsion of the oil from the reservoir. There are five distinct forces which can contribute to oil recovery:

1. Depletion Drive

This driving force may also be referred to as solution gas drive. This recovery mechanism is a result of gas liberation from solution in the reservoir oil, with subsequent expansion and expulsion of the oil. As will be shown in Chapter 4, this is usually the least efficient driving force and usually results in the recovery of only a small percentage of the total oil in place. As shown in Figure 3-1, this type driving mechanism is characterized by rapid reservoir pressure decline. Depletion drive is usually the predominant producing mechanism where the reservoir has no free gas cap or external water drive.

2. External Gas Drive

This type driving energy is the result of an expanding free gas cap. This is basically a displacement type drive, the gas displacing the oil ahead as it expands because of pressure reduction. The recovery efficiency of an external gas drive reservoir is dependent upon the displacing efficiency of the gas and the

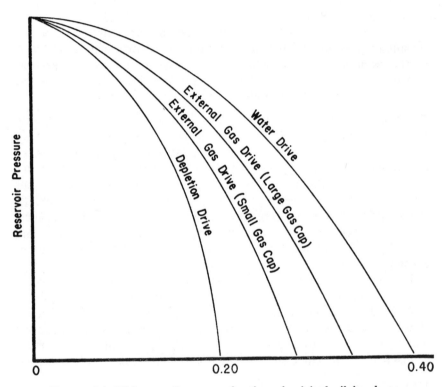

FIGURE 3-1. Ultimate oil recovery-fraction of original oil in place.

size of the gas cap because as the gas cap size increases, the actual number of barrels of expansion of the gas cap for a given pressure drop, will also increase accordingly. Therefore, as the gas cap size increases, a smaller pressure drop will be required to produce the oil to economic depletion. This will be discussed more fully in Chapter 5. Typical pressure-production history curves for reservoirs with both small gas caps and large gas caps are shown in Figure 3-1.

3. Water Drive

Water drive is usually the most efficient natural reservoir driving force. Water drive also is a displacing type drive and the efficiency of water displacement is usually greater than gas displacement regardless of the wetting characteristics of the reservoir rock. This is due to the more favorable mobility characteristics of the water-oil displacement process. Recovery from a water drive reservoir is dependent upon the activity of the water drive. As will be discussed more fully in Chapter 6, it has been determined that water invasion into the oil zone as a result of pressure reduction is accomplished primarily because of the expansion of the water in the adjacent aquifer. Therefore, the number of barrels of water invasion into the oil zone per unit pressure reduction will be proportional to the size of the aquifer, i.e. as the aquifer size increases, water encroachment per unit pressure drop increases. Pressure-production history for a typical water drive reservoir is also shown in Figure 3-1.

4. Gravity Segregation

In high-relief reservoirs where the producing wells are located low structurally, oil recovery by gravitational segregation may be quite substantial. Oil recovery by gravity segre-

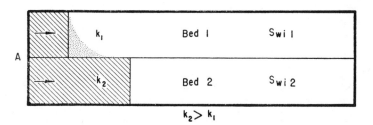

FIGURE 3-2. Flood-front distribution, water wet beds.

gation will be dependent primarily upon the relief, or dip, of the reservoir, the permeability in the direction of dip and the viscosities of the fluids. The recovery mechanism of gravity segregation can never be the sole driving force in a reservoir. Some pressure reduction must occur before the reservoir oil can be produced as no external fluids, such as water, are entering the reservoir to take the place of the produced oil. Therefore, once the reservoir pressure has been reduced to the saturation pressure of the reservoir oil some production by depletion drive must occur. In order to take maximum advantage of gravity segregation, for each unit volume of oil moving down structure there must be an equal volume of gas moving upstructure. Therefore, a reservoir producing under this type of drive must always have a gas cap, either a primary gas cap, or a secondary gas cap. Prediction of reservoir performance under gravitational segregation will be described in Chapter 7.

5. Capillary Forces

Capillary forces are always present in oil reservoirs. A large amount of laboratory work has been performed in an attempt to evaluate the effects of capillary forces. These forces are now reasonably well understood and their effects can be predicted where *known wettability conditions exist*, and where pore size distribution (reservoir heterogeneity) is known. For example, consider a water-wet porous medium, as shown in Figure 3-2, where there are two layers of different permeability, i.e. different pore sizes. It is assumed that the capillary forces are in equilibrium before any reservoir fluids are withdrawn. Therefore, there will be some interstitial water saturation, S_{wi1} in bed 1, and S_{wi2} in bed 2. If water encroachment begins in both beds at point A, water will travel faster in Bed 2 than in Bed 1 because the permeability k_2, of bed 2, is greater than the permeability of bed 1, which is k_1. After some period of water invasion the advancing water front will have advanced as shown by the shaded area in Figure 3-2. However, now there is an unbalance of capillary forces in the system. The capillary pressure in bed 1 is greater than that in bed 2, since this is a water-wet system, therefore water behind the flood front, where the water saturation is high, will be spontaneously imbibed into bed 1, as shown by the dotted areas in the figure ahead of the flood front where the water saturation is low. This will have a dual effect: it will add water to the low permeability bed, and will remove water from the high permeability bed. The net result of the action of capillary forces in this case is a more equal flood front in the two beds. Although the effects of capillary forces can often be explained when the system can be adequately described, in most cases so little is known of the wettability and the variation in pore geometry of the reservoir that the effects of capillarity are generally neglected. This is considered to be satisfactory in view of the assumptions which must be made concerning the gross characteristics of the reservoir.

6. Combination Drives

Production from most reservoirs is accomplished as a result of a combination of one or more of the previously-mentioned forces. Thus a reservoir will be referred to as a combination-drive reservoir when two or more of these driving forces are largely responsible for the oil production. It should be realized that in very few reservoirs will the production be accomplished as a result of only one of the major driving forces. However, when the reservoir is producing predominantly under only one driving force, and where other forces may contribute in only a small way to production, the reservoir, for convenience, is usually referred to as operating under a single driving force. Chapter 8 will discuss methods of predicting behavior of combination drive reservoirs.

Basic Equations and Tools

Several equations and techniques have evolved over the years into more or less standard tools for the reservoir engineer. Probably the most popular has been the volumetric balance, or the so-called material balance equation. Other commonly used equations include the instantaneous gas-oil ratio equation, the frontal drive equations, and various unsteady state flow equations. Many other equations, such as the perfect gas laws, are required in many reservoir performance calculations. Models have also become very important tools for reservoir engineers.

1. The Material Balance Equation

The Material Balance Equation is one of the reservoir engineer's most useful tools. This equation is based on a very simple physical law: the amount of product remaining plus the amount of product used must equal the original amount of product. The year-end inventory taken by most department stores is in reality a material balance. A simple material balance for a department store would be:

$$\text{Material on hand at beginning of year} = \text{Material remaining at end of year} + \text{Material sold during year} + \text{Losses}$$

The gasoline "plant balance" is another form of material balance. The plant balance, which is made at periodic intervals, shows the efficiency of operation of the gas plant. A simple gas plant material balance is:

$$\frac{\text{Wt. of products}}{\text{entering plant}} = \frac{\text{Wt. of products}}{\text{leaving plant}} + \frac{\text{Plant}}{\text{Consumption}} + \text{Losses}$$

Plant consumption and losses must be kept to a minimum in order to keep plant efficiency high.

Schilthuis[1] developed one of the first really usable oil reservoir material balance equations. This equation, or modifications of it, is still used by most reservoir engineers. The equation, which was based on work done originally by Moore, contained more than one unknown, and laborious trial and error calculations were required to predict reservoir performance.

In 1946, Tarner[2] published a method of predicting reservoir performance whereby the material balance equation was solved simultaneously with the instantaneous gas-oil ratio equation. The two unknowns in the material balance equation could be determined directly, using the two equations. This eliminated many of the trial-and-error calculations which had previously been required.

Schilthuis' material balance equation was based on the gas in the reservoir. This provided a relatively simple equation, and is developed as follows:

Standard Cu. Ft. of Gas Originally $\qquad$ (3-1)
$$= \text{SCF Gas Produced} + \text{SCF Gas Remaining}$$
where:
SCF Gas Originally = Gas Cap Gas + Gas in solution

$$= mNB_{oi}\frac{1}{B_{gi}} + NR_{si} \qquad (3\text{-}2)$$

SCF Gas Produced $= R_pN_p \qquad (3\text{-}3)$
where:

m = ratio of gas cap size to oil zone size

N = stock tank oil in place originally, barrels

B_{oi} = formation volume factor at original pressure

R_{si} = gas in solution at original pressure, SCF/stock tank bbl.

R_p = cumulative produced gas-oil ratio, SCF/stock tank bbl. obtained by dividing the cumulative gas produced by the cumulative oil produced.

---

[1] Schilthuis, R. J., "Active Oil and Reservoir Energy,' *Trans.* AIME, 1936, Vol. 127, p. 199.

[2] Tarner, J., "How Different Size Gas Caps and Pressure Maintenance Programs Affect Amount of Recoverable Oil," Oil Weekly, June 12, 1944, p. 32.

Note: Letter symbols conform to the standard AIME symbols which are shown in the appendix.

The gas conversion factor, B_g, which is equal to the volume in barrels of one SCF of gas at reservoir pressure and temperature, is derived as follows:

From the perfect gas laws:

$$\frac{P_1 V_1}{Z_1 T_1} = \frac{P_s V_s}{Z_s T_s}$$

where the subscript 1 refers to conditions at a specific time, and the subscript s, refers to standard conditions. By definitions B_g is equal to the volume in barrels, at reservoir temperature and pressure, occupied by one standard cubic foot of gas. Therefore, if V_s is equal to one, then V_1 shown in the above equation is equal to B_g, after conversion to barrel units. The calculation of B_g is accomplished by use of the following equation:

$$B_g = \frac{P_s V_s Z_1 T_1}{P_1 Z_s T_s \, 5.62}$$

As the quantities at standard conditions are known, this equation can be simplified as follows:

$$B_g = \frac{(14.7)\,(1.0)\,(Z_1)\,(T_1)}{(P_1)\,(1.0)\,(520)\,(5.62)}$$

$$= 0.00504 \, \frac{Z_1 T_1}{P_i}$$

The factor Z, used in the preceding equations is the gas deviation factor, or supercompressibility factor, as it is often called. The perfect gas laws were based on the hypotheses that the individual gas molecules neither occupied space nor exerted any attraction on each other. Actual gases do occupy space and they do exert an attractive force on other nearby molecules. The Z factor then is actually a conformance factor which permits the accurate use of the perfect gas laws for actual gases. The most accurate method of determining the proper Z factor to use for a certain gas is to actually measure, in the laboratory, the deviation of the gas from the behavior of an ideal gas. This would be laborious, and under most circumstances, would not be feasible. Fortunately, research scientists have determined the deviation factors for a large number of gases of varying composition. A correlation technique has been developed whereby, with a minimum amount of data, a reliable Z factor can be estimated. This correlation is based on the reduced temperature and reduced pressure of the gas. Reduced temperature and reduced pressure are defined as:

$$T_r = \frac{T}{T_c}$$

$$P_r = \frac{P}{P_c}$$

where the subscripts r and c refer to reduced and critical.

As reservoir gases are mixtures of pure components, they do not have true critical temperatures and critical pressures. However pseudo critical temperatures and pseudo critical pressures can be calculated, based on the molal composition of the gases. The pseudo critical temperature and pressure can then be used to estimate the Z factor for the gas. In many cases the specific gravity of the gas is known, but the composition is not known. Here again, experiments have been conducted on a large number of gases of varying specific gravities, and charts are available for estimating the critical temperature and critical pressure of the gas where only the specific gravity of the gas is known. The NGSMA Engineering Data Book has graphs showing average critical temperature and average critical pressure versus gas gravity. After obtaining the critical temperature and pressure, reduced temperature and reduced pressure are calculated using the preceding equations. These data are then used to obtain the graphs showing the variation of Z with critical temperature and critical pressure.

Continuing the development of the material balance equation:

$$\begin{array}{ccc} \text{SCF GAS} \\ \text{Remaining} \end{array} = \begin{array}{c} \text{Remaining} \\ \text{Free Gas} \end{array} + \begin{array}{c} \text{Remaining Gas} \\ \text{in solution} \end{array} \qquad (3\text{-}4)$$

where:

$$\begin{array}{c} \text{Remaining} \\ \text{Free Gas} \end{array} = \begin{array}{c} \text{Remaining} \\ \text{Gas Cap Gas} \end{array} + \begin{array}{c} \text{Remaining} \\ \text{Free Gas} \\ \text{Evolved from Solution} \end{array}$$

The size of the reservoir is comprised of the gas cap and the oil zone. In order to simplify the final solution, the assumption is made that the reservoir size always remains constant. Therefore, if water encroaches into the reservoir at some later date as a result of pressure decline, the reservoir size will remain unchanged, and will now be comprised of gas cap gas, free gas within the oil zone, oil in the oil zone, and water which has invaded the original oil zone. This is shown in Figure 3-3.

After the production of some oil and gas and after the influx of some water into the reservoir, the free gas remaining will occupy all space not occupied by liquid (oil and water).

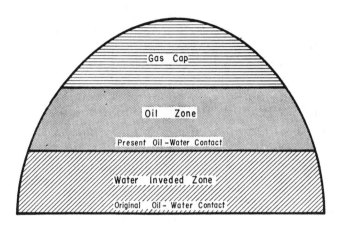

FIGURE 3-3. Oil reservoir showing water influx.

$$\text{Total reservoir space} = \frac{\text{Original oil}}{\text{zone size}} + \frac{\text{Original gas}}{\text{zone size}}$$

$$= NB_{oi} + mNB_{oi} \qquad (3\text{-}5)$$

Remaining liquid = Remaining Oil zone size + Net water influx

$$= (N - N_P) B_o + (W_e - W_p B_w) \qquad (3\text{-}6)$$

where:

B_w = Water formation volume factor
B_o = Oil formation volume factor at any pressure
W_e = Cumulative gross water influx into reservoir, barrels
W_P = Cumulative water produced, barrels

$$\frac{\text{Remaining free}}{\text{gas space}} = \frac{\text{Total reservoir}}{\text{space}} - \frac{\text{Remaining liquid}}{\text{volume}}$$

$$= (NB_{oi} + mNB_{oi}) - [(N - N_P) B_o + (W_e - W_p B_w)] \qquad (3\text{-}7)$$

therefore:

SCF free gas remaining =

$$\frac{(NB_{oi} + mNB_{oi}) - [(N - N_P) B_o + (W_e - W_p B_w)]}{B_g} \qquad (3\text{-}8)$$

Remaining gas in solution $= (N - N_p)\, R_s$ (3-9)

Combining Equations (3-1) through (3-9) yields:

$$mNB_{oi}\frac{1}{B_{gi}} + N\,R_{si} = N_p R_p$$
$$+\,\frac{(NB_{oi} + mNB_{oi}) - [\,(N - N_p)\,B_o + (W_e - W_p\,B_w)\,]}{B_g}$$
$$+ (N - N_p)R_s \qquad (3\text{-}10)$$

$$N_p R_p + \frac{N_p B_o}{B_g} - N_p R_s = mNB_{oi}\frac{1}{B_{gi}} + NR_{si} - \frac{NB_{oi}}{B_g}$$
$$-\,\frac{mNB_{oi}}{B_g} + \frac{NB_o}{B_g} - NR_s + \frac{(W_e - W_p\,B_w)}{B_g} \qquad (3\text{-}11)$$

multiplying both sides of Equation (3-11) by B_g:

$$N_p R_p + N_p B_o - N_p R_s B_g = mNB_{oi}\frac{B_g}{B_{gi}} + NR_{si}B_g - NB_{oi}$$
$$- mNB_{oi} + NB_o - NR_s B_g + (W_e - W_p\,B_w) \qquad (3\text{-}12)$$

however: $B_t = B_o + (R_{si} - R_s)\,B_g$ (3-13)

and $B_{ti} = B_{oi}$

where: B_t = two phase formation volume factor making the above substitutions result in:

$$N_p[B_o + (R_p - R_s)\,B_g]$$
$$= N\left[\,mB_{oi}\left(\frac{B_g}{B_{gi}} - 1\right) + B_o + (R_{si} - R_s)\,B_g - B_{oi}\,\right]$$
$$+ (W_e - W_p\,B_w) \qquad (3\text{-}14)$$

Combining Equations (3-13) and (3-14) and solving for N_p/N:

$$\frac{N_p}{N} = \frac{mB_{ti}\left(\dfrac{B_g}{B_{gi}} - 1\right) + (B_t - B_{ti}) + (W_e - W_p)/N}{B_o + (R_p - R_s)\,B_g} \qquad (3\text{-}15)$$

Equation (3-15) may have at least three unknowns, N, m, and W_e. Therefore, for it to have practical value other information must normally be available. Fortunately, this information is usually available, for to be of any real practical use the material balance equation can be used only after substantial volumes of fluid have been withdrawn from the reservoir. Production from other wells in the reservoir may yield information concerning the change in water-oil contact, and drill stem tests, logs, or core analysis data can be used to determine the size of the gas cap and oil zone.

Equation (3-15) can be rearranged as follows:

$$N_p [B_o + (R_p - R_s)B_g] = mNB_{ti} \left(\frac{B_g}{B_{gi}} - 1 \right) + N (B_t - B_{ti})$$
$$+ (W_e - W_p B_w) \qquad (3\text{-}16)$$

The left hand side of Equation (3-16) is equivalent to the reservoir oil and gas produced. The first term on the right hand side of the equation is the expansion of the gas cap, the second term is the expansion of the oil zone with the free gas which has been liberated from the oil zone, and the last term is the net water influx (or water expansion into the oil zone). Thus, it is seen from examination of Equation (3-16) that the reservoir oil and gas produced is equal to the sum of the gas cap expansion plus oil zone expansion, plus net water expansion into the oil zone. Equation (3-16) is a useful and interesting way to arrange the material balance equation because it shows the driving forces responsible for production of the reservoir oil and gas. A further discussion of the material balance equation in this form, for use in calculating indexes of drive, can be found in Chapter 8, *"Combination Drive Reservoirs."*

The previous development of the material balance equation assumed that the reservoir size did not change. In some reservoirs, the compressibility of the reservoir rock is of such magnitude that it should be considered. The effect of rock compressibility may be important in undersaturated depletion drive reservoirs and in water drive reservoirs. Normally it is not necessary to include the effects of rock compressibility in gas cap drive reservoirs because of the high compressibility of the gas cap gas.

Reservoir rock compressibility is the result of two factors: (1) expansion of the individual rock grains, and (2) formation compaction. Both of these factors are the results of a decrease of fluid pressure within the pore spaces, and both tend to reduce porosity. Hall[3] has published the results of laboratory studies of reservoir rock compressibility. Figure 3-4 is reproduced from his work. Hall found a good correlation between rock compressibility and rock porosity, which is considered applicable for most consolidated reservoir rocks. Hall's data for compressibility are reported as the change in pore volume per unit pore volume per psi. Therefore, in order to calculate the total change in reservoir pore volume, the equation is:

---

[3]Hall, H. N., "Compressibility of Reservoir Rocks," *Trans. AIME*, 1953, Vol. 198, p. 309.

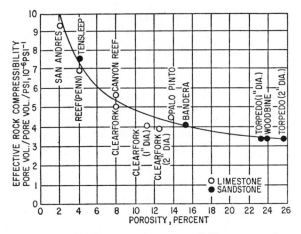

FIGURE 3-4. Effective rock compressibility vs. porosity.

Change in Pore Volume, Res. Bbls $= \dfrac{(C_t)\ (N\,B_{oi})\ \Delta P}{1 - S_{wi}}$ (3-17)

where:

$C_t = $ Effective rock compressibility, change in pore vol./unit pore vol./psi

$\dfrac{N\,B_{oi}}{1 - S_{wi}} = $ Reservoir pore volume, Reservoir barrels

$\Delta P = $ Change in reservoir pressure, psi

It should be noted that the reservoir pore volume term is obtained from the volumetric equation for calculating initial oil in place:

$$N = \frac{7758\,A\,h\,\phi\,(1 - S_{wi})}{B_{oi}}$$ (3-18)

Equation (3-18) is identical to Equation (2-7). The term 7758 Ahϕ is the pore volume of the reservoir, in units of reservoir barrels. Rearranging Equation (3-18):

$$7758\,Ah\phi = \frac{NB_{oi}}{1 - S_{wi}}$$ (3-19)

In the material balance equation it is usually more convenient to use the term $\dfrac{N\,B_{oi}}{1 - S_{wi}}$ rather than 7758 Ahϕ to express the reservoir pore volume.

As reservoir pressure declines the volume of the reservoir pore space decreases. In the material balance equation this will have the same effect as water influx. Therefore, a material balance equation which takes into consideration the rock compressibility can be derived by adding Equation (3-17) to the right hand side of Equation (3-16):

$$N_p [B_o + (R_p - R_s) B_g] = m NB_{ti} \left(\frac{B_g}{B_{gi}} - 1 \right) + N (B_t - B_{ti})$$

$$+ (W_e - W_p B_w) + \frac{C_f N B_{oi} \Delta P}{1 - S_{wi}} \qquad (3-20)$$

In some cases it may be desirable to include in the material balance equation the effects of formation water compressibility. In fact, this latter term may be as important as the rock compressibility term in some reservoirs. The expansion of the formation water can be expressed by:

$$\text{Formation Water Expansion} = C_w S_{wi} \frac{N B_{oi}}{1 - S_{wi}} \Delta P \qquad (3-21)$$

where:

C_w = Water compressibility, vol/vol/psi
S_{wi} = Formation water saturation, fraction

Including formation water expansion in the material balance equation provides a relationship which takes into consideration the effects of both rock and formation water compressibilities:

$$N_p [B_o + (R_p - R_s) B_g] = mNB_{ti} \left(\frac{B_g}{B_{gi}} - 1 \right) + N (B_t - B_{ti}) +$$

$$(W_e - W_p B_w) + \frac{C_f NB_{oi} \Delta P}{1 - S_{wi}} + \frac{C_w S_{wi} N B_{oi} \Delta P}{1 - S_{wi}} \qquad (3-22)$$

The principal utility of the material balance equation is in the prediction of reservoir behavior, and not in the estimation of initial oil in place. Large errors can be made by relying solely on the material balance equation for the estimation of initial oil in place. More weight should normally be applied to geologic data, logs, cores, and production data for the estimation of initial oil in place. The material balance is a useful auxiliary tool for estimating reserves. Cases have been reported where the material balance equation indicated a much larger initial oil in place than the best available geologic information showed. The unusually large initial oil in place calculated by the material balance equation resulted in a critical reexamination of the geologic data, which revealed a possible extension of the reservoir. On the basis of this information, an additional well was drilled, which proved the reservoir to be much larger than originally supposed.

Although it is unwise to use the material balance alone to calculate initial oil in place it can be reliably used with other equations and techniques to predict reservoir behavior, as will be discussed more fully in later chapters.

2. Instantaneous Gas-Oil Ratio Equation

In succeeding chapters it will be shown that the material balance equation contains at least two unknowns, even where good geologic data are available, when the equation is used in the prediction of reservoir behavior. Tarner, who was one of the first to develop a simplified method of predicting reservoir behavior, used the instantaneous producing gas-oil ratio equation in conjunction with the material balance equation. The gas-oil ratio equation is based on the Darcy flow equation. The radial flow form of this equation will be used in the following development, although any other form could be used equally as well. The instantaneous producing gas-oil ratio is:

$$R = \frac{\text{Gas producing rate, SCF/day}}{\text{Oil Producing rate, Stock tank barrel/Day}} \quad (3\text{-}23)$$

$$= \text{SCF/Stock tank barrel}$$

Gas production may be the result of free gas production and evolution of gas from solution in the reservoir oil. Free gas production can be stated in equation form as:

$$\text{free gas} = \frac{q_g}{B_g} \quad (3\text{-}24)$$

and the gas evolved from solution as:

$$\text{Gas evolved from solution} = Q_o R_s \quad (3\text{-}25)$$

where:

q_g = flow rate, reservoir barrels per day
B_g = gas conversion factor, bbls/SCF
Q_o = oil flow rate, stock tank (ST) barrels per day
R_s = gas solubility, SCF/ST barrel

Therefore, the total gas production rate is:

$$Q_g = \frac{q_g}{B_g} + Q_o R_s \qquad (3\text{-}26)$$

where:

Q_g = gas producing rate, SCF

The oil producing rate is:

$$Q_o = \frac{q_o}{B_o} \qquad (3\text{-}27)$$

where:

Q_o = oil producing rate, stock tank barrels/day
q_o = reservoir oil flow rate, reservoir barrels/day

Combining Equations (3-23), (3-26) and (3-27) yields:

$$R = \frac{\dfrac{q_g}{B_g} + Q_o R_s}{q_o/B_o} \qquad (3\text{-}28)$$

since $Q_o = \dfrac{q_o}{B_o}$, Equation (3-28) can be simplified:

$$R = \frac{\dfrac{q_g}{B_g}}{\dfrac{q_o}{B_o}} + R_s \qquad (3\text{-}29)$$

However, q_o and q_g represent reservoir flow rates, and these flow rates can be represented also by the Darcy flow equation:

$$q_g = \frac{2\pi k_g h \, \Delta p}{\mu_g \ln r_e/r_w} \qquad (3\text{-}30)$$

$$q_o = \frac{2\pi k_o h \, \Delta p}{\mu_o \ln r_e/r_w} \qquad (3\text{-}31)$$

Substituting Equations (3-30) and (3-31) into Equation (3-29) and simplifying yields:

$$R = \frac{\dfrac{2\pi k_g h \, \Delta p}{\mu_g \ln r_e/r_w \, B_g}}{\dfrac{2\pi k_o h \, \Delta p}{\mu_o \ln r_e/r_w \, B_o}} + R_s \qquad (3\text{-}32)$$

$$= \frac{k_g}{k_o} \cdot \frac{\mu_o}{\mu_g} \cdot \frac{B_o}{B_g} + R_s \qquad (3\text{-}33)$$

Equation (3-33) is the usual form of the instantaneous gas-oil ratio equation. In addition to its use in conjunction with the material balance equation, the gas-oil ratio equation can be used to calculate a field relative permeability curve or to check the validity of laboratory relative permeability data by rearranging Equation (3-33) as follows:

$$\frac{k_g}{k_o} = (R - R_s) \frac{\mu_g}{\mu_o} \frac{B_g}{B_o} \tag{3-34}$$

If data pertaining to the reservoir fluid characteristics (μ_g, μ_o, B_o, and R_s) are available, then Equation (3-34) will yield the k_g/k_o value at an instantaneous producing gas-oil ratio R. The value of R used in Equation (3-34) may have serious limitations in reservoirs where a gas cap is present. In order for the equation to be simplified to the form shown it was necessary to assume that the gas and oil were distributed uniformly throughout the reservoir in all directions, both vertically and laterally. If such were not the case, and in fact the gas and oil were essentially separated, then the nomenclature in Equations (3-30) and (3-31) would have to be revised as follows:

$$q_g = \frac{2\pi \, k_g \, h_g \, \Delta p}{\mu_g \ln r_e/r_w} \tag{3-35}$$

$$q_o = \frac{2\pi \, k_o \, h_o \, \Delta p}{\mu_g \ln r_e/r_w} \tag{3-36}$$

where:

h_g = reservoir thickness flowing gas
h_o = reservoir thickness flowing oil

It is obvious that the terms h_g and h_o would not cancel, but would remain in any simplification. Laboratory relative permeability data are taken with a core uniformly saturated with both gas and oil, and if the laboratory data are to be used in situations just described, the instantaneous gas-oil ratio equation should be used with caution.

3. Frontal Drive Equations

Leverett and Buckley[4, 5] were responsible for the development of a fluid displacement theory which has become known as the frontal

---

[4] Leverett, M. C., "Capillary Behavior in Porous Solids," *Trans.* AIME, 1941, Vol. 142, p. 152.
[5] Buckley, S. E., and Leverett, M. C., "Mechanism of Fluid Displacement in Sands," *Trans.* AIME, 1942, Vol. 146 p. 107.

drive theory. Frontal drive equations have one basic disadvantage which often seriously limits their application to practical reservoir engineering problems. This limitation is that in studying reservoirs which are stratified (i.e., layers of varying permeability) and have lateral variations in permeability, the calculated producing rates early in the life of the project may be substantially in error, Application of frontal drive equations to specific reservoir problems will be illustrated in Chapter 10, *Improving Oil Recovery*, where limitations of the method will also be discussed.

The frontal drive theory utilizes two equations, the fractional flow equation, and the rate-of-frontal-advance equation.

A. Fractional Flow Equation

The fractional flow equation is based on the principles governing fluid distribution and fluid flow within the reservoir. A generalized expression will be developed which will consider that flow may not necessarily be horizontal. Darcy's Law, for two fluids flowing downward (but parallel to the bedding plans) simultaneously through a reservoir which is inclined at some angle to the horizontal, can be written as follows:

$$q_g = - \frac{k_g A}{\mu_g} \left(\frac{\partial p_g}{\partial L} + \rho_g \operatorname{Sin} \alpha \right) \tag{3-37}$$

and:

$$q_o = - \frac{k_o A}{\mu_o} \left(\frac{\partial p_o}{\partial L} + \rho_o \operatorname{Sin} \alpha \right) \tag{3-38}$$

where:

q = flow rate, cc/sec.

k = permeability, darcies

A = cross-sectional area across which flow occurs, cm^2

μ = viscosity, centipoise

$\frac{\partial p}{\partial L}$ = pressure gradient, atmospheres/cm

ρ = density, gms/cc

α = angle of inclination of the reservoir, negative down dip

Subscripts "g" and "o" refer to gas and oil respectively. Capillary pressure can be represented by the following equations:

$$p_c = p_g - p_o \tag{3-39}$$

and

$$\frac{\partial p_c}{\partial L} = \frac{\partial p_g}{\partial L} - \frac{\partial p_o}{\partial L} \tag{3-40}$$

Solving Equations (3-37) and (3-38) for $\dfrac{\partial p_g}{\partial L}$ and $\dfrac{\partial p_o}{\partial L}$ and substituting these terms into Equation (3-40) yields:

$$\frac{\partial p_c}{\partial L} = \left[-\frac{q_g \mu_g}{k_g A} - \rho_g \, \text{Sin} \, \alpha \right] - \left[-\frac{q_o \mu_o}{k_o A} - \rho_o \, \text{Sin} \, \alpha \right] \quad (3\text{-}41)$$

$$= -\frac{q_g \mu_g}{k_g A} + \frac{q_o \mu_o}{k_o A} + (\rho_o - \rho_g) \, \text{Sin} \, \alpha \quad (3\text{-}42)$$

Solving for q_g, and substituting Δ_ρ for $(\rho_o - \rho_g)$ results in the following equation:

$$\frac{q_g \mu_g}{k_g A} = \frac{q_o \mu_o}{k_o A} + \Delta_\rho \, \text{Sin} \, \alpha - \frac{\partial p_c}{\partial L} \quad (3\text{-}43)$$

$$q_g = q_o \frac{\mu_o k_g}{\mu_g k_o} + \frac{k_g A}{\mu_g} \left(\Delta_\rho \, \text{Sin} \, \alpha - \frac{\partial p_c}{\partial L} \right) \quad (3\text{-}44)$$

By definition, the fraction of gas flowing in the sand is:

$$F_g = \frac{q_g}{q_t} = \frac{q_g}{q_g + q_o} \quad (3\text{-}45)$$

where:

F_g = fraction of gas flowing
q_t = total flow rate, cc/sec.

Dividing both sides of Equation (3-44) by $q_t \left(\dfrac{k_g \mu_o}{k_o \mu_g} \right)$ yields:

$$\frac{q_g}{q_t} \left(\frac{k_o}{k_g} \frac{\mu_g}{\mu_o} \right) = \frac{q_o}{q_t} + \frac{k_o A}{\mu_o q_t} \left(\Delta_\rho \, \text{Sin} \, \alpha - \frac{\partial p_c}{\partial L} \right) \quad (3\text{-}46)$$

however, $q_o/q_t = 1 - F_g$, and $q_g/q_t = F_g$. Substituting these relationships into Equation (3.46) yields:

$$F_g \left(\frac{k_o}{k_g} \frac{\mu_g}{\mu_o} \right) = (1 - F_g) + \frac{k_o A}{\mu_o q_t} \left(\Delta_\rho \, \text{Sin} \, \alpha - \frac{\partial p_c}{\partial L} \right) \quad (3\text{-}47)$$

rearranging Equation (3-47):

$$F_g \left(1 + \frac{k_o}{k_g} \frac{\mu_g}{\mu_o} \right) = 1 + \frac{k_o A}{\mu_o q_t} \left(\Delta_\rho \, \text{Sin} \, \alpha - \frac{\partial p_c}{\partial L} \right) \quad (3\text{-}48)$$

and solving for F_g:

$$F_g = \frac{1 + \dfrac{k_o}{\mu_o} \dfrac{A}{q_t} \left(\Delta_\rho \, \text{Sin} \, \alpha - \dfrac{\partial p_c}{\partial L} \right)}{1 + \dfrac{k_o}{k_g} \dfrac{\mu_g}{\mu_o}} \quad (3\text{-}49)$$

The development of Equation (3-49) is similar to the procedure used by Hocott.[6] As Hocott mentions in his discussion of the frontal drive theory the fractional flow Equation (3-49) states that flow through porous media is governed by viscous forces represented by

$\dfrac{k_o A}{\mu_o q_t}$; gravity forces, represented by Δ_ρ Sin α; and capillary forces,

represented by $\dfrac{\partial p_c}{\partial L}$.

The actual magnitude of the capillary forces is difficult, if not impossible, to evaluate, and therefore the $\dfrac{\partial p_c}{\partial L}$ term is generally omitted from Equation (3-49).

Gravity forces will be negligible if the flow is essentially horizontal, thereby making Sin α very small, or if the difference in density between the two fluids is small. If both the gravity forces (Δ_ρ Sin α) and the capillary forces are negligible, then Equation (3-49) reduces to:

$$F_g = \dfrac{1}{1 + \dfrac{k_o}{k_g}\dfrac{\mu_g}{\mu_o}} \tag{3-50}$$

which states that the fraction of gas in the flowing stream is dependent only upon the effective permeabilities and the viscosities of the flowing fluids.

B. Rate-of-Frontal-Advance Equation

The rate-of-frontal-advance equation can be developed by a material balance on a unit volume of the reservoir. Using a unit reservoir volume with the dimensions shown in Figure 3-5, the material balance equation is developed as follows:

$$\begin{matrix}\text{gas moving into} \\ \text{segment}\end{matrix} - \begin{matrix}\text{gas remaining in} \\ \text{segment}\end{matrix} = \begin{matrix}\text{gas moving out of} \\ \text{segment}\end{matrix} \tag{3-51}$$

$$q_t d\Theta F_{g1} \qquad - \phi A dx (S_{g2} - S_{g1}) = \qquad q_t d\Theta F_{g2} \tag{3-52}$$

Rearranging Equation (3-52) to solve for dx:

$$dx = \dfrac{q_t (F_{g1} - F_{g2}) d\Theta}{\phi A (S_{g2} - S_{g1})} \tag{3-53}$$

---

[6] Hocott, C. R., "Mechanics of Fluid Injection—Water," *Producers Monthly*, Sept. 1957, Vol. 21, No. 11, p. 20.

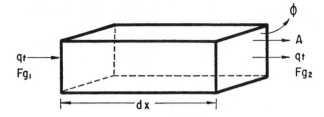

FIGURE 3-5. Unit reservoir volume.

Substituting ΔF_g for $(F_{g1} - F_{g2})$, ΔS_g for $(S_{g2} - S_{g1})$ and Δx for dx results in:

$$\Delta x = \frac{q_t d\Theta}{\phi A} \left(\frac{\Delta F_g}{\Delta S_g} \right) \tag{3-54}$$

however, $q_t d\Theta = Q_t$, and placing this value into Equation (3-54) yields:

$$\Delta x = \frac{Q_t}{\phi A} \left(\frac{\Delta F_g}{\Delta S_g} \right) \tag{3-55}$$

where:

$d\Theta$ = incremental time, sec.
dx = incremental length, cm.
S_g = gas saturation, fraction
ϕ = porosity, fraction
Δx = length, cm.
Q_t = total injected volume, cm^3

Equations (3-50) and (3-55) are used together in the frontal drive theory. Their use in the solution of reservoir flow problems will be discussed in the later chapters where specific problems are solved.

4. Unsteady State Equations

All of the flow equations developed previously in this book were *steady state* equations, which means that the mass rate of flow at one point in a system is exactly equal to the mass rate of flow at any other part of the system, or in other words, the mass rate of flow throughout the system is constant. When any compressible fluid is flowing the mass rate of flow is constantly changing due to the effect of pressure on the density; therefore, the flow is called *unsteady*. However, in many cases, Darcy's law, which is a steady state equation, can be used with a reasonable degree of accuracy, because the flow rate at mean pressure is used.

The influx of water into a reservoir is usually an important oil-displacing force. Taking maximum advantage of a natural water drive will usually result in the greatest possible oil recovery. Water is normally the most efficient displacing force available (excluding of course miscible displacing fluids such as liquid propane, pentane, etc.). This is because most reservoirs are not inclined at an angle sufficiently steep to take full advantage of gravitational segregation and also because gas is not an efficient displacing mechanism. Water is more efficient than gas as a displacing fluid because: (1) water viscosity is greater than gas viscosity, which results in a more favorable viscosity ratio, and (2) most reservoirs are believed to be water wet; thus the gas, which will be non-wetting will travel through the larger pores in the reservoir rock leaving oil trapped in the smaller pores, while water will pass through both the small pores and the large pores, leaving less residual oil behind.

Hurst[7] developed one of the most usable methods of predicting the behavior of water drive reservoirs. The method was later simplified by Hurst and van Everdingen,[8] and is now the most commonly-used method of predicting behavior of water drive reservoirs.

In the derivation of the method, Hurst applies Darcy's Law to the diffusivity equation to develop a usable technique. The mathematics in the development become somewhat complex to those who have little occasion to review basic mathematical principles from time to time. However, the method has been checked and verified both mathematically and in the field, and therefore the technique can be safely used without a thorough understanding of the development. The user should be familiar with the limitations of the equation, and these limitations will be discussed.

Where the reservoir pressure-time curve can be represented as a series of straight lines, the water influx into a reservoir can be represented as a series of step-wise calculations. Water influx into a reservoir can then be calculated by the following equation developed by Hurst:

$$W_e = B\Sigma\Delta p \times Q_{(t)} \qquad (3\text{-}56)$$

[7] Hurst, W., "Water Influx Into a Reservoir and Its Application to the Equation of Volumetric Balance," *Trans.* AIME, 1943, Vol. 151, p. 57.

[8] van Everdingen, A. F., and Hurst, W., "Application of the LaPlace Transformation to Flow Problems in Reservoirs," *Trans.* AIME, 1949, Vol. 186, p. 305.

where:

W_e = total water influx at any time, barrels
Δp = Pressure drop, psi
$Q_{(t)}$ = Dimensionless water influx.
B = Water influx constant

Equation (3-56) has the following limitations:

1. Water encroaches radially into the reservoir.
2. Gravitational forces are negligible.

The prediction of water-drive reservoir performance by this method is no more difficult than the prediction of performance of a depletion drive reservoir by the Tarner method. A simple procedure for using the Hurst method is outlined, with an example problem, in Chapter 6. Equation (3-56) is also derived in the same chapter.

5. Models

Models are used extensively in the study of petroleum reservoirs. Various electrical models and actual fluid flow models, including fluid mapper models, were the earliest models utilized. However, with the advent of high-speed computers, mathematical models came into wide use. During the 1960's, probably the greatest single development in reservoir engineering techniques has been the rapid advances in the development of usable, reliable mathematical models. These mathematical models can duplicate changes in lithology and changes in pressure from one part of the reservoir to another. The simultaneous influence of wells on each other can be determined. These reservoir mathematical models are powerful tools when properly used, and at the present time most oil companies and consultants have the models available for use. A discussion of the development and techniques used in model studies is beyond the scope of this book. Many excellent references are available in the literature if information is needed.

A. Reservoir Studies

A reservoir study concerns the factors governing the behavior of a petroleum reservoir, the end result of which is a recommended operating program which will yield the maximum net income from the property. Complete reservoir studies usually require months, or even years to complete, depending on the complexity of the reservoir and the thoroughness of the study. It should be emphasized that a thorough reservoir study can not be completed in a few days or a few weeks. So-called "thumb-nail" reservoir studies, requiring only a few days or a few weeks to complete, are often made, but these studies are of value only to indicate trends in reservoir behavior, or to determine the need for a full-scale study.

Stated broadly, a reservoir study is comprised of three basic parts: (1) matching past behavior, (2) predicting future behavior under various possible operating programs (various fluid withdrawal rates, water injection, gas injection), and (3) recommending the best overall operating plan for the reservoir.

The first step in any reservoir study after the data have been assembled is the matching of past behavior. Referring to Figure 3-6, the solid lines represent the actual pressure-production and gas-oil ratio history of the reservoir. If a reliable reservoir study is to be made the amount of past production from the reservoir must be substantial. The exact amount of past history which has to be accumulated before a reservoir study can be considered reliable is difficult to establish due to the many variable factors involved. However, a rule of thumb which many practicing reservoir engineers use is that it is safe to predict ahead the same number of years for which past production history is available. In other words, if a reservoir has been producing for 10 years then it should be safe to predict ahead for 10 additional years. As more and more data are accumulated the accuracy of reservoir predictions will normally increase.

Starting at a time when $N_p = 0$, and using the data which have been accumulated, a series of reservoir performance predictions are made. No attention at all is paid to the actual reservoir history. The reservoir performance predictions are made to cover the time from original production to the current data. These data, the "predicted" performance over the past producing history of the reservoir are then plotted on Figure 3-6, which also shows the actual production history. A typical plot is shown by the dashed lines in Figure 3-6. In the illustration, the calculated reservoir performance does not match the actual reservoir performance. This is often the result of the first attempt. It can be seen from Figure 3-6 that if future predictions of reservoir behavior had been begun immediately, in all probability the predicted future behavior would not have matched the actual future behavior. If the predicted past behavior does not match the actual past behavior, there is no basis for believing that the predicted future behavior will match the future actual behavior.

It is now necessary to determine why the predicted and actual past production histories do not match. There are two possible sources of error: (1) either incorrect equations, or (2) incorrect

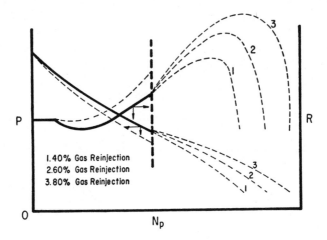

FIGURE 3-6. Predicting reservoir behavior.

data, are being used. In most cases, proper care has been taken in selecting the equations, and it must be assumed that these equations are correct. Occasionally equations used for predicting behavior of water drive reservoirs may need some change (this will be discussed at length in Chapter 6). The only remaining area of potential misinformation lies in the numbers used in the equations. The data which are used in the equations may be subdivided into four parts: (1) reservoir pressure data, (2) reservoir fluid data obtained from either subsurface or recombined samples, (3) oil, water, and gas production data, and (4) gross reservoir data, such as size of original oil zone, gas cap size, and water influx. If the equations used to predict the past behavior are correct, then if an incorrect answer is obtained it is obvious that incorrect data have been used in the equations. Therefore, the next step in the reservoir study is a re-evaluation of all the reservoir data in order to correct the discrepancies. This may be a tedious, time-consuming job, but nevertheless it is necessary if a sound reservoir study is to be made. A close appraisal of all the reservoir data may indicate possible errors in some of the data, in which case a tentative correction in the data is made and past reservoir performance is again "predicted." If this correction fails to yield a perfect match between predicted past behavior, then further study of the data must be made. In cases where a study of all reservoir data fails to yield a potential source of error, it may be simpler to examine the calculated results to determine what factors in the equations would have to be changed in order to yield the desired match. For example, it might be determined that a small change in original reservoir pressure would result in a match between predicted and actual behavior. Then the original reservoir pressure measurement could be critically examined to determine whether or not there would be any justification for the change. Likewise, it might be determined that a small change in the reported gas production would yield the desired match, in which case the gas production data could be examined very closely to locate possible errors in gas measurement.

Before finally changing any basic data to provide a match between predicted and actual past behavior there should be some justification for the change. Arbitrarily changing original reservoir pressure just because this would achieve the desired match is not good practice. This may temporarily solve the problem, but if the real problem is the omission of some of the gas production, then in future prediction work this may result in a compounding of errors.

A reservoir study is of value only if the future performance of the reservoir can be accurately predicted. Matching predicted past performance with actual past performance is a major step in the attainment of this goal.

The heart of a reservoir study lies in the information derived in predicting future behavior of the reservoir. Since the object of the reservoir study is to determine the operating methods which will yield the greatest net income for the property, it will usually be necessary to study the effects of: (1) different reservoir withdrawal rates, (2) varying amounts of gas injection, (3) varying amounts of water injection, and (4) other fluid injection or secondary recovery methods. All or part of these various parameters may be studied for any one reservoir. It becomes immediately obvious that the number of calculations becomes enormous if several combinations of varying factors are studied. For example, consider the number of complete calculations required if the effects of three different rates of oil production, three different rates of gas production, and three different rates of water production are studied. There are 27 different combinations of withdrawal rates. If to this, three different amounts of gas injection are added, this results in 81 sets of complete calculations, which would require several man-months of time if a standard desk calculator were used. Fortunately, computer facilities are available which reduce the calculation time to a matter of minutes, rather than months. Most routine methods of reservoir studies have been programmed, and therefore little preliminary work is required for solution of the problem on computers. The application of the computer to reservoir engineering studies has eliminated the laborious and unrewarding aspects of reservoir studies and permits the engineer to more effectively utilize his time in the development of good data, and in the interpretation of the results. It should be emphasized that, even with the aid of computer facilities, a thorough reservoir study still requires months for completion.

The results of the predicted future behavior under various operating plans is usually shown in graphical form. The dashed lines to the right of the vertical line in Figure 3-6 show typical results for three different gas injection rates with one set of fluid withdrawal rates. Because of the uncertain future actions of the various regulatory agencies in controlling reservoir fluid withdrawal rates, it is usually desirable to determine the effect of at least three different withdrawal rates for oil, and it may be necessary due to other uncertainties to also consider the effects of three different gas producing rates for each oil producing rate, and three water producing rates for each of these production rates.

After the effects of various operating methods on ultimate oil recovery have been predicted, it is necessary to select the best overall method of operation for recommendation to management. The method to be recommended will normally be the one which will yield the greatest ultimate net income, as there often will be factors present which will render uneconomic the recovery of a maximum amount of oil. For example, the return of 95% of the produced gas to the reservoir might result in the recovery of more oil than if only 50% of the produced gas were returned, but if the cost of additional gas and compressor facilities was more than the value of the additional oil recovered, there would be no incentive to construct the additional facilities.

B. Limitations of Reservoir Studies

The reliability of reservoir engineering studies is entirely dependent upon the validity of the data used in the calculations. If reliable data are not used then the calculated results will not be reliable. One of the most important parts of a reservoir study is the adjusting of the basic data (subsurface sample data and production data) to insure its reliability. This is also one of the most tedious tasks confronting the reservoir engineers in the overall study, and therefore the temptation to complete this phase of the work as rapidly as possible is often very great.

Volatile Oil Reservoirs

For many years petroleum reservoirs were classified either as gas, condensate, or oil reservoirs, and reservoir studies were performed on reservoirs in accordance with accepted principles for the particular type of reservoir under consideration. In recent years, with the advent of deeper drilling, reservoirs have been discovered which contain crude oil of markedly different character than the so-called "black-oil" reservoirs found at shallower depths. These deeper reservoirs contain an oil which is much more volatile than most previously-discovered crudes. These oils are characterized by a high API gravity, normally above 2000 SCF per stock tank barrel, but frequently above 3000 SCF per stock tank barrel.

Reservoir performance studies of these volatile oil reservoirs by conventional material balance methods are inadequate. In conventional material balance calculations the assumption is usually made that once the gas and oil phases have separated either in the reservoir, or in the well bore, the gas will not yield additional liquid, and the two fluids can be treated in a completely independent manner. This procedure is normally satisfactory for oils of low volatility although certain refinements in technique have been attempted from time to time. One of the most satisfactory techniques is the use of flash separation data to convert produced liquid to a stock tank basis where oils of medium volatility are encountered.

In volatile oil reservoirs, significant volumes of liquid may be obtained from the reservoir gas phase, and for this reason the previously-used material balance techniques are unsuitable. It was therefore necessary to develop techniques which would adequately describe the phenomenon. Several methods which appear to have merit have been developed.[9, 10, 11]

[9] Cook A. B., Spencer, G. B., and Bobrowski, F. B., "Special Consideraitons in Predicting Reservoir Behavior of Highly Volatile Type Oil Reservoirs," *Trans.* AIME, 1951, Vol. 192, p. 37.

[10] Reudelhuber, F. O., and Hinds, R. F., "A Compositional Material Balance Method for Prediction of Recovery from Volatile Oil Depletion Drive Reservoirs," *Trans.* AIME, 1957, Vol. 210, p. 19.

[11] Jacoby, R. H., and Berry, V. J., Jr., "A Method for Predicting Depletion Performance of a Reservoir Producing Volatile Crude Oil," *Trans.* AIME, 1957, Vol. 210, p. 27.

Identification of Volatile Oil Reservoirs

In addition to the high API gravity, high solution gas-oil ratios, and high formation volume factors that are characteristic of volatile oil reservoirs, there are other factors which can also be used in their identification. It has been observed that in these volatile oil reservoirs the API gravity of the stock tank liquid will increase in the later life of the reservoir. Figure 3-7 shows a graph of API Gravity vs Cumulative Oil Production for the volatile oil reservoir described by Woods.[12]

Another characteristic of volatile oil reservoirs is the relatively high initial gas-oil ratios, usually exceeding 2000 SCF per stock

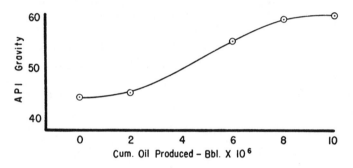

FIGURE 3-7. API gravity history of a volatile oil reservoir. *(After Woods, Trans., AIME, 1955.)*

tank barrel, exhibited by structurally low wells. This is a result of the unusually high gas solubility of the volatile oils. Figure 3-8 shows produced gas-oil ratio history of the volatile oil reservoir discussed by Woods. Note the unusually high initial producing gas oil ratios. Typical gas solubility and formation volume factor data for a volatile oil reservoir are shown in Figure 3-9.

Ultimate Recovery

Ultimate recovery from volatile oil reservoir is dependent upon the same general factors which govern recovery from other oil reservoirs, but due to the peculiarities of the reservoir oil, other factors are particularly important. Volatile oil reservoirs may be subjected to a water drive, and where an effective water drive is present, ultimate recovery can be expected to be reasonably good,

[12] Woods, R. W., "Case History of Reservoir Performance of a Highly Volatile Type Oil Reservoir," *Trans.* AIME, 1955, Vol. 204, p. 156.

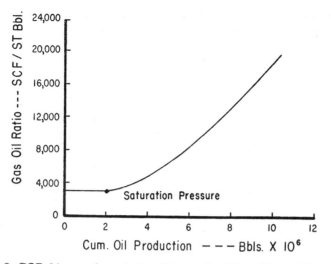

FIGURE 3-8. GOR history of a volatile oil reservoir. *(After Woods, Trans., AIME, 1955, Vol. 204, p. 159.)*

possibly on the order of 40 to 60 percent of the initial oil in place depending upon the activity of the water drive. The literature has few references to water drive volatile oil reservoirs, most of the reported volatile oil reservoirs having been the depletion drive type. It is not known whether this lack of reported water-drive volatile oil reservoirs has any significance.

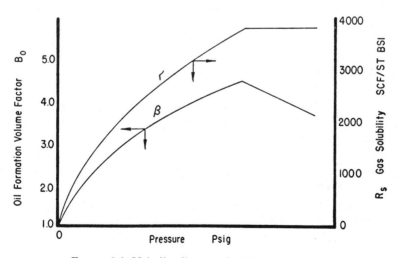

FIGURE 3-9. Volatile oil reservoir fluid characteristics.

There have been several reported cases of depletion drive volatile oil reservoirs. Ultimate recovery from these reservoirs has been

Table 3-1

Basic Experimental Data - - - Constant Volume Depletion,
Hydrocarbon Analyses of Equilibrium Gas Phase

Component	Reservoir Pressure—psig						
	4,795 *	3,990	3,100	2,310	1,410	690	0
			Values are Mol Per Cent				
Carbon Dioxide	0.27	0.27	0.27	0.28	0.29	0.32	
Nitrogen	0.24	0.27	0.28	0.29	0.29	0.28	
Methane	66.83	75.94	79.34	80.87	80.74	77.75	
Ethane	8.28	8.23	8.29	8.44	8.85	9.90	
Propane	5.15	4.59	4.41	4.35	4.65	5.69	
iso-Butane	1.04	0.90	0.77	0.75	0.77	0.94	
n-Butane	2.27	1.93	1.73	1.57	1.61	2.08	
iso-Pentane	1.00	0.78	0.64	0.55	0.54	0.64	
n-Pentane	1.04	0.84	0.67	0.57	0.57	0.70	
Hexanes	1.85	1.24	0.90	0.72	0.65	0.73	
Heptanes plus	12.03	5.01	2.70	1.61	1.04	0.97	
Totals	100.00	100.00	100.00	100.00	100.00	100.00	
Molecular Weight Heptanes plus	182	144	123	115	112	112	
Density Heptanes plus—gms/cc	0.801	0.773**	0.752**	0.745**	0.741**	0.741**	
Deviation Factor—Z	1.042	0.924	0.848	0.845	0.879	0.929	1.000
Cumulative Volume Produced Gas— Mol Per Cent	0	9.054	22.100	36.318	55.083	70.880	88.659
Liquid Phase Volume Per Cent of Initial Hydrocarbon Pore Space	100.00	50.35	45.80	42.50	37.93	34.50	28.59 26.40 @60°F

* Reservoir fluid composition at saturation pressure.
** These values are based upon the characterization factor of the initial heptanes plus and are obtained from Brown, Katz, Oberfell and Alden, *Natural Gasoline and the Volatile Hydrocarbons,* (Section One), Natural Gasoline Association of America, Tulsa, p. 79, 1948.

low, varying from less than 10 percent to more than 20 percent of the initial oil in place.

Due to the high shrinkage factors of volatile oils, a reduction in reservoir pressure as a result of oil production will cause an abnormally high reduction in reservoir liquid volume with a consequent rapid increase in gas saturation. This results in an early high permeability to gas, which in turn causes further decreases in reservoir pressure. The net result is low ultimate oil recovery from the reservoir.

If it were not for the fact that substantial quantities of liquid are recoverable from the reservoir gas phase, ultimate liquid recovery would be even less.

Predicting Reservoir Behavior

As mentioned previously several methods have been developed which appear to have merit for predicting behavior of volatile oil reservoirs. The technique developed by Reudelhuber and Hinds is straightforward and involves a minimum number of assumptions; and although it requires some special laboratory data, the extra trouble appears to be worthwhile because of the simplicity of the calculations. The basic experimental data required are the hydrocarbon analyses of both liquid and gas phases at various pressures for a constant volume depletion process. Table 3-1 shows the basic experimental data from analysis of an oil sample from the Mid-Continent oil reservoir reported by Reudelhuber and Hinds.

The prediction of reservoir behavior of a volatile oil reservoir is subject to the same limitations and restrictions as predictions for normal oil reservoirs. The limitations and procedures for predicting reservoir behavior have already been outlined. The principal requirement in predicting reservoir behavior is the matching of past reservoir history. This aspect of a reservoir study is particularly important in volatile oil reservoir studies due to the increased complexity of the laboratory data required. If the laboratory data do not yield a match with the actual past production history of the reservoir then some of the data will have to be adjusted until the laboratory data do yield a match with past reservoir performance.

Chapter 4

DEPLETION DRIVE RESERVOIRS

In depletion drive reservoirs, as previously discussed in Chapter 3, the principal source of energy displacing oil from the reservoir is the expansion of the gas which has been evolved from solution from the oil as the reservoir pressure is reduced. Depletion drive reservoirs are often referred to as solution gas drive or internal gas drive reservoirs. These reservoirs have no initial free gas cap and no active water drive. Stratigraphic trap reservoirs are often depletion drive reservoirs, due to the nature of the trap, which precludes the presence of a large aquifer underlying the oil zone.

A reservoir operating under a depletion drive producing mechanism has the following characteristics:

1. Rapid pressure decline. No extraneous fluids or large free gas caps are available to occupy the space vacated by the produced oil.

2. Water-free oil production. The absence of a water drive means there will be little or no water produced with the oil during the entire producing life of the reservoir. The interstitial water saturation in the oil zone will not be produced as it has already been reduced to a minimum saturation.

3. Rapidly increasing gas-oil ratio from all wells, regardless of their structural position. After reservoir pressure has been reduced below the saturation pressure, gas will be evolved from solution throughout the reservoir. Once this gas saturation has increased to the point where it can flow (equilibrium saturation), then this free gas will begin to flow toward the well bore. The gas will also begin a vertical movement due to the gravitational forces, which may result in the formation of a secondary gas cap. Vertical permeability is an important factor in the formation of a secondary gas cap.

4. Low ultimate oil recovery. Oil production by depletion drive is usually the least efficient recovery method. This is a direct result of the formation of a gas saturation throughout the reservoir. Very early in the life of a reservoir a high relative permeability to gas is developed, and before oil recovery has reached very large proportions, the reservoir is flowing essen-

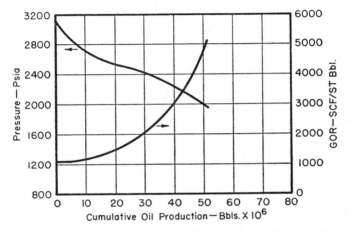

FIGURE 4-1. Performance history—West Edmond Hunton Lime. (*After Little-field, Gray and Godbold, Trans., AIME, 1948, Vol. 174.*)

tially gas only. Thus, the economic limit is reached relatively early. This problem could be alleviated somewhat if the gas could be made to form a *bank* to displace oil ahead of it. This is often impossible, but where the vertical permeability is such that gravity forces can be brought into play, one solution to this problem is to shut in the reservoir for a short time (2 or 3 months) to allow the gas to migrate upstructure and the oil to migrate downstructure. This will reduce the gas saturation in the lower portion of the reservoir, with a consequent reduction in gas-oil ratios. Gravity segregation will be discussed more fully in Chapter 7. Figure 4-1 shows pressure and gas-oil ratio histories of the West Edmond Hunton Lime reservoir prior to initiation of pressure maintenance operations. This reservoir was operating primarily under a depletion drive mechanism, although a small amount of water had encroached into the reservoir.

Ultimate recovery from depletion drive reservoirs may vary from less than five percent to about 25 percent. Relative permeability (k_g/k_o) relationships determine to a large extent the ultimate recovery from depletion drive reservoirs. In turn, individual factors which govern the relative permeability relationships can be examined to determine their effects on ultimate oil recovery. Reservoir oil viscosity is also an important factor in determining ultimate recovery. As reservoir oil viscosity increases, ultimate oil recovery decreases. The amount of gravitational segregation of the oil and gas will also be a function of the oil and gas viscosities.

Predicting Reservoir Performance

Future reservoir performance of a depletion drive reservoir can be predicted with reasonable accuracy provided reliable subsurface sample and relative permeability data are available. The method developed by Tarner[1] provides a convenient method of predicting future reservoir performance. This method utilizes the Schilthuis material balance equation, the instantaneous gas-oil ratio equation, and an equation for determining the oil saturation existing at any time.

If the original reservoir pressure is greater than the saturation pressure (undersaturated oil), then two entirely different material balance equations should be used. Reservoir saturation pressure is defined as the highest pressure (going in the direction of decreasing pressure) at which a bubble of gas is first evolved from solution from the oil. The general material balance equation developed in Chapter 3 is applicable both above and below the saturation pressure after clearing terms from the equation which are zero, and also realizing that the numerical value of N in the equation is different, depending on whether the equation is to be used above or below the saturation pressure. The same value of N should not be used both above and below the saturation pressure because of the change in the slope of the formation volume factor curve at the saturation pressure. Above the saturation pressure B_o increases as the pressure is reduced. This is a direct result of the compressibility of the oil, for as the pressure is reduced the oil volume increases. Below the saturation pressure, the oil volume continues to increase as pressure is decreased; however, now gas is being evolved from solution from the oil, which causes a reduction in volume of a unit of reservoir oil. Thus, the two factors of oil compressibility and gas evolution are working in exactly opposite directions. The effect of gas evolution from the oil has a much greater effect on the size

---

[1] Tarner, J., "How Different Size Gas Caps and Pressure Maintenance Affect Ultimate Recovery," *Oil Weekly,* June 12, 1944, p. 32.

of a unit volume of reservoir oil, and therefore below the saturation pressure B_o decreases as reservoir pressure is decreased.

The material balance equation for use above the saturation pressure will be developed by referring to the general material balance equation shown in Equation (3-15), which includes a gas cap and water encroachment. For convenience, Equation (3-15) is repeated here:

$$\frac{N_p}{N} = \frac{mB_{ti}\left(\dfrac{B_g}{B_{gi}} - 1\right) + (B_t - B_{ti}) + \left(\dfrac{W_e - W_p B_w}{N}\right)}{B_o + (R_p - R_s)B_g} \quad (3\text{-}15)$$

For a depletion drive reservoir, m, W_e, and W_p are all equal to zero, and since no free gas is flowing above the saturation pressure, R_p must be exactly equal to R_s. Therefore a material balance equation for a depletion drive reservoir above the saturation pressure reduces to:

$$\frac{N_{ps}}{N_s} = \frac{B_t - B_{ti}}{B_o} \quad (4\text{-}1)$$

however, above the saturation pressure, $B_t = B_o$, therefore Equation (4-1) can be rewritten as:

$$\frac{N_{ps}}{N_s} = \frac{B_o - B_{oi}}{B_o} \quad (4\text{-}2)$$

where:

N_{ps} = Cumulative oil produced, stock tank barrels.
N_s = Oil in place originally, stock tank barrels.

The fractional oil recovery above the saturation pressure is simply a function of the change in formation volume factors.

Equation (4-2) can be used above to calculate oil recovery down to the saturation pressure. From the saturation pressure to abandonment pressure Equation (3-15) is again modified to fit the specific conditions of a depletion drive reservoir, as shown:

$$\frac{N_p}{N} = \frac{B_t - B_{ti}}{B_o + (R_p - R_s)B_g} \quad (4\text{-}3)$$

where:

N_p = Cumulative oil produced, beginning at time when reservoir pressure has declined to the saturation pressure, stock tank barrels.

N = Oil in place after reservoir pressure has declined to the saturation pressure, stock tank barrels.

To find the total oil produced from the reservoir by the depletion drive mechanism the oil produced above the saturation pressure must be added to the oil produced below the saturation pressure, or:

$$N_{pt} = N_{ps} + N_p \qquad (4\text{-}4)$$

where:

N_{pt} = Total cumulative oil produced from a depletion drive reservoir, stock tank barrels.

The instantaneous gas-oil ratio equation is the second equation used in the prediction of reservoir performance. This equation was developed in Chapter 3, and is shown here again for convenience:

$$R = \frac{k_g}{k_o} \; \frac{\mu_o}{\mu_g} \; \frac{B_o}{B_g} + R_s \qquad (3\text{-}33)$$

The other major equation required for the technique is an equation for determining oil saturation in the reservoir at any time. Oil saturation is defined as:

$$S_o = \frac{\text{Remaining Oil Volume}}{\text{Total Pore Volume}}$$

$$= \frac{(N - N_p) B_o}{N B_{os}/1 - S_{wi}} \qquad (4\text{-}5)$$

$$= \left(1 - \frac{N_p}{N}\right) \frac{B_o}{B_{os}} (1 - S_{wi}) \qquad (4\text{-}6)$$

where:

S_o = Oil saturation at any time, fraction.

S_{wi} = Interstitial water saturation, fraction.

The foregoing development assumes that the gas saturation is distributed uniformly throughout the reservoir at all times. The oil saturation required for the solution which follows is the saturation in that part of the reservoir which is supplying fluids to the well bore. If a secondary gas cap is being formed then another equation should be developed for the determination of oil saturation, which takes this vertical movement of fluids into consideration. An example will be used to illustrate the procedure to be employed to develop a reliable method of calculating oil saturation, using an oil reservoir which has no original free gas cap. Vertical permeability in the reservoir is unusually good, and a secondary gas cap has been formed, the magnitude of which can be determined by production data from wells located structurally high. The oil saturation of interest for reservoir performance studies is that oil saturation existing in the vicinity of the completion interval. This can be determined by using the following reasoning:

$$S'_o = \frac{\text{Remaining Oil Volume}}{\text{Pore Volume within which Rem. Oil is located}}$$

$$= \frac{\text{Remaining Oil Volume}}{\text{Original Total Volume} - \text{Secondary Gas Cap Volume}}$$

$$= \frac{(N - N_p) B_o}{(NB_{os} - m'NB_{os})/(1 - S_{wi})}$$

$$= \frac{(N - N_p) B_o (1 - S_{wi})}{NB_{os} (1 - m')}$$

$$= \frac{\left(1 - \dfrac{N_p}{N}\right) \dfrac{B_o}{B_{os}} (1 - S_{wi})}{(1 - m')} \tag{4-7}$$

where:

S'_o = Oil saturation within the oil zone of the reservoir, fraction.

m' = Ratio of secondary gas cap size to original oil zone size.

The development of Equation (4-7) was simplified by assuming that the oil saturation in the secondary gas cap is zero. Although this is obviously an impossibility, the error involved in the assumption is believed to be small, and is justified as a result of the simplified final equation.

Similar reasoning will enable the engineer to develop reliable oil saturation equations for situations encountered in most reservoir engineering problems. Equations for calculating oil saturation equations using other assumptions are shown in Chapter 8, *"Combination Drive Reservoirs."*

Mechanics of the Reservoir Performance Prediction Procedure

When making a reservoir study of a depletion drive reservoir the principal objectives are to determine:

(1) the ultimate recovery by primary recovery methods,

(2) the rate at which the oil and gas will be recovered, and

(3) the variation of reservoir pressure with oil production.

All of these objectives can be answered by the Tarner method of predicting reservoir performance. A step-by-step procedure for performing a reservoir study follows.

Procedure for Reservoir Performance Predictions

I. Assemble production data and all necessary information concerning the reservoir fluids. The information can be grouped into the following categories:

A. Reservoir Fluid Data

    1. Oil Formation Volume Factor (B_o)

    2. Gas Solubility Data (R_s)

    3. Gas Deviation Factor (Z)

    This can be calculated if any one of the following are available:

        a. Laboratory measured values of Z.

        b. Gas composition.

        c. Gas specific gravity.

    4. Reservoir Oil Viscosity (μ_o)

    5. Reservoir Gas Viscosity (μ_g)

Prepare graphs of all the above factors versus pressure.

B. Past Production Data

    1. Oil production data

    2. Gas production data

    3. Water production data

    4. Net water influx

Prepare graphs of the above data versus pressure.

C. Fluid Flow Data

    1. Laboratory relative permeability data (k_g/k_o vs S_o) or (k_w/k_o vs S_o)

    2. Field relative permeability data. Calculated from past production data using the instantaneous gas-oil ratio equation and the oil saturation equation.

D. Geological Data

    1. Initial oil in place (N)

    2. Ratio of gas zone size to oil zone size (m)

3. Interstitial water saturation (S_{wi})

4. Porosity (ϕ).

As previously listed, both a laboratory relative permeability curve and a field relative permeability curve should be available. The field relative permeability curve can be calculated by using the instantaneous gas-oil ratio equation and the oil saturation equation. This provides a reliable index of the past flow characteristics of the reservoir, which is a critical factor in the behavior of a depletion drive reservoir. However, since the behavior of the reservoir in the future is one of the principal objectives of the study, it will be necessary to extrapolate the field relative permeability curves to lower oil saturations. This is best accomplished by using laboratory relative permeability data, adjusting the curve obtained in the laboratory until it fits the field curve over the past history of the reservoir. This will usually provide a reliable index of future behavior.

II. Arrange the material balance equation in the following form:

$$N_p R_p = \frac{N(B_t - B_{ts}) - (N_p(B_t - R_{ss}B_g)}{B_g} \qquad (4\text{-}8)$$

where:

$N_p R_p$ = Cumulative gas produced, SCF.

III. Using the past production history of the reservoir, and the best available data, *predict* reservoir behavior, as if the actual reservoir behavior were unknown, and compare this *predicted* performance with the actual reservoir performance. This technique is a necessary preliminary step in any reservoir study and was discussed more fully in Chapter 3. Make any necessary adjustments in basic data as dictated by this matching process.

IV. **First Prediction Step**

A. Select a future reservoir pressure, and assume a value of N_p. Solve Equation (4-8) for $N_p R_p$. It is obvious that to solve the equation for $N_p R_p$ that N must be known. In most instances where sufficient data are available to prepare a reservoir study, there will also be sufficient geologic data available to calculate N.

B. Using the assumed value of N_p solve the oil saturation Equation (4-6) for S_o. Using this calculated value of S_o, determine the applicable k_g/k_o from the relative permeability curve. Then calculate R, the instantaneous gas-oil ratio, from the instantaneous flowing gas-oil ratio (GOR) equation.

C. Calculate the total gas produced during the first period by:

$$\left(\frac{R_i + R_{i+1}}{2}\right) N_{p1} \qquad (4\text{-}9)$$

where:

R_i = Initial instantaneous flowing gas-oil ratio, SCF/stock tank (ST) barrel.

R_{i+1} = Instantaneous GOR at end of first period, SCF/ST barrel.

N_{p1} = Cumulative oil produced to the end of the first period, ST barrels.

For the first period, the value $\left(\dfrac{R_i + R_{i+1}}{2}\right) N_p$ is equal to $\left(\dfrac{R_{ss} + R_{i+1}}{2}\right) N_{p1}$. It should be noted that Equation (4-9) yields the total gas produced only if the variation between R_i and R_{i+1} is linear. Since a plot of R vs N_p is not linear in nature, it is necessary to assume small pressure drops in order to have successive values of R which are close together. In actual practice, pressure decrements in the order of 50 psi are normally used.

D. The total gas produced during the period, as calculated by the material balance equation, is compared to the total gas produced during the period, as calculated by the GOR equation. These two equations represent independent methods of arriving at the same answer. Therefore, if the total gas produced, as calculated by the two different methods, is the same, then the correct value of N_p has been assumed. However, if the two values are not in agreement, then this process must be repeated until a value of N_p is found which will yield the same answer from both equations.

E. In order to simplify this estimating process, three values of N_p can be assumed, which will yield three different solutions of gas produced for each of the equations. If these values are then plotted on a graph of $N_p R_p$ vs N_p, the plot of the two lines will intersect. This intersection is the only place where one value of N_p will satisfy both equations.

V. Second Prediction Step

A. Choose a second pressure and assume a new value of N_p. This will be N_{p2}.

B. Solve the material balance equation for $N_{p2}R_{p2}$. This is equivalent to the total gas produced from initial conditions to the end of Step 2. In order to find the amount of gas produced during Step 2, it is necessary to subtract the amount of gas produced during Step 1 from the total gas produced to the end of Step 2. This is done as follows:

$$G_2 = N_{p2}R_{p2} - N_{p1}R_{p1} = \frac{N(B_t - B_{ts}) - N_p(B_t - R_{ss}B_g)}{B_g} - N_{p1}R_{p1}$$

(4-10)

C. Using the assumed value of N_p calculate S_o. Using the calculated value of S_o determine the value of k_g/k_o. Calculate R from the GOR equation. This will be R_2.

D. Calculate the amount of gas produced during the second period by:

$$\left(\frac{R_{1+1} + R_2}{2}\right)(N_{p2} - N_{p1}) = G_2$$

(4-11)

where:

G_2 = Total gas produced during the period, SCF.

E. If the correct value of N_{p2} has been assumed, the amount of gas produced as calculated by Equations (4-10) and (4-11) will agree. As in Step 8, in order to simplify the estimating process, three values of N_{p2} can be assumed.

F. This step-wise procedure is continued until the economic limit has been reached.

G. The final results of this series of calculations are usually shown in the form of graphs of R vs N_p/N and p vs N_p/N, where R and p are plotted on the ordinate.

H. It may be more convenient to assume values of N_p in terms of N, rather than in terms of barrels. For instance, N_p can be assumed as 0.01 N, rather than as 10,000 barrels. In this method, a true value of N is not required, and where N appears in the material balance, the letter symbol is left in the equation.

Example Problem 4-1

Example calculations for a depletion drive reservoir will be made in order to clarify the preceding discussion of the method.

Table 4-1 lists reservoir data necessary for the study, and Figures 4-2 through 4-4 provide the additional data necessary for the study. Table 4-2 shows calculated data which will be required for the study. Performance predictions will be made at the following pressures: 2600, 2400, 2100, 1800, 1500, 1200, 1000, 700 and 400. In an actual reservoir study it would probably be desirable to predict performance in pressure steps not greater than 50 psi. The larger pressure steps are used here in order to simplify the presentation and reduce the number of repetitive calculations. It should be noted

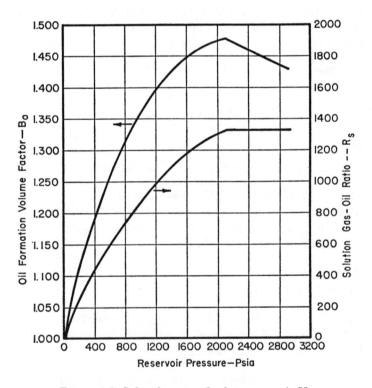

FIGURE 4-2. Subsurface sample data, reservoir X.

Table 4-1
Engineering Data for Reservoir X Depletion Drive Reservoir

Structure: Low-relief stratigraphic trap.

Average depth: 6500 feet

Original reservoir pressure: 2925 psia

Reservoir saturation pressure: 2100 psia

Reservoir temperature: 175° F.

Interstitial water saturation: 15%

Original oil in place: 100,000,000 stock tank barrels
(from geologic data)

No original gas cap

No water drive

Average specific gravity of produced gas: 0.70

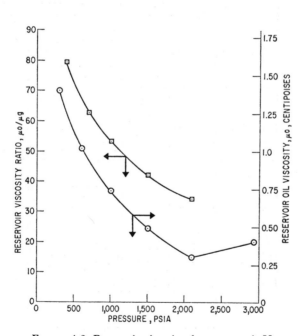

FIGURE 4-3. Reservoir viscosity data, reservoir X.

that above the saturation pressure the B_t and B_g data are not required as the oil is produced solely by expansion of the liquid phase. The gas-oil ratio does not change, as no gas is being liberated in the reservoir.

Tables 4-3 through 4-7 and Figures 4-5 through 4-7 show the results of the performance predictions. Example calculations are provided to illustrate clearly in a step-by-step fashion the procedure used.

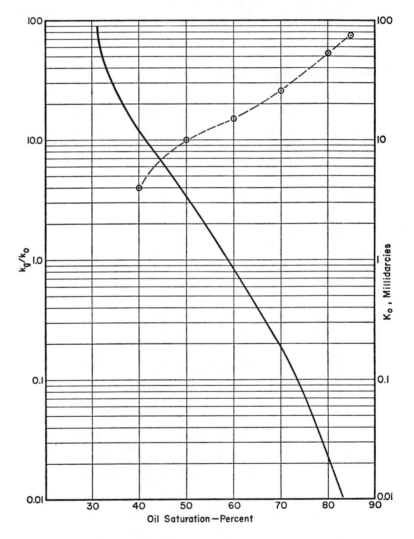

FIGURE 4-4. Permeability data, reservoir X.

Table 4-2
Basic Data — Reservoir X

Pressure	Z	R_s	B_o	B_g	B_t	B_o/B_g	μ_o/μ_g
2100(p_s)	0.842	1340	1.480	0.001283	1.480	1152	34.1
1800	0.854	1280	1.468	0.001518	1.559	967	38.3
1500	0.869	1150	1.440	0.001853	1.792	777	42.4
1200	0.888	985	1.399	0.002365	2.239	590	48.8
1000	0.901	860	1.360	0.002885	2.745	471	53.6
700	0.929	662	1.287	0.004250	4.167	303	62.5
400	0.960	465	1.202	0.007680	7.922	156	79.0

Example calculations: p = 1200 psia

1. Calculation of Z: sp. gr. of gas = 0.70

p_c = 667 psia (from NGSMA *Data Book*, 1957, p. 103)
T_c = 385° R

$$T_r = \frac{T}{T_c} = \frac{175 + 460}{385} = 1.65$$

$$p_r = \frac{p}{p_c} = \frac{1200}{667} = 1.80$$

Z = 0.888 (from NGSMA *Data Book*, 1957, p. 102)

2. Calculation of B_g:

$$B_g = \frac{p_s \, v_s \, Z_1 \, T_p}{p_1 \, Z_s \, T_s \times 5.62} = \frac{(14.7) \, (1) \, (0.888) \, (635)}{(1200) \, (1) \, (520) \, (5.62)} = 0.002365$$

3. Calculation of B_t:

$$B_t = B_o + (R_{si} - R_s)B_g$$
$$= 1.399 + (1340 - 985) \, 0.002365$$
$$= 2.239$$

Table 4-3
Summary of Reservoir Performance Calculations
(Above the Saturation Pressure)

Pressure	N_{ps}	R_p
2600	1,380,000	1340
2400	2,260,000	1340
2100	3,445,000	1340[1]

[1] The producing GOR does not change because no gas is being liberated in the reservoir as long as the pressure is greater than the saturation pressure.

Example calculation: p = 2400 psia

$$N_{ps} = \frac{N_s(B_o - B_{oi})}{B_o} = \frac{100,000,000 \, (1.462 - 1.429)}{1.462}$$
$$= 2,260,000 \text{ stock tank barrels}$$

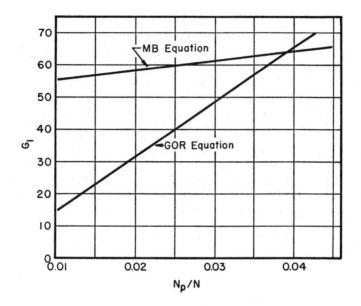

FIGURE 4-5. Determining true value of N_{p1}.

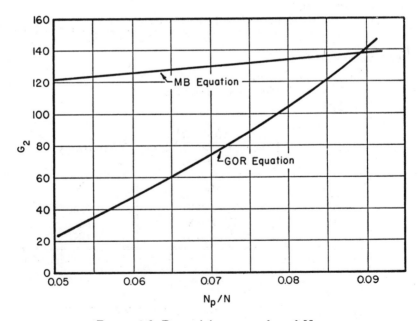

FIGURE 4-6. Determining true value of N_{p2}.

Table 4-4
Reservoir Performance Calculations
(Below the Saturation Pressure)

Pressure Psia	N_p/N	R_p SCF/Bbl	N_p Bbls $\times 10^6$	Total Oil Produced[1] Bbls $\times 10^6$
2100	0	1340	0	3.445
1800	0.0393	1936	3.795	7.240
1500	0.0889	3584	8.584	12.029
1200	0.1230	6230	11.876	15.321
1000	0.1396	8580	13.479	16.924
700	0.1578	13010	15.236	18.681
400	0.1715	16625	16.559	20.004

[1] Includes oil produced above the saturation pressure.

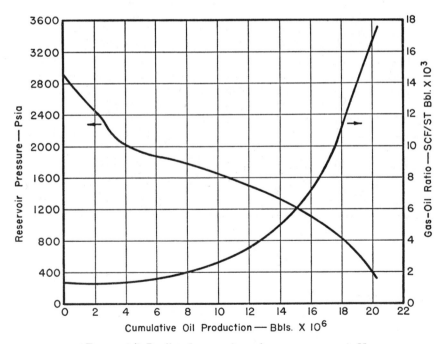

FIGURE 4-7. Predicted reservoir performance, reservoir X.

Table 4-5
Summary of Reservoir Performance Calculations
(Below the Saturation Pressure)

Pressure	N_p/N Assumed	G_{mb}	S_o Calcu- lated	k_g/k_o	R_p Calcu- lated	G_{gor}	Actual G
1800	0.010	55.17N	0.835	0.0100	1650	14.95N	
	0.030	61.43N	0.817	0.0142	1806	47.19N	
	0.040	64.56N	0.810	0.0180	1946	65.72N	
(actual)	0.0393				1936		64.34N
1500	0.050	122.36N	0.786	0.0342	2278	22.56N	
	0.080	133.86N	0.761	0.0628	3220	104.95N	
	0.090	137.56N	0.753	0.0742	3594	140.19N	
(actual)	0.0889				3584		136.06N
1200	0.120	166.80N	0.707	0.180	6060	150.0N	
	0.130	170.70N	0.700	0.192	6530	207.8N	
	0.150	178.10N	0.683	0.255	8340	364.3N	
(actual)	0.1230				6230		167.9N
1000	0.130	119.3N	0.680	0.272	7730	48.86N	
	0.140	123.6N	0.672	0.311	8720	127.10N	
	0.150	127.4N	0.664	0.354	9810	216.50N	
(actual)	0.1396				8580		123.3N
700	0.150	193.4N	0.628	0.601	12062	107.3N	
	0.155	195.4N	0.624	0.624	12460	161.9N	
	0.160	197.4N	0.620	0.663	13210	222.3N	
(actual)	0.1578				13010		196.3N
400	0.170	202.5N	0.573	1.280	16300	178.8N	
	0.175	204.1N	0.570	1.314	16715	255.8N	
	0.180	205.7N	0.566	1.395	17745	341.5N	
(actual)	0.1715				16625		203.1N

Table 4-6
Example Calculations — Reservoir X
First Period — $p = 1800$ psia

A. Trial 1—Assume $N_{p1} = 0.01$ N

$$G_{mb1} = N_{p1}R_{p1} = \frac{N(B_t - B_{ts}) - N_p(B_t - R_{ss}B_g)}{B_g}$$

$$= \frac{N(1.559 - 1.480) - 0.01\, N(1.559 - 1340 \times 0.001518)}{0.001518}$$

$$= \mathbf{55.17\ N}$$

$$S_o = \left(1 - \frac{N_p}{N}\right)\frac{B_o}{B_{os}}(1 - S_{wi}) = \left(1 - \frac{0.01\ N}{N}\right)\frac{1.468}{1.480}(1 - 0.15) = 0.835$$

$$k_g/k_o = 0.0100 \text{ (from Fig. 4-4 where } S_o = 0.835)$$

$$R_1 = \frac{k_g}{k_o} \times \frac{\mu_o}{\mu_g} \times \frac{B_o}{B_g} + R_s = (0.0100)(38.3)(967) + 1280 = 1650$$

$$G_{gor1} = \left(\frac{R_1 + R_{ss}}{2}\right)(N_{p1}) = \left(\frac{1650 + 1340}{2}\right)(0.01\ N) = \underline{14.95\ N}$$

B. Trial 2—Assume $N_{p1} = 0.03$ N

$$G_{mb1} = \frac{N(1.559 - 1.480) - 0.03\, N(1.559 - 1340 \times 0.001518)}{0.001518}$$

$$= \underline{61.43\ N}$$

$$S_o = 0.97 \times 0.991 \times 0.85 = 0.817$$

$$k_g/k_o = 0.0142$$

$$R_1 = 0.0142 \times 38.3 \times 967 + 1280 = 1806$$

$$G_{gor1} = \left(\frac{1806 + 1340}{2}\right) \times 0.03\ N = \mathbf{47.19\ N}$$

C. Trial 3—Assume $N_{p1} = 0.04$ N

$$G_{mb1} = \frac{N(1.559 - 1.480) - 0.04\, N(1.559 - 1340 \times 0.001518)}{0.001518}$$

$$= \underline{64.56\ N}$$

$$S_o = 0.96 \times 0.991 \times 0.85 = 0.810$$

$$k_g/k_o = 0.0180$$

$$R_1 = 0.018 \times 38.3 \times 967 + 1280 = 1946$$

$$G_{gor1} = \left(\frac{1946 + 1340}{2}\right) \times 0.04\ N = \mathbf{65.72\ N}$$

Table 4-7
Example Calculations — Reservoir X
Second Period — p = 1500 psia

A. Trial 1—Assume $N_{p2} = 0.05\ N$

$$N_{p2}R_{p2} = \frac{N\ (B_t - B_{ts}) - N_p(B_t - R_{ss}B_g)}{B_g}$$

$$= \frac{N\ (1.792 - 1.480) - 0.05\ N\ (1.792 - 1340 \times 0.001853)}{0.001853}$$

$$= \underline{186.7\ N}$$

$$G_{mb2} = N_{p2}R_{p2} - N_{p1}R_{p1} = 186.7\ N - 64.34\ N = \underline{122.36\ N}$$

$$S_o = \left(1 - \frac{N_p}{N}\right)\frac{B_o}{B_{os}}\ (1 - S_{wl}) = \left(1 - \frac{0.05\ N}{N}\right)\frac{1.440}{1.480}\ (1 - 0.15) = 0.786$$

$$k_g/k_o = 0.0342 \text{ (from Fig. 4-4 where } S_o = 0.786)$$

$$R_2 = \frac{k_g}{k_o}\frac{\mu_o}{\mu_g}\frac{B_o}{B_g} + R_s = 0.0342 \times 42.4 \times 777 + 1150 = 2278$$

$$G_{gor2} = \frac{R_1 + R_2}{2}\ (N_{p2} - N_{p1}) = \left(\frac{2278 + 1936}{2}\right)(0.05\ N - 0.0393\ N)$$

$$= \underline{22.56\ N}$$

B. Trial 2—Assume $N_{p2} = 0.08\ N$

$$N_{p2}R_{p2} = \frac{N\ (1.792 - 1.480) - 0.08\ N\ (1.792 - 1340 \times 0.001853)}{0.001853}$$

$$= \underline{198.2\ N}$$

$$G_{mb2} = 198.2\ N - 64.34\ N = \underline{133.86\ N}$$

$$S_o = 0.92 \times 0.973 \times 0.85 = 0.761$$

$$k_g/k_o = 0.0628$$

$$R_2 = 0.0628 \times 42.4 \times 777 + 1150 = 3220$$

$$G_{gor2} = \left(\frac{1936 + 3220}{2}\right)(0.08\ N - 0.0393\ N) = \underline{104.95\ N}$$

C. Trial 3—Assume $N_{p2} = 0.090\ N$

$$N_{p2}R_{p2} = \frac{N\ (1.792 - 1.480) - 0.09\ N\ (1.792 - 1340 \times 0.001853)}{0.001853}$$

$$= \underline{201.9\ N}$$

$$G_{mb2} = 201.9 \text{ N} - 64.34 \text{ N} = \underline{137.56 \text{ N}}$$

$$S_o = 0.91 \times 0.973 \times 0.85 = 0.753$$

$$k_g/k_o = 0.0742$$

$$R_2 = 0.0742 \times 42.4 \times 777 + 1150 = 3594$$

$$G_{gor2} = \left(\frac{1936 + 3594}{2} \right) (0.09 \text{ N} - 0.0393 \text{ N}) = \underline{140.19 \text{ N}}$$

Limitations of Predictions

The prediction of behavior of a depletion drive reservoir involves the same general limitations described in Chapter 3. Predictions normally become more accurate as the amount of production data increases, but in general, reliable predictions can usually be made in advance for a period equal to the length of the past production history.

It should be noted that theoretically, withdrawal rates do not affect the ultimate oil recovery from a depletion drive reservoir. This is due to the fact that no extraneous fluids are moving into the reservoir, and that recovery is dependent almost entirely on the relative permeability characteristics of the reservoir. It has been demonstrated conclusively that, under properly controlled laboratory conditions, flow rate does not affect the relative permeability curve. Of course, where gravity segregation of the fluids permits the formation of a secondary gas cap, then lower withdrawal rates would increase recovery from the reservoir by maintaining a lower gas saturation in the vicinity of the completion interval.

Relating Reservoir Performance to Time

The Tarner performance prediction technique shows the relationship of cumulative oil production and instantaneous producing gas-oil ratio to reservoir pressure, but it does not show the oil producing rate and cumulative oil production as a function of time. After the Tarner performance prediction has been completed, reservoir performance can be related to time by the use of productivity index data.

Productivity index, J, has units of stock tank barrels per day per psi, or:

$$J = \frac{Q_o}{P_e - P_w} \qquad (4\text{-}12)$$

where:

Q_o = Oil Producing rate, ST bbls/day

P_e = Reservoir pressure, psia

P_w = Well bore producing pressure, psia

Replacing Q_o in Equation (4-12) with the Darcy radial flow equation results in the following equation:

$$J = \frac{7.07 \, k_o \, h \, (P_e - P_w)}{\mu_o \ln r_e/r_w \, B_o \, (P_e - P_w)} \qquad (4\text{-}13)$$

For most reservoir producing conditions:

$$\frac{7.07 \, h}{\ln r_e/r_w} = constant = C \qquad (4\text{-}14)$$

Combining Equations (4-13) and (4-14), and eliminating the identical $(P_e - P_w)$ terms in numerator and denominator:

$$J = \frac{C \, k_o}{\mu_o \, B_o} \qquad (4\text{-}15)$$

The constant, C, can be calculated from actual field operating conditions by rearranging Equation (4-15):

$$C = \frac{J \, \mu_o \, B_o}{k_o} \qquad (4\text{-}16)$$

Once determined, i.e., at initial conditions, this value can then be used for future performance predictions.

The use of the productivity index in relating reservoir performance to time is illustrated by an example problem using the performance prediction results from Reservoir X. The following additional data are needed:

1. The allowable producing rate for the reservoir is 15,000 ST Bbls/day.

2. Reservoir average depth is 6500 feet.

3. There are 60 producing wells.

4. Bottom hole flowing pressure is 1500 psia.

5. The initial measured per well productivity index is 0.75 barrels/day/psi. Therefore the reservoir productivity index is 0.75 × 60 = 45.0.

6. Other appropriate data can be found in the previous example problem where the Tarner performance prediction was illustrated.

Table 4-8
Results from the Performance Prediction

	Pressure Psia P_e	Prod. GOR SCF / STB R	Oil Saturation % S_o	Cum. Oil Prod. STB x 10^6 N_p
1.	2925 (P_i)	1340	85	0
2.	2600	1340	85	1.380
3.	2400	1340	85	2.260
4.	2100 (P_b)	1340	85	3.445
5.	1800	1936	81.2	7.240
6.	1500	3584	75.4	12.029
7.	1200	6230	70.5	15.321
8.	1000	8580	67.2	16.924
9.	700	13010	62.2	18.681
10.	400	16625	57.2	20.004

$$J_i = 0.75 \, (60) = 45.0 = \frac{C \, K_{oi}}{B_{oi} \, \mu_{oi}} \text{ STB/day/psia}$$

$$C = \frac{J_i \, B_{oi} \, \mu_{oi}}{K_{oi}} = \frac{(45) \, (1.429) \, (0.4)}{0.074} = 347.6$$

The value for the constant C is assumed to remain constant throughout the producing life of the reservoir.

Example Problem 4-2

1. P = 2925 psia (P_i)

$$J_i = 45 = \frac{Q_o}{P_e - P_w}$$

The maximum producing capacity (flowing) =

$Q_o = J_i \, (P_e - P_w) = 45 \, (2925 - 1500) = 64,100$ ST bbls/day,

which is greater than the 15,000 barrels per day, allowable producing rate.

Therefore, initially the reservoir will be producing less than its capacity.

2. P = 2600 psia:

$$J = \frac{C \, K_o}{B_o \, \mu_o} = \frac{(347.6) \, (0.074)}{(1.444) \, (0.367)} = 49.5 \text{ bbls/day/psia}$$

$Q_o = J (P_e - P_w) = 49.5 (2600 - 1500) = 54,500$ bbls/day,

which is still greater than the allowable producing rate.

Therefore, the producing rate during the first period (from initial pressure until $P = 2600$), is 15,000 barrels per day. The time required to produce the oil is:

$$\Delta_{ti} = \frac{1,380,000 \text{ bbls}}{15,000 \text{ bbls/day}} = 92 \text{ days}$$

3. $P = 2400$ psia:

$$J = \frac{C K_o}{B_o \mu_o} = \frac{(347.6) (0.074)}{(1.462) (0.328)} = 53.6 \text{ bbls/day/psia}$$

$$Q_o = J (P_e - P_w)$$
$$= 53.6 (2400 - 1500) = 48,200 \text{ ST bbls/day}$$

Since the producing capacity of the reservoir exceeds the allowable producing rate, the actual producing rate during the second period will be 15,000 barrels per day.

$$\Delta N_{p2} = (N_{p2400} - N_{p2600}) = 2,260,000 - 1,380,000$$
$$= 880,000 \text{ ST bbls.}$$

$$\Delta t_2 = \frac{\Delta N_{p2}}{Q_{o2}} = \frac{880,000}{15,000} = 59 \text{ days}$$

Cumulative Time $= \Sigma \Delta t = 92 + 59 = 151$ days

4. $P = 2100$ psia:

$$J = \frac{C K_o}{B_o \mu_o} = \frac{(347.6) (0.074)}{(1.480) (0.30)} = 57.9 \text{ ST bbls/day/psia}$$

$$Q_o = J (P_e - P_w)$$
$$= 57.9 (2100 - 1500) = 34,700 \text{ ST bbls/day,}$$

which is more than the allowable producing rate.

$$\Delta N_{p3} = (N_{p2100} - N_{p2400}) = 3,445,000 - 2,260,000$$
$$= 1,185,000 \text{ barrels}$$

$$\Delta t_3 = \frac{\Delta N_{p3}}{Q_{o3}} = \frac{1,185,000 \text{ ST bbls}}{15,000 \text{ ST bbls/day}} = 79 \text{ days}$$

Cumulative Time $= \Sigma \Delta t = 151 + 79 = 230$ days

5. $P = 1800$ psia:

$$J = \frac{C K_o}{B_o \mu_o} = \frac{(347.6) (0.058)}{(1.468) (0.38)} = 36.1 \text{ ST bbls/day/psia}$$

$$Q_o = J (P_e - P_w) = 36.1 (1800 - 1500)$$
$$= 10,800 \text{ ST bbls/day}$$

The producing rate, under flowing conditions, has declined below the allowable producing rate. Therefore, artificial lift equipment should be installed before pressure declines to 1800 psia.

It is assumed that subsurface pumps will be installed and that the producing well bore pressure, P_w, can now be reduced to 200 psia. Under these conditions, the reservoir productivity will be:

$$Q_o = J (P_e - P_w) = 36.1 (1800 - 200)$$
$$= 57,800 \text{ ST bbls/day, which is more than the}$$

allowable producing rate. Therefore, during this period the actual producing rate will be 15,000 barrels per day.

$$\Delta N_{p4} = (N_{p1800} - N_{p2100}) = 7,240,000 - 3,445,000$$
$$= 3,795,000 \text{ ST bbls}$$

$$\Delta t_4 = \frac{3,795,000 \text{ ST bbls}}{15,000 \text{ ST bbls/day}} = 253 \text{ days}$$

Cumulative Time $= \Sigma \Delta t = 230 + 253 = 483$ days

6. P $=1500$ psia:

$$J = \frac{C K_o}{B_o \, \mu_o} = \frac{(347.6) \, (0.038)}{(1.440) \, (0.48)} = 19.1 \text{ ST bbls/day/psia}$$

$$Q_o = J (P_e - P_w) = 19.1 (1500 - 200) = 24,800 \text{ ST bbls/day}$$

$$\Delta N_{p5} = N_{p1500} - N_{p1800} = 12,029,000 - 7,240,000$$
$$= 4,789,000 \text{ ST bbls}$$

$$\Delta t_5 = \frac{\Delta N_{p5}}{Q_o} = \frac{4,789,000 \text{ ST bbls}}{15,000 \text{ ST bbls/day}} = 319 \text{ days}$$

Cumulative Time $= \Sigma \Delta t = 483 + 319 = 802$ days

7. P $= 1200$ psia:

$$J = \frac{(347.6) \, (0.028)}{(1.399) \, (0.63)} = 11.0 \text{ ST bbls/day/psia}$$

$$Q_o = 11 (1200 - 200) = 11,000 \text{ ST bbls/day}$$

The maximum producing capacity of the reservoir has declined below the allowable producing rate. By a series of trial-and-error calculations it was determined that a producing capacity of 15,000 barrels per day occurs at a reservoir pressure of 1350 psia. At this latter pressure, the cumulative oil produced, N_p, is 14,000,000 stock tank barrels.

The time elapsed during the pressure decline from 1500 psia to 1350 psia is:

$$\Delta N_p = N_{p1350} - N_{p1500} = 14,000,000 - 12,029,000$$
$$= 1,971,000 \text{ ST bbls}$$

$$\Delta t = \frac{1,971,000 \text{ ST bbls}}{15,000 \text{ ST bbls/day}} = 131 \text{ days}$$

Cumulative Time $= \Sigma \Delta t = 802 + 131 = 933$ days

During the pressure drop from 1350 psia to 1200 psia, the average oil producing rate can be assumed to be the arithmetic average of the beginning and ending producing rates:

$$Q_{o(avg)} = \frac{15,000 + 11,000}{2} = 13,000 \text{ ST bbls/day}$$

$$\Delta N_p = N_{p1200} - N_{p1350} = 15,321,000 - 14,000,000$$
$$= 1,321,000 \text{ ST bbls}$$

$$\Delta t = \frac{\Delta N_p}{Q_{o(avg)}} = \frac{1.321,000}{13,000} = 102 \text{ days}$$

Cumulative Time $= \Sigma \Delta t = 933 + 102 = 1035$ days

8. P = 1000 psia:

$$J = \frac{(347.6) \ (0.023)}{(1.360) \ (0.74)} = 7.95 \text{ ST bbls/day/psia}$$

$$Q_o = 7.95 \ (1000 - 200) = 6350 \text{ ST bbls/day}$$

$$Q_{o(avg)} = \frac{11,000 + 6350}{2} = 8675 \text{ ST bbls/day}$$

$$\Delta N_{p7} = N_{p1000} - N_{p1200} = 16,924,000 - 15,321,000$$
$$= 1,603,000 \text{ ST bbls}$$

$$\Delta t = \frac{1,603,000}{8675} = 185 \text{ days}$$

Cumulative Time $= 1035 + 185 = 1220$ days

9. P = 700 psia:

$$J = \frac{(347.6) \ (0.018)}{(1.287) \ (0.94)} = 5.17 \text{ ST bbls/day/psia}$$

$$Q_o = 5.17 \ (700 - 200) = 2590 \text{ ST bbls/day}$$

$$Q_{o(avg)} = \frac{6350 + 2590}{2} = 4470 \text{ ST bbls/day}$$

$$\Delta N_{p8} = N_{p700} - N_{p1000} = 18{,}681{,}000 - 16{,}924{,}000$$
$$= 1{,}757{,}000 \text{ ST bbls}$$

$$\Delta t = \frac{1{,}757{,}000}{4470} = 393 \text{ days}$$

Cumulative Time $= 1220 + 393 = 1613$ days

10. $P = 400$ psia:

$$J = \frac{(347.6)\ (0.014)}{(1.202)\ (1.25)} = 3.24 \text{ ST bbls/day/psia}$$

$$Q_o = 3.24\ (400 - 200) = 648 \text{ ST bbls/day}$$

$$Q_{o(avg)} = \frac{2590 + 648}{2} = 1619 \text{ ST bbls/day}$$

$$\Delta N_{p9} = N_{p400} - N_{p700} = 20{,}004{,}000 - 18{,}681{,}000$$
$$= 1{,}323{,}000 \text{ ST barrels}$$

$$\Delta t = \frac{1{,}323{,}000}{1619} = 818 \text{ days}$$

Cumulative Time $= 1613 + 818 = 2431$ days

Note: Because of the rapid decline in producing rates at the lower reservoir pressures, it would have been preferable to use smaller pressure intervals.

Figure 4-8 shows producing rate and cumulative oil production as a function of time.

Factors Affecting Ultimate Recovery

Arps and Roberts[2] have presented statistical data showing the effects of relative permeability ratio, oil gravity, and solution gas-oil ratio, on primary recovery from a depletion drive reservoir. A number of graphs were prepared to visually illustrate the results of their investigation. Wahl, Mullins, and Elfrink[3] have developed a set of charts which can be used for the estimation of ultimate recovery from depletion drive reservoirs. These charts are very convenient where a minimum amount of data are available, and

---

[2] Arps, J. J. and Roberts, T. G., "The Effect of the Relative Permeability Ratio, the Oil Gravity, and the Solution Gas-Oil Ratio on the Primary Recovery from a Depletion Type Reservoir," *Trans.* AIME, Vol. 204, (1955), p. 120.

[3] Wahl, W. L., Mullins, L. D. and Elfrink, E. B., "Estimation of Ultimate Recovery from Solution Gas-Drive Reservoirs," *Trans.* AIME (1958), Vol. 213, p. 132.

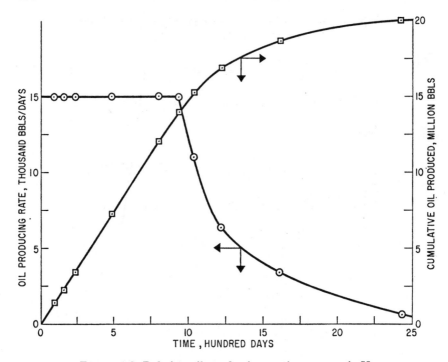

FIGURE 4-8. Relating oil production to time, reservoir X.

where time does not permit a more detailed study. For convenience, these charts have been reproduced in the Appendix.

Craze and Buckley[4] analyzed 103 reservoirs in their study of the well spacing problem. Many of these reservoirs were producing by depletion drive, and the effects of the various parameters on oil recovery can be studied by analyzing their data.

Analyzing Gas-Oil Ratio History

The producing gas-oil ratio history of a depletion drive reservoir can provide valuable reservoir engineering information when this information is analyzed in the light of the events which must occur in the reservoir. Figure 4-9 shows the gas-oil ratio history of a theoretical depletion drive reservoir. The changes in the GOR history have been exaggerated to more clearly illustrate the underlying reasons for the changes.

---

[4] Craze, R. C. and Buckley, S. E., "A Factual Analysis of the Effect of Well Spacing on Recovery," *Drilling and Production Practice,* API, 1945, p. 144.

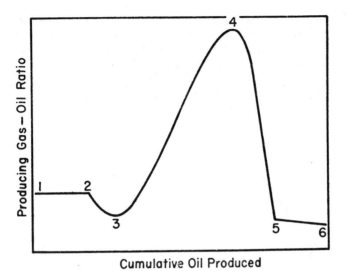

FIGURE 4-9. GOR history of a depletion drive reservoir.

From Point 1 to Point 2 in Figure 4-9, reservoir pressure is above the saturation pressure, therefore, there can be no change in the solution gas-oil ratio or the producing gas-oil ratio. At Point 2 the reservoir saturation pressure is reached, and gas is evolved from solution. However, this free gas cannot flow until a free gas saturation equivalent to the equilibrium gas saturation (minimum gas saturation necessary to permit gas flow) has been built up. Therefore, the surface gas-oil ratio will begin to decrease, still being exactly equal to the solution gas-oil ratio at the reservoir pressure.

At Point 3 the equilibrium gas saturation is reached, and free gas now begins to flow. The gas-oil ratio increases from Point 3 to Point 4. The rapidity of the gas-oil ratio increase will depend upon the rate of pressure decline. The more rapid the rate of pressure decline, the more rapid will be the increase in producing gas-oil ratio because the sole source of gas is that evolved from solution from the oil. The gas-oil ratio increases because gas is being evolved from all of the oil in the reservoir, while only a small part of this oil is being produced.

At Point 4 the maximum gas-oil ratio is reached for the simple reason that the supply of gas has reached a maximum and the "blow-down" cycle is beginning. From Point 4 to Point 5, the free gas saturation is being depleted rapidly due to the small amount of gas coming out of solution compared to the gas produced.

At Point 5 all of the producible free gas has been produced and the producing gas-oil ratio now is equal to the solution gas-oil ratio, which now is small due to the low reservoir pressure. This same cycle continues from Point 5 to Point 6.

The line from Point 5 to Point 6 seldom is seen in an actual case because the economic limit usually falls somewhere between Point 4 and Point 5.

Chapter 5

GAS CAP DRIVE RESERVOIRS

Gas cap drive reservoirs can be identified by the presence of a relatively large gas cap with little or no water drive. Due to the ability of the gas cap to expand readily, these reservoirs are characterized by less rapid pressure decline than the same size depletion drive reservoir. Other characteristics of gas cap drive reservoirs are their lack of water production and rapidly increasing gas-oil ratio in structurally high wells as the gas cap expands into the oil zone.

Oil recovery by gas cap expansion is actually a frontal drive displacing mechanism. Recovery efficiency is therefore normally considerably larger than in depletion drive reservoirs, since a gas saturation is not being formed throughout the reservoir at the same time. Figure 5-1 shows the relative positions of the gas and oil at different times in the producing life of the reservoir.

As the size of the gas cap increases, the ultimate oil recovery will also be increased. This is illustrated graphically in Figure 5-2. Vertical permeability and reservoir oil viscosity are also important factors in determining the recovery efficiency. Good vertical permeability will permit the oil to move downward with less bypassing of gas. As oil viscosity increases the amount of gas bypassing will also increase.

In order to conserve gas, and thereby increase ultimate oil recovery, it is necessary to shut in wells which produce excessive gas. In areas where production is subject to proration or where inequities with royalty owners may occur, it is usually desirable to transfer the allowables of wells producing with high gas-oil ratios to wells producing with low gas-oil ratios. This has the desirable effect of reducing the gas withdrawal rate without reducing the oil producing rate.

Gas, as a displacing fluid, is limited in its efficiency primarily because of two factors: (1) the unfavorable viscosity ratios promote fingering of gas with consequent early breakthrough and (2) gas is normally the non-wetting phase and will preferentially pass through the larger pore spaces, leaving oil trapped in the smaller pore spaces. Once this oil has been bypassed, much of it will never be recovered. Figure 5-3 shows a comparison of displacement in individual pores of a reservoir rock by water and by gas. Water will usually maintain a more uniform front than the gas, the capillary forces causing the water to invade the smaller pore spaces while the viscous pressure forces the water into the larger pores. The result is more complete oil displacement at water breakthrough.

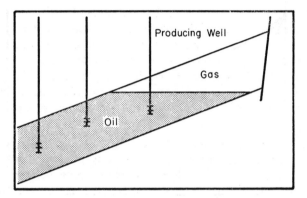

A. Initial fluid distribution.

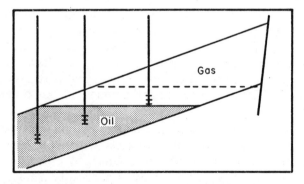

B. Gas cap expansion due to oil production.

FIGURE 5-1. Gas cap drive reservoir.

Ultimate oil recovery from gas cap drive reservoirs is greater than comparable recovery from depletion drive reservoirs. Recovery will vary, depending on the size of the original gas cap, the vertical permeability, reservoir oil viscosity, and the degree of conservation of the gas, but as a rule of thumb ultimate recovery will vary from 20% to 40% of the original oil in place.

Where the size of the original gas cap is not large, and reservoir pressure decreases rapidly as oil and gas withdrawals continue, a gas saturation throughout the oil zone is formed by release of gas from solution from the oil. With the creation of this uniform gas saturation throughout the oil zone, it becomes increasingly difficult to maintain a gas "front" to displace the oil. Gas

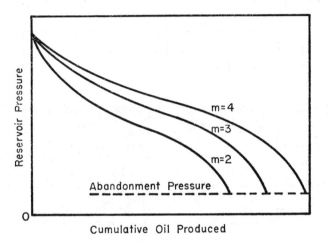

FIGURE 5-2. Effect of gas cap size on ultimate oil recovery.

begins to flow very readily at even small saturations; therefore, if prohibitive gas-oil ratios are to be prevented, reservoir pressure should be maintained as near the saturation pressure as possible. Recovery efficiency is dependent to a large extent on the ability to maintain the reservoir pressure near the saturation pressure.

As a gas cap can expand only as a result of pressure reduction in the reservoir, it follows that some gas will also be evolved from solution from the oil. If this gas saturation is increased by successive pressure reductions to the point where the free gas will flow in the oil zone two important events will occur: (1) the effective permeability to oil will be decreased as a result of the increased gas saturation, and (2) the effective permeability to gas will be increased, thereby increasing the flow of gas. This may result in a producing mechanism which is actually a solution gas drive mechanism.

The formation of the free gas saturation in the oil zone cannot be prevented without resorting to pressure maintenance operations.

Therefore, in order to achieve maximum benefit from a gas cap drive producing mechanism, gas saturation in the oil zone must be kept to an absolute minimum. This can be accomplished by taking advantage of gravitational segregation of the fluids. In fact, an efficiently-operated gas cap drive reservoir must also have an efficient gravity segregation drive. As the gas saturation is formed in the oil zone it must be allowed to migrate upstructure to the gas cap. Thus, a gas cap drive reservoir is in reality a combination drive reservoir, although it is not usually considered as such.

Lower producing rates will permit the maximum amount of free gas in the oil zone to migrate to the gas cap. Therefore gas cap drive reservoirs are rate sensitive, as lower producing rates will usually result in increased recovery.

   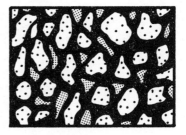

A. Oil displacement by gas.   B. Displacement by water.

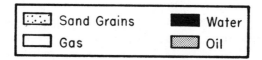

FIGURE 5-3. Comparison of oil displacement by gas and by water—water-wet reservoir.

In a large number of cases it will be desirable to install gas return facilities in order to maintain reservoir pressure. This is especially true where, due to some structural features of the reservoir, it is impossible to control gas-oil ratios. The installation of gas return facilities is largely an economic measure, it being necessary to first determine whether the cost of the pressure maintenance facilities will be more than repaid by the increased oil recovery. The installation of pressure maintenance facilities is described in Chapter 9.

Effect of Producing Rate on Ultimate Recovery

The effectiveness of oil displacement from the reservoir is dependent largely on the maintenance of a uniform gas front. Slow withdrawal rates will promote the uniformity of this front by causing less fingering of the advancing gas and also allowing maximum gravitational segregation. Therefore, low production rates will increase ultimate recovery.

Unfortunately, it is difficult to calculate the effect on ultimate recovery of varying withdrawal rates. All of the equations normally used in predicting reservoir behavior are not rate sensitive, and therefore the rate effect cannot be studied. Past experience with the reservoir or similar reservoirs can usually be relied upon to show the effect of producing rate.

Predicting Reservoir Performance

The material balance equation, the instantaneous gas-oil ratio equation, and the oil saturation equation are used to determine the future behavior of the reservoir. The Tarner method, outlined in Chapter 4, usually provides a reliable solution to the problem.

The principal objectives in a study of a gas drive reservoir are:

1. Determination of past changes in gas-oil contact.

2. Determine maximum efficient producing rate for the reservoir.

3. Determine future changes in the gas-oil contact at various times. This will be invaluable in determining the need for additional wells, remedial work, and shutting in of high gas-oil ratio wells.

The objective in operating any reservoir is to take advantage of the most efficient displacing mechanism available. In the case of a reservoir with a large gas cap and no water drive, the expansion of the gas cap will normally provide the most efficient displacing energy. It is particularly important in any reservoir with an original free gas cap to prevent shrinkage of the gas cap. If the gas cap is permitted to shrink, then an oil saturation will be established in a portion of the reservoir which hitherto had no oil saturation. There is always some minimum oil saturation below which it is impossible to reduce the oil saturation. Therefore, the residual oil saturation remaining in the gas zone is lost oil which would have been recoverable if the gas cap had not been permitted to shrink. Calculation of the amount of oil lost as a result of gas cap shrinkage is discussed in Chapter 13, *Economics*.

Equations Used

1. The Tarner method is generally used in predicting performance of gas cap drive reservoirs. The material balance equation and the instantaneous gas oil ratio equation are solved simultaneously for the amount of gas produced during the period selected. It may be necessary to also revise the equation for calculating oil saturation, as some of the gas may move upstructure to the gas cap. The material balance equation is rearranged as follows:

$$N_p \times R_P = \frac{N\left[(B_t - B_{ti}) + m \times B_{ti}\left(\dfrac{B_g - B_{gi}}{B_{gi}}\right)\right] - N_P(B_t - R_{si} \times B_g)}{B_g}$$

$$(5\text{-}1)$$

Prediction of reservoir performance is then made following the procedure outlined in Chapter 4.

2. The frontal drive method can occasionally be used to satisfactorily predict gas cap drive reservoir performance. An example problem using the frontal drive will not be worked for a gas drive reservoir, due to its similarity to gas drive frontal advance calculations in secondary recovery, where a problem of this nature is solved.

Example Problem 5-1

An example reservoir performance prediction using the Tarner method is illustrated. Table 5-1 lists the required data for the reservoir study. Subsurface sample data and relative permeability ratio data are shown in Figures 5-4 and 5-5, while the results of the reservoir performance prediction are shown graphically in Figure 5-8. Table 5-2 shows a summary of the performance predictions, and Tables 5-3 through 5-6 show calculations for the study.

Table 5-1
Essential Data Required for Reservoir Study, Reservoir A

Structure: Elongated dome.

Original Reservoir Pressure, = 1710 psia.
Original oil in place = 40,000,000 stock tank barrels.
Ratio of gas zone size to oil zone size, m = 4.0.
Reservoir Temperature: 125°F.
Connate water saturation = 15%.
Gas gravity = 0.78.

Table 5-2
Summary of Performance Predictions, Reservoir A

Pressure Psia	Np/N	R SCF/ST Bbl.	Np Bbls. x 10^6
1710 (p_i)	0	462	0
1400	0.176	8490	7.04
1200	0.217	15160	8.68
1000	0.248	22166	9.92
800	0.268	28872	10.71
600	0.283	34900	11.32
400	0.296	35638	11.84

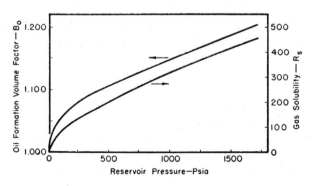

FIGURE 5-4. Subsurface sample fluid data, reservoir A.

Table 5-3
Basic Data — Gas Cap Drive, Reservoir A

Pressure Psia	Z	R_s	B_o	B_t	B_g	μ_o/μ_g
1710	0.755	462	1.205	1.205	0.00129	——
1400	0.784	399	1.180	1.283	0.00164	113.5
1200	0.809	359	1.164	1.367	0.00197	122.0
1000	0.835	316	1.148	1.506	0.00245	137.5
800	0.865	272	1.131	1.731	0.00316	163.0
600	0.895	225	1.115	2.148	0.00436	197.0
400	0.930	176	1.097	3.037	0.00680	239.0
200	0.965	122	1.075	5.935	0.01430	284.0

Example Calculations for Table 5-3

1. Calculation of Z at 1710 psia:

$$Sp. Gr. = 0.78$$

$p_c = 662$ psia; $T_c = 407$ °R. (From 1957 *NGSMA Data Book*, p. 103)

$$T_r = \frac{T}{T_c} = \frac{125 + 460}{407} = 1.44$$

$$p_r = \frac{p}{p_c} = \frac{1710}{662} = 2.58$$

$Z = 0.755$ (from 1957 *NGSMA Data Book*, p. 103)

2. Calculation of B_g at 1710 psia:

$$B_g = \frac{p_{sc} \times V_{sc} \times Z_1 \times T_f}{p_1 \times Z_{sc} \times T_{sc} \times 5.62} = \frac{14.7 \times 1 \times 0.755 \times 585}{1710 \times 1 \times 520 \times 5.62} = 0.00129$$

3. Calculation of B_t at 1400 psia:

$$B_t = B_o + (R_{si} - R_s) B_g$$
$$= 1.180 + (462 - 399) 0.00164$$
$$= 1.283$$

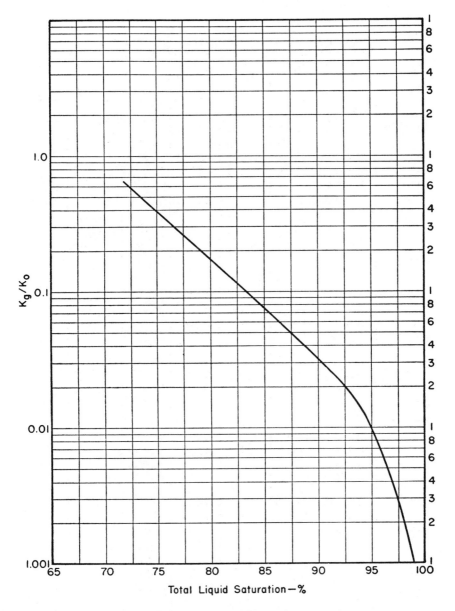

FIGURE 5-5. Relative permeability ratio, reservoir A.

Table 5-4
Summary of Calculations, Prediction of Reservoir
Performance, Reservoir A

Pressure	Assumed N_p/N	G_{mb}	S_o	k_g/k_o	R	G_{gor}	G (Actual)
1400	0.10	810N	0.750	0.0316	2,980	172.1N	
	0.15	795N	0.709	0.0630	5,550	451.0N	
	0.20	780N	0.666	0.1350	11,410	1187.2N	
Result:	0.176				8,490		790N
1200	0.20	485N	0.655	0.164	12,169	249N	
	0.215	480N	0.642	0.205	15,160	446N	
	0.217	479N	0.641	0.206	15,170	482N	
Result:	0.217				15,160		480N
1000	0.23	590N	0.623	0.275	18,000	215.5N	
	0.25	584N	0.606	0.350	22,816	625.0N	
	0.248	583N	0.608	0.340	22,166	580.0N	
Result:	0.248				22,166		583N
800	0.27	507N	0.585	0.495	29,172	565N	
	0.268	507N	0.587	0.490	28,872	509N	
Result:	0.268				28,872		507N
600	0.285	470N	0.560	0.720	36,400	555N	
	0.283	470N	0.563	0.690	34,900	479N	
Result:	0.283				34,900		470N
400	0.290	475N	0.550	0.850	32,876	237N	
	0.295	475N	0.545	0.920	35,576	424N	
Result:	0.296				35,638		475N
200	0.305	445N	0.526	1.25	26,822	281N	
	0.310	445N	0.523	1.30	27,872	445N	
Result:	0.310				27,872		445N

Table 5-5

Example Calculations — First Period — p = 1400 psia

Gas Cap Drive Reservoir A

Trial 1: Assume $N_p = 0.10$ N

$$G_{mb1} = N_{p1} \times R_{p1} = \frac{\left\{N\left[(B_t - B_{ti}) + m \times B_{ti}\left(\dfrac{B_g - B_{gi}}{B_{gi}}\right)\right] - N_p(B_t - R_{si} \times B_g)\right\}}{B_g}$$

$$= N\frac{\left\{\left[(1.283 - 1.205) + 4 \times 1.205\left(\dfrac{0.00164 - 0.00129}{0.00129}\right)\right] - 0.10\ N\ (1.283 - 462 \times 0.00164)\right\}}{0.00164}$$

$$= \underline{810\ N}$$

$$S_o = (1 - N_p/N)\frac{B_o}{B_{oi}}(1 - S_{wi})$$

$$= \left(1 - \frac{0.10\ N}{N}\right)\frac{1.180}{1.205}(1 - 0.15) = 0.75$$

$$S_t = S_o + S_{wi} = 0.75 + 0.15 = 0.90$$

k_g/k_o (from Fig. 5-5 where $S_t = 0.90$) = 0.0316

$$R_1 = k_g/k_o \times \mu_o/\mu_g \times \frac{B_o}{B_g} + R_s$$

$$= 0.0316 \times 113.5 \times \frac{1.180}{0.00164} + 399 = 2980$$

$$G_{gor1} = \left(\frac{R_1 + R_{si}}{2}\right) \times N_{p1} = \left(\frac{2980 + 462}{2}\right) \times 0.1\ N = \underline{172.1\ N}$$

Trial 2: Assume $N_p = 0.015\ N$

$G_{mb1} = N_{p1} \times R_{p1}$

$$= \frac{\left\{ N\left[(1.283 - 1.205) + 4 \times 1.205\left(\dfrac{0.00164 - 0.00129}{0.00164} \right) \right] - 0.15\ N\ (1.283 - 462 \times 0.00164) \right\}}{0.00164}$$

$= \underline{795\ N}$

$S_o = \left(1 - \dfrac{0.15N}{N} \right)\dfrac{1.180}{1.205}\ (1 - 0.15)\ = 0.709$

$S_t = 0.709 + 0.15 = 0.859$

$k_g/k_o = 0.063$ (from Fig. 5-5)

$R_1 = 0.063 \times 113.5 \times \dfrac{1.180}{0.00164} + 399 = 5550$

$G_{gor1} = \left(\dfrac{5550 + 462}{2} \right) \times 0.15\ N = \underline{451\ N}$

Trial 3: Assume $N_p = 0.20\ N$

$G_{mb1} = N_{p1} \times R_{p1}$

$$= \frac{\left\{ N\left[(1.283 - 1.205) + 4 \times 1.205\left(\dfrac{0.00164 - 0.00129}{0.00129} \right) \right] - 0.20\ N\ (1.283 - 462 \times 0.00164) \right\}}{0.00164}$$

$= \underline{780\ N}$

$S_o = \left(1 - \dfrac{0.20\ N}{N} \right)\dfrac{1.180}{1.205}\ (1 - 0.15) = 0.666$

$S_t = 0.666 + 0.15 = 0.816$

$k_g/k_o = 0.135$ (from Fig. 5-5)

$R_1 = 0.135 \times 113.5 \times \dfrac{1.180}{0.00164} + 399 = 11,410$

$G_{gor1} = \left(\dfrac{11,410 + 462}{2} \right) \times 0.20\ N = \underline{1187.2\ N}$

Table 5-6
Example Calculation — Second Period — p = 1200 psia
Gas Cap Drive Reservoir A

Trial 1: Assume $N_p = 0.20 \, N$

$$N_{p2} \times R_{p2} = \frac{\left\{ N\left[(B_t - B_{ti}) + m \times B_{ti}\left(\dfrac{B_g - B_{gi}}{B_{gi}}\right)\right] - N_p (B_t - R_{si} \times B_g) \right\}}{B_g}$$

$$= \frac{\left\{ N\left[(1.367 - 1.205) + 4 \times 1.205\left(\dfrac{0.00197 - 0.00129}{0.00129}\right)\right] - 0.2 \, N \, (1.367 - 462 \times 0.00197) \right\}}{0.00197}$$

$$= 1275 \, N$$

$$G_{mb2} = N_{p2} \times R_{p2} - G_1 = 1275 \, N - 790 \, N = \underline{485 \, N}$$

$$S_o = \left(1 - \frac{N_p}{N}\right)\frac{B_o}{B_{oi}} \, (1 - S_{wi})$$

$$= \left(1 - \frac{0.20 \, N}{N}\right)\frac{1.164}{1.205} \, (1 - 0.15) = 0.655$$

$k_g/k_o = 0.164$ (from Fig. 5-5 where $S_t = 0.655 + 0.150 = 0.805$)

$$R_2 = \frac{k_g}{k_o} \times \frac{\mu_o}{\mu_g} \times \frac{B_o}{B_g} + R_s$$

$$= 0.164 \times 122 \times \frac{1.164}{0.00197} + 359 = 12{,}169$$

$$G_{gor2} = \left(\frac{R_2 + R_1}{2}\right)(N_{p2} - N_{p1})$$

$$= \left(\frac{12169 + 8490}{2}\right)(0.200 \, N - 0.176 \, N)$$

$$= \underline{249 \, N}$$

Trial 2: Assume $N_p = 0.215$

$$N_{p2} \times R_{p2} = \frac{\left\{ N \left[(1.367 - 1.205) + 4 \times 1.205 \left(\frac{0.00197 - 0.00129}{0.00129} \right) \right] - 0.215\ N\ (1.367 - 462 \times 0.00197) \right\}}{0.00197}$$

$$= 1270\ N$$

$$G_{mb2} = N_{p2} \times R_{p2} - G_1 = 1270\ N - 790\ N = \underline{480\ N}$$

$$S_o = 0.785 \times \frac{1.164}{1.205} \times 0.85 = 0.642$$

$$k_g/k_o = 0.205$$

$$R_2 = 0.205 \times 122 \times \frac{1.164}{0.00197} + 359 = 15{,}160$$

$$G_{gor2} = \left(\frac{15{,}160 + 8{,}490}{2} \right)(0.215\ N - 0.176\ N) = \underline{446\ N}$$

Trial 3: Assume $N_p = 0.217\ N$

$$N_{p2} \times R_{p2} = \frac{\left\{ N \left[(1.367 - 1.205) + 4 \times 1.205 \left(\frac{0.00197 - 0.00129}{0.00129} \right) \right] - 0.217\ N\ (1.367 - 462 \times 0.00197) \right\}}{0.00197}$$

$$= 1269\ N$$

$$G_{mb2} = N_{p2} \times R_{p2} - G_1 = 1269\ N - 790\ N = \underline{479\ N}$$

$$S_o = 0.783 \times \frac{1.164}{1.205} \times 0.85 = 0.641$$

$$k_g/k_o = 0.206$$

$$R_2 = 0.206 \times 122 \times \frac{1.164}{0.00197} + 359 = 15{,}165$$

$$G_{gor2} = \left(\frac{15{,}165 + 8{,}490}{2} \right)(0.217\ N - 0.176\ N) = \underline{482\ N}$$

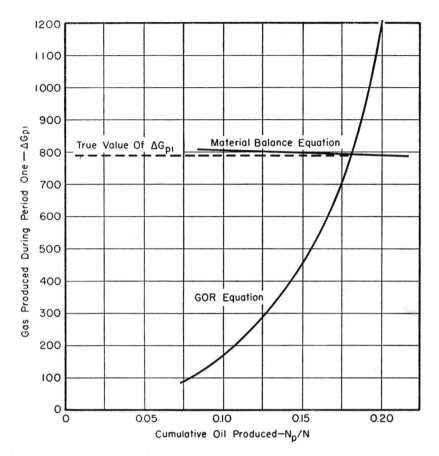

FIGURE 5-6. Determination of true value of ΔG_{p1}.

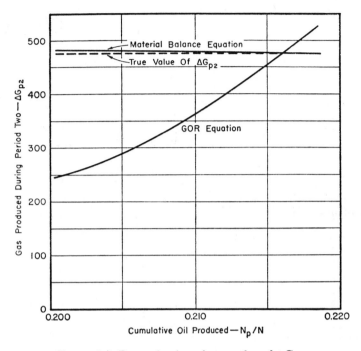

FIGURE 5-7. Determination of true value of ΔG_{p2}.

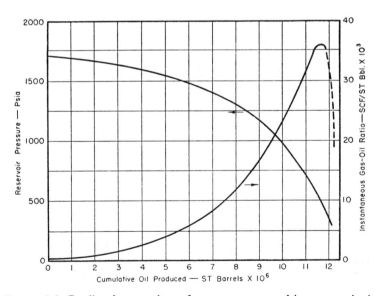

FIGURE 5-8. Predicted reservoir performance gas cap drive, reservoir A.

Chapter 6

WATER DRIVE RESERVOIRS

The production of oil by a water-displacing process is usually the most efficient displacing agent naturally available in the reservoir. However, even water drive reservoirs leave behind large percentages of oil at abandonment.

Water drive reservoirs have several characteristics which can be used for identification of the driving mechanism:

1. Pressure decline is very gradual. Figure 6-1 shows the pressure-production history of a typical water drive reservoir. It is not uncommon for many thousands of barrels of oil to be produced for each pounds per square inch drop in reservoir pressure. The reason for the small decline in reservoir pressure is that oil and gas withdrawals from the reservoir are replaced almost volume for volume by water encroaching into the oil zone. Several large oil reservoirs in the Gulf Coast areas of the U. S. have such active water drives that the reservoir pressure has declined only about one psi per million barrels of oil produced. Although pressure history is normally plotted versus cumulative oil production, it should be understood that total reservoir fluid withdrawals are the really important criteria in the maintenance of reservoir pressure. In a water drive reservoir, only a certain number of barrels of water can move into the reservoir as a result of a unit pressure drop within the reservoir. Since the principal income production is from oil, if the withdrawals of water and gas can be minimized, then the withdrawal of oil from the reservoir can be maximized with minimum pressure decline. Therefore, it is extremely important to reduce water and gas production to an absolute minimum. This can usually be accomplished by shutting in wells producing large quantities of these fluids, and where possible transferring their allowables to other wells producing with lower water-oil or gas-oil ratios.

2. Early excess water production occurs in structurally low wells. This is characteristic of a water drive reservoir, and provided the water is encroaching in a uniform manner, nothing can or should be done to restrict this encroachment, as the water will probably provide the most efficient displacing mechanism possible. If the reservoir has one or more lenses of very high

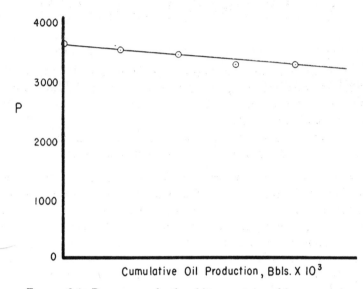

FIGURE 6-1. Pressure-production history—water drive reservoir.

permeability, then the water may be moving through this more permeable zone. In this case, it may be economically feasible to perform remedial operations to shut off this permeable zone producing water. It should be realized that in most cases the oil which is being recovered from a structurally low well will be recovered from wells located higher on the structure and any expenses involved in remedial work to reduce the water-oil ratio of structurally low wells may be needless expenditure.

3. There is normally little change in the producing gas-oil ratio during the life of the reservoir. This is especially true if the reservoir does not have an initial free gas cap. Pressure will be maintained as a result of water encroachment and therefore there will be relatively little gas released from solution.

4. Initial reservoir pressure is normal for the area, since either a sub-normal pressure reservoir or an abnormal pressure reservoir is usually a closed reservoir of limited extent. Since water influx is primarily the result of expansion of the water, a large aquifer is required for an active water drive due to the low expansibility of water. Therefore, highly faulted reservoirs seldom have active water drives.

If the reservoir has an initial free gas cap some of the wells located high on the structure may produce excess gas. In a water drive reservoir containing an original free gas cap, control of the gas cap is very important. In fact, control of the gas cap is usually the best criterion of the efficiency of reservoir operation. Since the objective in reservoir control is to utilize the most efficient displacing mechanism available, the gas cap must be carefully controlled. Where a water drive is present, maximum advantage should be taken of this displacing force since it will normally be more effective than an expanding gas cap. However, it is even more important to prevent shrinkage of the gas cap as this will permit oil to move up into the gas cap where there was no previous oil saturation. When the reservoir is finally depleted some residual oil saturation will remain in the original gas zone, since according to all flow concepts the saturation of any fluid can never be reduced to zero. The procedure used in calculating the actual amount of oil lost as a result of a shrinking gas cap is discussed more completely in Chapter 13.

In many reservoirs having a gas cap it will be impossible to prevent the production of gas cap gas due to the necessity of producing some of the structurally high wells. Therefore, it may be economically desirable to return gas to the reservoir to maintain the original size of the gas cap. Where the reservoir has a very active water drive, the objective should be to maintain the exact size of the original gas cap, so that the gas cap neither shrinks nor expands. This will permit the water drive to displace the oil from the reservoir. Where the water drive is not sufficiently strong to provide good pressure maintenance, it may be desirable to return gas to the reservoir to such an extent that the gas cap *expands*. Then the reservoir would be producing under a *combination* drive—that is, a combination of gas cap drive and water drive. This type of reservoir will be described in Chapter 8.

Typical pressure, gas-oil ratio, and salt water percentage curves for a water drive reservoir are shown in Figure 6-2. The reservoir shown does not have an original free gas cap, as evidenced by the continued low producing gas-oil ratio. Salt water production begins early in the producing life of the reservoir and continues to increase until the economic limit is reached. Reservoir pressure is still 2600 psia at abandonment, indicating an effective water drive.

Ultimate recovery from water drive reservoirs is usually much larger than recovery under any other producing mechanism. Recovery is dependent upon the efficiency of the flushing action of the water as it displaces the oil. In general, as the reservoir heterogeneity increases, the recovery will decrease, due to the uneven advance of the displacing water. The rate of water advance is normally faster in the zones of high permeability. This results in earlier high water-oil ratios and consequent earlier economic limits. Where the reservoir is more-or-less homogeneous, the advancing water front will be more uniform, and when the economic limit, due primarily to high water-oil ratio, has been reached, a greater portion of the reservoir will have been contacted by the advancing water.

Ultimate oil recovery is also affected by the degree of activity of the water drive. In a very active water drive where the degree of pressure maintenance is good, the role of solution gas in the recovery process is reduced to almost zero, with maximum ad-

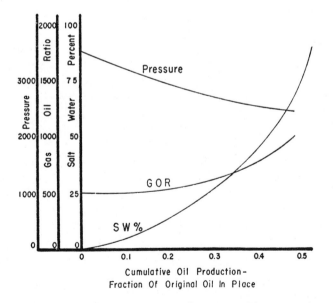

FIGURE 6-2. Performance curves of a water drive reservoir.

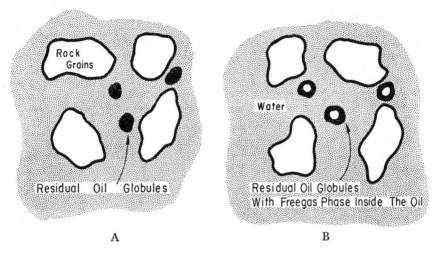

FIGURE 6-3. Theoretical effect of free gas saturation on residual oil saturation.

vantage being taken of the water as a displacing force. This should result in maximum oil recovery from the reservoir.

Effect of Free Gas Saturation on Recovery

Laboratory experiments have demonstrated that oil recovery by water displacement is improved as a result of the establishment of a free gas saturation in the reservoir. Several reasons for this phenomenon have been postulated, some of which appear to have merit. One of these theories postulates that since the interfacial tension of a gas-oil system is less than the interfacial tension of a gas-water system, in a three-phase system containing gas, water, and oil, the reservoir fluids will tend to arrange themselves in a minimum energy relationship.[1] In this case, this would dictate that the gas molecules enclose themselves in an oil "blanket." This increases the effective size of any oil globules which have enclosed some gas. When the oil is displaced by water, the oil globules are reduced to some size dictated by the flow mechanics. If a gas bubble existed on the inside of the oil globule, the amount of residual oil left in the reservoir would be reduced by the size of the gas bubble within the oil globule. This is illustrated in Figure 6-3. It can be seen that the external diameters of the residual oil globules

---

[1] Holmgren, C. R., and Morse, R. A., "Effect of Free Gas Saturation on Oil Recovery by Water Flooding," *Trans.* AIME, 1951, Vol. 192, p. 135.

are the same in both views. However, in view B, the center of the residual oil globule is not oil, but is gas. Therefore, in view B, the actual residual oil saturation is reduced by the size of the gas bubble within the oil globule.

If the above hypotheses were strictly true, then for very small gas saturations where all of the gas could be located inside the oil phase, there should be no change in the k_w/k_o relationships over that observed with no free gas saturation present. This would be true because the displacing water could not "see" the gas if it were all located within the oil phase. Most reported data, however, do show some difference in the relative permeability relationships. Thus, some of the free gas must be present outside of the oil phase. It is recognized that the enclosed gas bubble could alter the oil viscosity, but this should not affect the relative permeability relationships.

Reports on other laboratory experiments have noted the increased recovery obtained by flooding a core with air after water flooding.[2,3] These laboratory studies were performed on large radial cores cut from Nellie Bly sandstone. This formation was apparently water wet at the time the laboratory experiments were conducted. On the basis of these experiments, it was postulated that the residual oil saturation was located in the larger pore spaces, since the water would be preferentially pulled into the smaller pore spaces by capillary action in the water-wet sandstone. At a later time, when air was flooded through the core, it moved preferentially through the larger pore spaces since it was non-wetting. However, in passing through these large pore spaces, the air displaced some of the residual oil left by water displacement.

This latter theory is more nearly compatible with fluid flow observations, as the gas saturation does not have to exist inside the oil phase. If this theory were correct, the increased recovery due to the presence of a free gas saturation could be explained quite simply for water-wet porous media. As the gas saturation formed, it displaced oil from the larger pore spaces, as it is more non-wetting to the reservoir rock than the oil. Then, as water displaced the oil from the reservoir rock, the amount of residual oil left in the

---

[2] Jackson, M. L., "Oil Recovery by Combination of Water and Miscible Fluid Injection in Radial System," Master of Petroleum Engineering Thesis, University of Oklahoma, 1957.

[3] Cowan, J. V., "The Effect of a Free Gas Saturation on Recovery Efficiency of an LPG Flood," Master of Geological Engineering Thesis, University of Oklahoma, 1957.

larger pore spaces would be reduced because of occupancy of a portion of this space by gas. This phenomenon is illustrated in Figure 6-4. In view A, there is no free gas saturation and the residual oil occupies the larger pore spaces. In view B, a free gas saturation is present and this free gas now occupies a portion of the space originally occupied by the oil. The combined residual saturations of oil and gas in view B are approximately equal to the residual oil saturation of view A.

It is difficult to determine the actual reasons for the increased oil recovery by water displacement in the presence of a free gas saturation, because it is impossible at the present time to examine the flow characteristics inside a porous medium. However, it is generally agreed that oil recovery is increased in the presence of a free

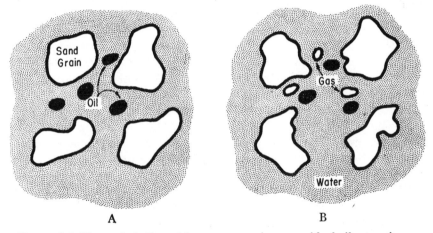

A   B

FIGURE 6-4. Theoretical effect of free gas saturation on residual oil saturation—water wet reservoir.

gas saturation. Although the actual mechanism is not completely understood this phenomenon can be taken advantage of in water drive reservoirs. Where original pressure is above the saturation pressure of the reservoir oil it may be desirable to reduce reservoir pressure below the saturation pressure as rapidly as possible in order to create a free gas saturation in the oil zone. After the free gas saturation has been established it is then desirable to maintain reservoir pressure as much as possible in order to prevent an excessive gas saturation from developing in the reservoir. At least one company received permission from a state regulatory body to withdraw oil at a rapid rate in order that reservoir pressure could be lowered below the saturation pressure, and a free gas saturation established in the oil zone prior to initiating a water-injection program in the reservoir. It is possible to substantially increase oil recovery from a reservoir by this technique and it should be taken advantage of at every opportunity.

Ultimate recovery from water drive reservoirs is dependent upon the efficiency of the water displacement process and also upon the degree of activity of the water drive. Recovery from water drive reservoirs will vary from 40 percent to more than 80 percent as a rule of thumb.

Reservoir wettability is apparently a key factor. Intermediate wettability apparently yields best recovery. Water wet reservoirs have lower recovery than intermediate wettability reservoirs, but greater recovery than from oil wet reservoirs. One statistical study[4] of active water drive reservoirs, where wettability conditions were believed to be known, showed that reservoirs having intermediate wetting properties yielded recoveries as high as 80 percent of the initial oil in place, while water wet reservoirs had recoveries as high as 60 percent of the initial oil in place. Oil wet reservoirs had the lowest recovery, about 40 percent of the initial oil in place, as a maximum.

These recoveries are in general agreement with wettability theories. In a highly water wet reservoir, the advancing water will be pulled into the smaller pore spaces by capillary forces and at the same time the viscous forces will push the water into the larger pore spaces. However, the water may advance more rapidly in the smaller pore spaces, and residual oil will be trapped in the larger pore spaces. In an oil wet reservoir the capillary forces will tend to prevent the water from entering the smaller pore spaces, resulting in relatively large residual oil saturations. In those reservoirs having an intermediate wettability, the capillary forces will not govern the advance of the water front, but the viscous forces will push the water into all the pore spaces, resulting in maximum oil recovery.

Measurement of reservoir wettability is probably very difficult. It has been shown that most drilling mud filtrates will alter the wetting properties of reservoir rock, and it has also been reported that weathering and aging of cores will alter their wetting characteristics. Probably the most reliable method of determining reservoir wettability is an imbibition test at the well site, on fresh, uncontaminated parts of cores which have not been in contact with the mud filtrate.

---

[4]Cole, Frank W., Private Report, 1966.

Predicting Reservoir Performance

As one of the principal functions of the reservoir engineer is the evaluation of future reservoir behavior, mathematical tools which can be reliably used to predict future reservoir performance are needed.

Schilthuis[5] developed one of the first useful approximations for calculating water influx into a hydrocarbon reservoir. This equation is:

$$W_e = k \int_0^t (p_i - p) \, dt \qquad (6\text{-}1)$$

or:

$$\frac{dW_e}{dt} = k \, (p_i - p) \qquad (6\text{-}2)$$

where:

W_e = gross water influx, barrels
p_i = initial boundary pressure, psi
p = boundary pressure at some later time, psi
t = time, days
k = water influx constant, bbls/day/psi

Equations (6-1) and (6-2) are steady state equations. This becomes evident, when after examination of the equations, it becomes obvious that regardless of the magnitudes of the pressures involved or length of time involved, a given pressure drop during a specified time interval will always yield identical values of water influx.

Water can move into a reservoir as a result of: (1) expansion of the water due to pressure drop within the hydrocarbon reservoir, and (2) artesian flow of water where the outcrop is located structurally higher than the hydrocarbon accumulation, and the water is replenished at the surface. Occurrence of the latter is probably rare, although there are some reservoirs which purportedly have this type of drive. Due to faulting or pinchouts, most hydrocarbon-bearing formations are not continuous from the hydrocarbon reservoir to the surface outcrop. In addition, for artesian flow to contribute substantially to water influx into a reservoir there must be sufficient ground water moving into the outcrop to replace the fluid

[5] Schilthuis, R. J., "Active Oil and Reservoir Energy," *Trans.* AIME, 1936, Vol. 118, p. 27.

withdrawals from the reservoir, and this water must move through the entire distance from outcrop to reservoir at this same rate. Thus it is believed that water influx is usually the result of expansion as a result of pressure drop. The existence of tilted oil-water contacts, which lends support to the hydrodynamic theory of oil accumulation, does not necessarily indicate that ground water is *currently* capable of moving into the reservoir at a rate equal to the reservoir voidage rate.

The compression of the void spaces in the reservoir rock as a result of pressure decline in the pore spaces can affect reservoir performance in a manner identical to water influx into the reservoir. The compression of the void spaces results in a reduction in the pore volume of the reservoir as withdrawals continue. Thus, for a given volume of reservoir fluid withdrawals, the pressure reduction is less. In several areas throughout the world, notably in California and South America, this phenomenon is believed to exist.

From a practical standpoint it is usually difficult to separate the water expansion from the rock compression. Therefore, these two effects, which are additive, are usually combined into one term which, for convenience, is referred to as effective water compressibility. The compressibility of water, as well as the compressibility of other liquids, will vary slightly, according to the pressure and temperature imposed on the water. Increasing the pressure will reduce the compressibility of water and increasing the temperature will increase the compressibility of water. The compressibility of fresh water at one atmosphere pressure and 60°F is 3.3×10^{-6} bbls./bbl/psi. Effective water compressibilities which have been used in reservoir engineering calculations with good results vary from 1.0×10^{-6} bbls/bbl/psi to 1.0×10^{-4} bbls/bbl/psi.

Examination of the mechanics of water expansion into a hydrocarbon reservoir shows that it must be an unsteady state process. However, for combination drive reservoirs, where the water influx rate is small compared to the other driving forces, the use of the Schilthuis steady state Equations (6-1) and (6-2) can usually be used with reliable results. The water influx constant, k, can be determined from past production data, and then this same value of k can be used to aid in predicting reservoir performance.

For active water drive reservoirs, the use of a steady state water influx equation will not usually result in reliable predictions of reservoir performance. As the pressure drop due to water expansion moves out further into the aquifer, the expanding water will not move into the hydrocarbon reservoir at the same rate, because for

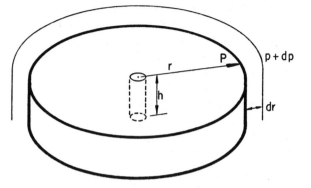

FIGURE 6-5. Unsteady state flow model.

a given pressure drop, the water has to move a greater distance in order to enter the oil or gas zone.

Hurst[6] and van Everdingen and Hurst[7] have developed a method for calculating the rate of water influx into a reservoir. The continuity equation is the basis for the development of the technique. Using the radial flow system shown in Figure 6-5, the continuity equation can be developed as follows:

The volume in some element with a radius r is:

$$V = \pi r^2 h \phi \qquad (6\text{-}3)$$

Differentiating Equation (6-3) results in:

$$dV = 2\pi r h\phi dr \qquad (6\text{-}4)$$

Where dV is the elemental volume developed as a result of increasing the radius of the element from r to r + dr. The compressibility of a slightly compressible fluid can be expressed as the change in volume per unit volume per unit pressure drop; or

$$c = \frac{1}{V} \frac{dV}{dp} \qquad (6\text{-}5)$$

The V term in Equation (6-5) is equivalent to the dV term in Equation (6-4).

Substituting Equation (6-4) into Equation (6-5) and solving for dV, the change in volume of the incremental element with a change in pressure dp results in:

[6] Hurst W., Water Influx into a Reservoir and its Application to the Equation of Volumetric Balance," *Trans.* AIME, 1943, Vol. 151, p. 57.
[7] van Everdingen, A. F., and Hurst, W., "The Application of the Laplace Transformation to Flow Problems in Reservoirs," *Trans.* AIME, 1949, Vol. 186, p. 305.

$$dV = c \, V \, dp$$
$$= c2\pi rh\phi \, (dr) \, (dp) \tag{6-6}$$

The time rate of change of this incremental volume is:

$$\frac{\delta V}{\delta t} = 2\pi rh\phi c \, (dr) \, \frac{\delta p}{\delta t} \tag{6-7}$$

however:

$$\frac{\delta V}{\delta t} = dq \tag{6-8}$$

Combining Equations (6-7) and (6-8) yields:

$$dq = 2\pi rh\phi c \, (dr) \, dp/dt \tag{6-9}$$

Rearranging Equation (6-9):

$$\frac{\delta q}{\delta r} = 2\pi rh\phi c \, (dp/dt) \tag{6-10}$$

Darcy's equation for radial flow is:

$$q = \frac{2\pi khr}{\mu} \frac{\delta p}{\delta r} \tag{6-11}$$

Differentiating Equation (6-11) with respect to r:

$$\frac{\delta q}{\delta r} = \frac{2\pi kh}{\mu} \, r\frac{\delta^2 p}{\delta r^2} + \frac{\delta p}{\delta r} \tag{6-12}$$

Combining Equations (6-10) and (6-12):

$$2\pi h\phi c \left(\frac{\delta p}{\delta t}\right) = \frac{2\pi kh}{\mu} \left(\frac{r\delta^2 p}{\delta r^2} + \frac{\delta p}{\delta r}\right) \tag{6-13}$$

After cancelling terms and simplifying, Equation (6-13) reduces to:

$$\frac{\delta^2 p}{\delta r^2} + \frac{1}{r} \frac{\delta p}{\delta r} = \frac{\mu\phi c}{k} \frac{\delta p}{\delta t} \tag{6-14}$$

The term $\frac{\mu\phi c}{k}$ will be essentially constant for any given reservoir.

If $\eta = \frac{k}{\mu\phi c}$, then Equation (6-14) becomes:

$$\frac{\delta^2 p}{\delta r^2} + \frac{1}{r} \frac{\delta p}{\delta r} = \frac{1}{\eta} \frac{\delta p}{\delta t} \tag{6-15}$$

Equation (6-15) is referred to as the diffusivity equation. This same basic equation has been used to calculate heat flow and electrical flow, as well as fluid flow through porous media. The term η is usually defined as the diffusivity constant.

A solution of Equation (6-15) will allow the calculation of the rate of water influx into a reservoir, provided the proper data are available.

A more general solution of Equation (6-15) can be obtained by substituting dimensionless time, t_D, in place of real time, t, in Equation (6-15), which now becomes:

$$\frac{\delta^2 p}{\delta r^2} + \frac{1}{r} \frac{\delta p}{\delta r} = \frac{\delta p}{\delta t} = \frac{\delta p}{\delta t_D} \qquad (6\text{-}16)$$

where:

$$t_D = \frac{kt}{\mu \phi c R^2} \qquad (6\text{-}17)$$

Since only basic equations have been utilized, the units for the above quantities are:

t_D = time, dimensionless
t = time, seconds
k = permeability, darcys
μ = viscosity, centipoises
ϕ = porosity, fraction
c = effective water compressibility, vol./ vol./atmosphere
R = reservoir radius, centimeters.

Converting Equation (6-17) to more commonly used units of t = days; k = millidarcies; μ = centipoises; ϕ = fraction; c = vol./psi; and R = feet; results in:

$$t_D = \frac{k \times t \times 24 \times 60 \times 60}{\mu \phi c \times 14.7 \times R^2 \times (2.54) \times 12)^2}$$

$$= 6.323 \times 10^{-3} \frac{kt}{\mu \phi c R^2} \qquad (6\text{-}18)$$

Van Everdingen and Hurst have utilized the Laplace transformations to solve Equation (6-16): Their resulting equation is:

$$W_e = \frac{2\pi \phi c R^2 h \Delta p Q_{(t)}}{5.615} \qquad (6\text{-}19)$$

$$= 1.119 \phi c R^2 h \Delta p Q_{(t)}$$

where:

W_e = cumulative water influx, barrels
Δp = pressure drop, psi

$Q_{(t)}$ = dimensionless water influx
5.615 = conversion factor, cubic feet to barrels

Equation (6-20) may also be expressed as:

$$W_e = B \times \Delta p \, Q_{(t)} \qquad \qquad (6\text{-}21)$$

where:

$$B = 1.119 \, \phi \, c \, R^2 \, h \qquad \qquad (6\text{-}22)$$

Van Everdingen and Hurst have presented the solution of Equation (6-21) in the form of dimensionless time, t_D, and dimensionless water influx, $Q_{(t)}$. Thus the solutions to the diffusivity equation are general, and can be applied to any reservoir where the flow of water into the reservoir is essentially radial in nature. Solutions were derived for the cases of aquifers of infinite extent and for aquifers of limited extent. Tables 6-1 and 6-2 show some of their solutions, and Figure 6-6 presents these same data in graphical form. Equations (6-20) and (6-21) assume that water is encroaching in a radial form. Quite often, water does not encroach on all sides of the reservoir, or the reservoir is not circular in nature. In these cases some modification must be made in order to properly describe the flow mechanism. One of the simplest modifications which can be made is to determine the fraction of a circular area through which water is encroaching. Equation (6-21) can be modified to:

$$B = 1.119 \, \phi \, c \, R^2 \, h \, f \qquad \qquad (6\text{-}23)$$

where:

f = fraction of the reservoir periphery into which water
is encroaching.

Figure 6-7 shows two reservoirs where the factor, f, could probably be used with reasonably good results. Other reservoirs, however, with more complex shapes, present greater problems. For example, the reservoirs shown in Figure 6-8 present problems in determining both R and f. However, since these two factors are somewhat related, small errors can be tolerated in one of the factors, as the other factor will be compensating.

Fortunately, it is usually unnecessary to determine these values with great accuracy, because the magnitude of B is determined as a single value when predicting reservoir behavior. This technique will be discussed at length later in this chapter.

Table 6-1
Radial Flow, Constant Terminal Pressure and Constant Terminal Rate Cases for Infinite Reservoirs*

t	P(t)	Q(t)	t	P(t)	Q(t)	t	P(t)	Q(t)	t	P(t)	Q(t)
$1.0(10)^{-2}$	0.112	0.112	$1.5(10)^{3}$		$4.136(10)^{2}$	$1.5(10)^{7}$		$1.828(10)^{6}$	$1.5(10)^{11}$		$1.17(10)^{10}$
5.0 "	0.229	0.278	2.0 "		5.315 "	2.0 "		2.398 "	2.0 "		1.55 "
$1.0(10)^{-1}$	0.315	0.404	2.5 "		6.466 "	2.5 "		2.961 "	2.5 "		1.92 "
1.5 "	0.376	0.520	3.0 "		7.590 "	3.0 "		3.517 "	3.0 "		2.29 "
2.0 "	0.424	0.606	4.0 "		9.757 "	4.0 "		4.610 "	4.0 "		3.02 "
2.5 "	0.469	0.689	5.0 "		11.88	5.0 "		5.689 "	5.0 "		3.75 "
3.0 "	0.503	0.758	6.0 "		13.95	6.0 "		6.758 "	6.0 "		4.47 "
4.0 "	0.564	0.898	7.0 "		15.99	7.0 "		7.816 "	7.0 "		5.19 "
5.0 "	0.616	1.020	8.0 "		18.00	8.0 "		8.866 "	8.0 "		5.89 "
6.0 "	0.659	1.140	9.0 "		19.99	9.0 "		9.911 "	9.0 "		6.58 "
7.0 "	0.702	1.251	$1.0(10)^{4}$		21.96	$1.0(10)^{8}$		10.95	7.28 "		7.28 "
8.0 "	0.735	1.359	1.5 "		$3.146(10)^{3}$	1.5 "		$1.604(10)^{7}$	$1.0(10)^{12}$		$1.08(10)^{11}$
9.0 "	0.772	1.469	2.0 "		4.079 "	2.0 "		2.108 "	1.5 "		1.42 "
1.0	0.802	1.570	2.5 "		4.994 "	2.5 "		2.607 "	2.0 "		
1.5	0.927	2.032	3.0 "		5.891 "	3.0 "		3.100 "			
2.0	1.020	2.442	4.0 "		7.634 "	4.0 "		4.071 "			
2.5	1.101	2.838	5.0 "		9.342 "	5.0 "		5.032 "			
3.0	1.169	3.209	6.0 "		11.03	6.0 "		5.984 "			
4.0	1.275	3.897	7.0 "		12.69	7.0 "		6.928 "			
5.0	1.362	4.541	8.0 "		14.33	8.0 "		7.865 "			
6.0	1.436	5.148	9.0 "		15.95	9.0 "		8.797 "			
7.0	1.500	5.749	$1.0(10)^{5}$		17.56	$1.0(10)^{9}$		9.725 "			
8.0	1.556	6.314	1.5 "		$2.538(10)^{4}$	1.5 "		$1.429(10)^{8}$			
9.0	1.604	6.861	2.0 "		3.308 "	2.0 "		1.880 "			
$1.0(10)^{1}$	1.651	7.417	2.5 "		4.066 "	2.5 "		2.328 "			
1.5 "	1.829	9.965	3.0 "		4.817 "	3.0 "		2.771 "			
2.0 "	1.960	$1.229(10)^{1}$	4.0 "		6.267 "	4.0 "		3.645 "			
2.5 "	2.067	1.455 "	5.0 "		7.699 "	5.0 "		4.510 "			
3.0 "	2.147	1.681 "	6.0 "		9.113 "	6.0 "		5.368 "			
4.0 "	2.282	2.088 "	7.0 "		10.51	7.0 "		6.220 "			
5.0 "	2.388	2.482 "	8.0 "		11.89	8.0 "		7.066 "			
6.0 "	2.476	2.860 "	9.0 "		13.26	9.0 "		7.909 "			
7.0 "	2.550	3.228 "	$1.0(10)^{6}$		14.62	$1.0(10)^{10}$		8.747 "			
8.0 "	2.615	3.599 "	1.5 "		$2.126(10)^{5}$	1.5 "		$1.288(10)^{9}$			
9.0 "	2.672	3.942 "	2.0 "		2.781 "	2.0 "		1.697 "			
$1.0(10)^{2}$	2.723	4.301 "	2.5 "		3.427 "	2.5 "		2.103 "			
1.5 "	2.921	5.980 "	3.0 "		4.064 "	3.0 "		2.505 "			
2.0 "	3.064	7.586 "	4.0 "		5.313 "	4.0 "		3.299 "			
2.5 "	3.173	9.120 "	5.0 "		6.544 "	5.0 "		4.087 "			
3.0 "	3.263	10.58	6.0 "		7.761 "	6.0 "		4.868 "			
4.0 "	3.406	13.48	7.0 "		8.965 "	7.0 "		5.643 "			
5.0 "	3.516	16.24	8.0 "		10.16	8.0 "		6.414 "			
6.0 "	3.608	18.97	9.0 "		11.34	9.0 "		7.183 "			
7.0 "	3.684	21.60	$1.0(10)^{7}$		12.52	$1.0(10)^{11}$		7.948 "			
8.0 "	3.750	24.23									
9.0 "	3.809	26.77									
$1.0(10)^{3}$	3.860	29.31									

* After Trans. AIME. Vol. 186, P. 314

Table 6-2
Constant Terminal Pressure Case Radial Flow, Limited Reservoirs*

R = 1.5 a₁ = 2 8899 a₂ = 9.3452		R = 2.0 a₁ = 1.3606 a₂ = 4.6458		R = 2.5 a₁ = 0.8663 a₂ = 3.0875		R = 3.0 a₁ = 0.6256 a₂ = 2.3041		R = 3.5 a₁ = 0.4851 a₂ = 1.8374		R = 4.0 a₁ = 0.3925 a₂ = 1.5267		R = 4.5 a₁ = 0.3296 a₂ = 1.3051	
t	$Q_{(t)}$	t	$Q_{(t)}$	t	$Q_{(t)}$	t	$Q_{(t)}$	t	$Q_{(t)}$	t	$Q_{(t)}$	t	$Q_{(t)}$
$5.0(10)^{-2}$	0.276	$5.0(10)^{-2}$	0.278	$1.0(10)^{-1}$	0.408	$3.0(10)^{-1}$	0.755	1.00	1.571	2.00	2.442	2.5	2.835
6.0 "	0.304	7.5 "	0.345	1.5 "	0.509	4.0 "	0 895	1.20	1.761	2.20	2.598	3.0	3.196
7.0 "	0.330	$1.0(10)^{-1}$	0.404	2.0 "	0.599	5.0 "	1.023	1.40	1.940	2.40	2.748	3.5	3.537
8.0 "	0.354	1.25 "	0.458	2.5 "	0.681	6.0 "	1.143	1.60	2.111	2.60	2.893	4.0	3.859
9.0 "	0.375	1.50 "	0.507	3.0 "	0.758	7.0 "	1.256	1.80	2.273	2.80	3.034	4.5	4.165
$1.0(10)^{-1}$	0.395	1.75 "	0.553	3.5 "	0.829	8.0 "	1.363	2.00	2.427	3.00	3.170	5.0	4.454
1.1 "	0.414	2.00 "	0.597	4.0 "	0.897	9.0 "	1.465	2.20	2.574	3.25	3.334	5.5	4.727
1.2 "	0.431	2.25 "	0.638	4.5 "	0.962	1.00	1.563	2.40	2.715	3.50	3.493	6.0	4.986
1.3 "	0.446	2.50 "	0.678	5.0 "	1.024	1.25	1.791	2.60	2.849	3.75	3.645	6.5	5.231
1.4 "	0.461	2.75 "	0.715	5.5 "	1.083	1.50	1.997	2.80	2.976	4.00	3.792	7.0	5.464
1.5 "	0.474	3.00 "	0.751	6.0 "	1.140	1.75	2.184	3.00	3.098	4.25	3.932	7.5	5.684
1.6 "	0.486	3.25 "	0.785	6.5 "	1.195	2.00	2.353	3.25	3.242	4.50	4.068	8.0	5.892
1.7 "	0.497	3.50 "	0.817	7.0 "	1.248	2.25	2.507	3.50	3.379	4.75	4.198	8.5	6.089
1.8 "	0.507	3.75 "	0.848	7.5 "	1.299	2.50	2.646	3.75	3.507	5.00	4.323	9.0	6.276
1.9 "	0.517	4.00 "	0.877	8.0 "	1.348	2.75	2.772	4.00	3.628	5.50	4.560	9.5	6.453
2.0 "	0.525	4.25 "	0.905	8.5 "	1.395	3.00	2.886	4.25	3.742	6.00	4.779	10	6.621
2.1 "	0.533	4.50 "	0.932	9.0 "	1.440	3.25	2.990	4.50	3.850	6.50	4.982	11	6.930
2.2 "	0.541	4.75 "	0.958	9.5 "	1.484	3.50	3.084	4.75	3.951	7.00	5.169	12	7.208
2.3 "	0.548	5.00 "	0.983	1.0	1.526	3.75	3.170	5.00	4.047	7.50	5.343	13	7.457
2.4 "	0.554	5.50 "	1.028	1.1	1.605	4.00	3.247	5.50	4.222	8.00	5.504	14	7.680
2.5 "	0.559	6.00 "	1.070	1.2	1.679	4.25	3.317	6.00	4.378	8.50	5.653	15	7.880
2.6 "	0.565	6.50 "	1.108	1.3	1.747	4.50	3.381	6.50	4.516	9.00	5.790	16	8.060
2.8 "	0.574	7.00 "	1.143	1.4	1.811	4.75	3.439	7.00	4.639	9.50	5.917	18	8.365
3.0 "	0.582	7.50 "	1.174	1.5	1.870	5.00	3.491	7.50	4.749	10.00	6.035	20	8.611
3.2 "	0.588	8.00 "	1.203	1.6	1.924	5.50	3.581	8.00	4.846	11	6.246	22	8.809
3.4 "	0.594	9.00 "	1.253	1.7	1.975	6.00	3.656	8.50	4.932	12	6.425	24	8.968
3.6 "	0.599	1.00	1.295	1.8	2.022	6.50	3.717	9.00	5.009	13	6.580	26	9.097
3.8 "	0.603	1.1	1.330	2.0	2.106	7.00	3.767	9.50	5.078	14	6.712	28	9.200
4.0 "	0.606	1.2	1.358	2.2	2.178	7.50	3.809	10.00	5.138	15	6.825	30	9 283
4.5 "	0.613	1.3	1.382	2.4	2.241	8.00	3.843	11.00	5.241	16	6.922	34	9.404
5.0 "	0.617	1.4	1.402	2.6	2.294	9.00	3.894	12.00	5.321	17	7.004	38	9.481
6.0 "	0.621	1.6	1.432	2.8	2.340	10.00	3.928	13.00	5.385	18	7.076	42	9.532
7.0 "	0.623	1.7	1.444	3.0	2.380	11.00	3.951	14.00	5.435	20	7.189	46	9.565
8.0 "	0.624	1.8	1.453	3.4	2.444	12.00	3.967	15.00	5.476	22	7.272	50	9.586
		2.0	1.468	3.8	2.491	14.00	3.985	16.00	5.506	24	7.332	60	9.612
		2.5	1.487	4.2	2.525	16.00	3.993	17.00	5.531	26	7.377	70	9.621
		3.0	1.495	4.6	2.551	18.00	3.997	18.00	5.551	30	7.434	80	9.623
		4.0	1.499	5.0	2.570	20.00	3.999	20.00	5.579	34	7.464	90	9.624
		5.0	1.500	6.0	2.599	22.00	3.999	25.00	5.611	38	7.481	100	9.625
				7.0	2.613	24.00	4.000	30.00	5.621	42	7.490		
				8.0	2.619			35.00	5.624	46	7.494		
				9.0	2.622			40.00	5.625	50	7.497		
				10.0	2.624								

* After Trans. AIME, Vol. 186, P. 315

Calculating Water Influx

It has previously been stated that water encroaches into a reservoir primarily by expansion of water as a result of a pressure drop. For any given reservoir the water influx at various times as a result of some pressure drop, Δp, can be calculated.

Example Problem 6-1

Calculate water influx at the end of 1, 2, and 5 years, into a circular reservoir with an aquifer of infinite extent. Effective water permeability is 100 mds., reservoir water viscosity is 0.8 cp., effective water compressibility is 1.0×10^{-6} bbl/bbl/psi, the radius of

Table 6-2 (Cont.)
Constant Terminal Pressure Case Radial Flow, Limited Reservoirs*

R = 5.0 a_1 = 0.2823 a_2 = 1.1392		R = 6.0 a_1 = 0.2182 a_2 = 0.9025		R = 7.0 a_1 = 0.1767 a_2 = 0.7534		R = 8.0 a_1 = 0.1476 a_2 = 0.6438		R = 9.0 a_1 = 0.1264 a_2 = 0.5740		R = 10.0 a_1 = 0.1104 a_2 = 0.4979	
t	$Q_{(t)}$	t	$Q_{(t)}$	t	$Q_{(t)}$	t	$Q_{(t)}$	t	$Q_{(t)}$	t	$Q_{(t)}$
3.0	3.195	6.0	5.148	9.00	6.861	9	6.861	10	7.417	15	9.965
3.5	3.542	6.5	5.440	9.50	7.127	10	7.398	15	9.945	20	12.32
4.0	3.875	7.0	5.724	10	7.389	11	7.920	20	12.26	22	13.22
4.5	4.193	7.5	6.002	11	7.902	12	8.431	22	13.13	24	14.09
5.0	4.499	8.0	6.273	12	8.397	13	8.930	24	13.98	26	14.95
5.5	4.792	8.5	6.537	13	8.876	14	9.418	26	14.79	28	15.78
6.0	5.074	9.0	6.795	14	9.341	15	9.895	28	15.59	30	16.59
6.5	5.345	9.5	7.047	15	9.791	16	10.361	30	16.35	32	17.38
7.0	5.605	10.0	7.293	16	10.23	17	10.82	32	7.10	34	18.16
7.5	5.854	10.5	7.533	17	10.65	18	11.26	34	17.82	36	18.91
8.0	6.094	11	7.767	18	11.06	19	11.70	36	18.52	38	19.65
8.5	6.325	12	8.220	19	11.46	20	12.13	38	19.19	40	20.37
9.0	6.547	13	8.651	20	11.85	22	12.95	40	19.85	42	21.07
9.5	6.760	14	9.063	22	12.58	24	13.74	42	20.48	44	21.76
10	6.965	15	9.456	24	13.27	26	14.50	44	21.09	46	22.42
11	7.350	16	9.829	26	13.92	28	15.23	46	21.69	48	23.07
12	7.706	17	10.19	28	14.53	30	15.92	48	22.26	50	23.71
13	8.035	18	10.53	30	15.11	34	17.22	50	22.82	52	24.33
14	8.339	19	10.85	35	16.39	38	18.41	52	23.36	54	24.94
15	8.620	20	11.16	40	17.49	40	18.97	54	23.89	56	25.53
16	8.879	22	11.74	45	18.43	45	20.26	56	24.39	58	26.11
18	9.338	24	12.26	50	19.24	50	21.42	58	24.88	60	26.67
20	9.731	25	12.50	60	20.51	55	22.46	60	25.36	65	28.02
22	10.07	31	13.74	70	21.45	60	23.40	65	26.48	70	29.29
24	10.35	35	14.40	80	22.13	70	24.98	70	27.52	75	30.49
26	10.59	39	14.93	90	22.63	80	26.26	75	28.48	80	31.61
28	10.80	51	16.05	100	23.00	90	27.28	80	29.36	85	32.67
30	10.98	60	16.56	120	23.47	100	28.11	85	30.18	90	33.66
34	11.26	70	16.91	140	23.71	120	29.31	90	30.93	95	34.60
38	11.46	80	17.14	160	23.85	140	30.08	95	31.63	100	35.48
42	11.61	90	17.27	180	23.92	160	30.58	100	32.27	120	38.51
46	11.71	100	17.36	200	23.96	180	30.91	120	34.39	140	40.89
50	11.79	110	17.41	500	24.00	200	31.12	140	35.92	160	42.75
60	11.91	120	17.45			240	31.34	160	37.04	180	44.21
70	11.96	130	17.46			280	31.43	180	37.85	200	45.36
80	11.98	140	17.48			320	31.47	200	38.44	240	46.95
90	11.99	150	17.49			360	31.49	240	39.17	280	47.94
100	12.00	160	17.49			400	31.50	280	39.56	320	48.54
120	12.0	180	17.50			500	31.50	320	39.77	360	48.91
		200	17.50					360	39.88	400	49.14
		220	17.50					400	39.94	440	49.28
								440	39.97	480	49.36
								480	39.98		

* After Trans. AIME, Vol. 186, P. 315

the reservoir is 2000 feet, reservoir thickness is 25 feet, porosity is 20%, initial reservoir pressure is 2500 psi, and present reservoir pressure is 2490 psi.

$$B = 1.119\, \phi\, c\, R^2\, h\, f$$
$$= 1.119 \times 0.20 \times 1.0 \times 10^{-6} \times (2000)^2 \times 25 \times 1.0$$
$$= 20.4$$
$$t_D = \frac{6.323 \times 10^{-3}\, k\, t}{\mu\, \phi\, c\, R^2}$$

After one year:

$$t_D = \frac{6.323 \times 10^{-3} \times 100 \times 365}{0.80 \times 0.20 \times 1.0 \times 10^{-6} \times (2000)^2}$$
$$= 361$$

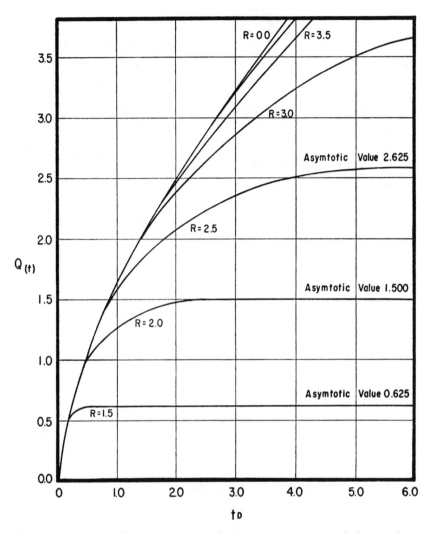

FIGURE 6-6. Radial flow constant terminal pressure case, cumulative production vs. time for limited reservoir. *(After Trans. AIME, Vol. 186, p. 309.)*

Referring to Table 6-1, where $t_D = 361$, $Q_{(t)} = 123.7$ Using Equation (6-21):

$$W_e = B \times \Delta p \times Q_{(t)}$$
$$= 20.4 \times (2500 - 2490) \times 123.5$$
$$= 25{,}200 \text{ barrels}$$

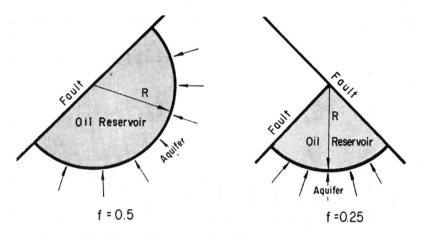

FIGURE 6-7. Water drive reservoirs with restricted encroachment.

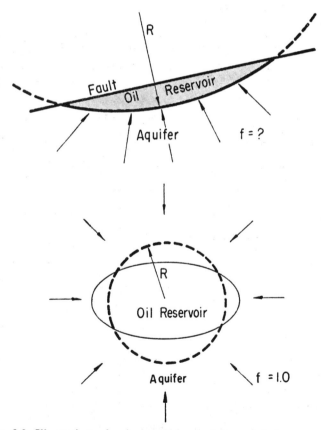

FIGURE 6-8. Illustrations showing variations of R and f for water drive reservoirs.

After two years:

$$t_D = \frac{6.323 \times 10^{-3} \times 100 \times 365 \times 2}{0.80 \times 0.20 \times 1.0 \times 10^{-6} \times (2000)^2} = 722$$

$Q_{(t)} = 22.18$ (from Table 6-1)
$W_e = 20.4 \times (2500 - 2490) \times 221.8$
     $= 45,200$ barrels

After five years:

$$t_D = \frac{6.323 \times 10^{-3} \times 100 \times 365 \times 5}{0.80 \times 0.20 \times 1.0 \times 10^{-6} \times (2000)^2}$$
$$= 1805$$

$Q_{(t)} = 484.6$ (From Table 6-1)
$W_e = 20.4 \times (2500 - 2490) \times 484.6$
     $= 98,800$ barrels

Example 6-1 shows that for a given pressure drop, doubling the time interval will not double the water influx. This example also shows how to calculate water influx as a result of a single pressure drop. The solutions of the diffusivity equation shown in Tables 6-1

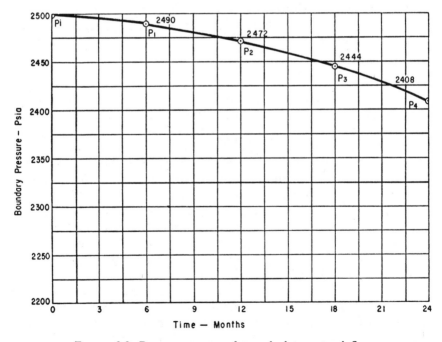

FIGURE 6-9. Pressure steps used to calculate water influx.

and 6-2 are for a constant terminal pressure. It is well known that in an actual reservoir the pressure is declining continuously. In order to use this method it is necessary to assume that the boundary (reservoir) pressure declines in a series of pressure steps. Referring to Figure 6-9 it is assumed that at the end of six months the pressure everywhere in the reservoir drops suddenly from p_i to p_1. It is further assumed that the pressure stays constant for another six months period, at the end of which it again drops suddenly throughout the reservoir to p_2. These stepwise decreases in reservoir pressure are continued for the length of time desired in the water influx calculations.

Example 6-1 showed how to calculate the water influx as a result of one pressure drop in the reservoir. As there will usually be many of these pressure drops occurring throughout the prediction period it is necessary to analyze the procedure to be used where these multiple pressure drops are present. Referring again to Figure 6-9 it is noted that at the end of six months it is assumed that pressure declines instantly to some new pressure p_1 (2490 psia in the example shown).

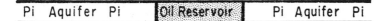

FIGURE 6-10. Pressure relationships within a hypothetical oil reservoir and its surrounding aquifer.

The pressures which have been discussed in the preceding examples are actually the boundary pressures between the hydrocarbon reservoir and the aquifer. The principal interest at the present time is the determination of the water expansion due to pressure decline. Figure 6-10 illustrates the pressure relationships within a hypothetical reservoir and its surrounding aquifer. If the boundary pressure in the reservoir shown in Figure 6-10 is suddenly reduced from p_i to p_1, a pressure drop, $p_i — p_1$ will be imposed across the aquifer. Water will continue to expand and the new reduced pressure will continue to move outward into the aquifer. Given a sufficient length of time the pressure at the outer edge of the aquifer will finally be reduced to p_1.

If some time after the boundary pressure has been reduced to p_1, a second pressure p_2 is suddenly imposed at the boundary, and a new pressure wave will begin moving outward into the aquifer. This new pressure wave will also cause water expansion and therefore encroachment into the reservoir. However, this new pressure drop will not be $p_i - p_2$, but will be $p_1 - p_2$. This second pressure wave will be moving behind the first pressure wave. Just ahead of the second pressure wave will be the pressure at the end of the first pressure drop, p_1.

Since these pressure waves are assumed to occur at different times, they are entirely independent of each other. Thus, water expansion will continue to take place as a result of the first pressure drop, even though additional water influx is also taking place as a result of one or more later pressure drops. In order to determine the total water influx into a reservoir at any given time, it is necessary to determine the water influx as a result of each successive pressure drop which has been imposed on the reservoir and aquifer.

In calculating cumulative water influx into a reservoir at successive intervals, it is necessary to calculate the total water influx from the beginning. This is required because of the different times during which the various pressure drops have been effective. An example calculation will be used to explain this procedure more clearly.

The term B in Equation (6-21) is usually a constant for a given reservoir. Thus where the water influx must be calculated for several different pressure drops, each of which has been effective for varying lengths of time, instead of calculating the water influx for each pressure step, the total water influx as a result of all the pressure steps can be calculated as follows:

$$W_{e1} = B \times (p_i - p_1)\, Q_{(t)1} \qquad (6\text{-}24)$$
$$W_{e2} = B \times (p_1 - p_2)\, Q_{(t)2} \qquad (6\text{-}25)$$
$$W_{en} = B \times (p_{n-1} - p_n)\, Q_{(t)n} \qquad (6\text{-}26)$$

Combining Equations (6-24), (6-25) and (6-26):

$$W_e = B\, \Sigma\, \Delta p \times Q_{(t)} \qquad (6\text{-}27)$$

Equation (6-27) is the form usually used to calculate water influx.

It has been reported[8] that instead of using the entire pressure drop for the first period a better approximation is to consider that

---

[8] van Everdingen, A. F., Timmerman, E. H., and McMahon, J. J., "Application of the Material Balance Equation to a Partial Water Drive Reservoir," *Trans.* AIME, 1953, Vol. 198, p. 51.

one-half of the pressure drop, $\frac{1}{2}$ $(p_i - p_1)$, is effective during the entire first period. For the second period the effective pressure drop then is one-half of the pressure drop during the first period, $\frac{1}{2}$ $(p_i - p_1)$, plus one-half of the pressure drop during the second period, $\frac{1}{2}$ $(p_1 - p_2)$, which simplifies to:

$$\tfrac{1}{2}\ (p_i - p_1) + \tfrac{1}{2}\ (p_1 - p_2) = \tfrac{1}{2}\ (p_i - p_2)$$

Similarly, the effective pressure drop for use in the calculations for the third period would be one-half of the pressure drop during the second period, $\frac{1}{2}$ $(p_1 - p_2)$, plus one-half of the pressure drop during the third period, $\frac{1}{2}$ $(p_2 - p_3)$, which simplifies to $\frac{1}{2}$ $(p_1 - p_3)$. The time intervals must all be equal in order to preserve the accuracy of these modifications.

Example Problem 6-2

Using reservoir data from Example 6-1 calculate the cumulative water influx at the end of: (1) 6 months, (2) one year, (3) 18 months, and (4) 2 years. The pressure-time relationship is shown in Figure 6-9.

1. Water influx at the end of 6 months:

$$B = 20.4 \text{ (from example 6-1)}$$
$$t_D = \frac{6.323 \times 10^{-3} \times 100 \times 182.5}{0.20 \times 0.80 \times 1.0 \times 10^{-6} \times (2000)^2}$$
$$= 180.5$$
$$W_e = B \times \Delta p \times Q_{(t)}$$
$$= 20.4 \times \tfrac{1}{2}\ (2500 - 2490) \times 69.46$$
$$= 7080 \text{ barrels}$$

2. Water influx at the end of one year.

$$B = 20.4$$
$$t_D = \frac{6.323 \times 10^{-3} \times 100 \times 365}{0.20 \times 0.80 \times 1.0 \times 10^{-6} \times (2000)^2} = 361$$

The first pressure drop, $p_i - p_1$, has been effective for one year, but the second pressure drop, $p_1 - p_2$, has been effective only 6 months. Separate calculations must be made for the two pressure drops because of this time difference, and the results added in order to determine the total water influx.

Equation (6-27) will now be used and the $\Delta p \times Q_{(t)}$ values for each pressure drop will be determined:

Table 6-3

Calculating Water Influx After One Year

Time Days	t_D	Pressure Psia	Effective Δp Pressure Drop Psi	$Q_{(t)}$	$\Delta p \times Q_{(t)}$
365	361	2490	5	123.5	617
182.5	180.5	2472	14*	69.46	971

$$\Sigma \, \Delta p \times Q_{(t)} = 1588$$

*Effective $\Delta p = \frac{1}{2} \, (p_1 - p_1) + \frac{1}{2} \, (p_1 - p_2) = \frac{1}{2} \, (p_1 - p_2)$
$\qquad = \frac{1}{2} \, (2500 - 2472) = 14$ psi

$W_e = B \, \Sigma \, \Delta p \times Q_{(t)}$
$\qquad = 20.4 \times 1588 = 32,400$ barrels

3. Water influx at the end of 18 months (third period) :

The first pressure drop will have been effective the entire 18 months, the second pressure drop will have been effective for 12 months, and the last pressure drop will have been effective only 6 months. Table 6-4 summarizes the calculations:

Table 6-4

Water Influx at the End of 18 Months

Time Days	t_D	Pressure Psia	Effective Δp Psi	$Q_{(t)}$	$\Delta p \times Q_{(t)}$
547.5	541.5	2490	5	173.7	868
365	361	2472	14	123.5	1729
182.5	180.5	2444	23	69.46	1596

$$\Sigma \, \Delta p \times Q_{(t)} = 4193$$

$W_e = B \, \Sigma \, \Delta p \times Q_{(t)}$
$\qquad = 20.4 \times 4193 = 85,600$ barrels

4. Water influx at the end of 2 years:

The first pressure drop has now been effective for the entire two years, the second pressure drop has been effective for 18 months, the third pressure drop has been effective for 12 months, and the fourth pressure drop has been effective only 6 months. Table 6-5 summarizes the water influx calculations:

Table 6-5
Water Influx at the End of Two Years

Time Days	t_D	Pressure Psia	Effective Δp Psi	$Q_{(t)}$	$\Delta p \times Q_{(t)}$
730	722	2490	5	221.8	1109
547.5	541.5	2472	14	173.7	2430
365	361	2444	23	123.5	2840
182.5	180.5	2408	32*	69.46	2220

$$\Sigma \Delta p \times Q_{(t)} = 8599$$

*Effective $\Delta p = \frac{1}{2} (p_2 - p_3) + \frac{1}{2} (p_3 - p_4) = \frac{1}{2} (p_2 - p_4)$
$= \frac{1}{2} (2472 - 2408) = 32\ \text{psi}$
$W_e = B \Sigma \Delta p \times Q_{(t)}$
$= 20.4 \times 8599 = 175,500\ \text{barrels}$

Use of the Unsteady State Equation in Predicting Reservoir Performance

The principal utility of the unsteady state water influx equation is in the prediction of reservoir performance, although very useful information can be developed by using the equation to analyze past behavior.

In the prediction of future reservoir performance, the unsteady state equation can not be used alone because there are two unknowns, water influx and pressure. It is necessary to utilize another equation to develop a solution. The material balance equation is commonly used in conjunction with the unsteady state equation to predict reservoir performance.

The following procedure is used to analyze a water drive reservoir:

1. Assemble all necessary reservoir and subsurface sample data.

2. Using the best available data, calculate a value for the constant, B, in the unsteady state equation.

3. In order to determine the validity of the constant B, an evaluation is also made by determining gross water influx at several times by the material balance equation. Values of B at these various times are calculated by:

$$B = \frac{W_{e(mb)}}{\Sigma \Delta p \times Q_{(t)}} \tag{6-28}$$

The apparent B, as determined by this method is then plotted versus cumulative oil production as shown in Figure 6-11. The best horizontal line is then drawn through the various points. This is the value of B which is normally used for all future calculations, although it is checked against the value computed from the various factors comprising B.

4. Water influx over the past history of the reservoir is next calculated using both the unsteady state equation and the material balance equation. These two should agree if the average value of B has been used in the unsteady state equation.

5. On the basis of the past production history of the reservoir the following curves are usually drawn:

A. Gross Water Influx vs. Time (and Cum. Oil)
B. Net Water Influx vs. Time (and Cum. Oil)
C. Net Change in Gas Cap vs. Time (and Cum. Oil)
These calculated values are then compared to actual performance data to determine whether the calculated values are indicative of actual behavior.

6. Prediction of Future Reservoir Behavior.

A. Select a combination of oil, gas and water production rates which will hold throughout the prediction period.

B. The first step is the estimation of the reservoir pressure at the end of the first trial period (suggested 6 months). Gross water influx is calculated by both equations. If the results agree then the first estimated pressure is correct; if not, then another pressure must be selected and the procedure repeated until agreement is reached.

C. Additional calculations are repeated for additional equal time intervals until the desired range of reservoir history has been studied.

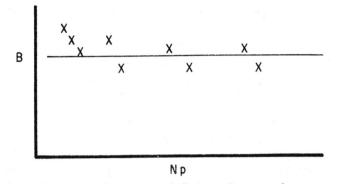

FIGURE 6-11. Evaluation of the constant B from the unsteady state equation.

7. Several different combinations of oil, gas and water producing rates should be used, and a complete prediction made for each set of values. For example, after selecting the combination of producing rates which appears to be the most reasonable, it is desirable to select one producing rate which is greater, and one producing rate which is smaller for oil, gas and water. Thus, there would be three different oil producing rates, three different gas producing rates, and three different water producing rates. This will result in 27 different combinations of producing rates. Since most reservoir engineering calculations of this nature are solved on computing machines, the additional time required for 27 completely different solutions is insignificant. The advantage of having these different combinations of withdrawal rates is that if for any reason the withdrawal rates are changed in the future from those expected, a set of performance curves will already be available for the altered producing condition, and an entirely new study will not be required.

Validity of Performance Predictions

The effectiveness of the previously described procedure for predicting reservoir behavior by the simultaneous solution of the unsteady state and material balance equations is largely the result of three characteristics of the technique:

1. The two equations represent independent methods of solving for identical quantities.

2. An error in boundary pressure results in a deviation in the calculated water influx by the unsteady state equation which

is opposite in direction from the same deviation in water influx as calculated by the material balance equation.

3. Errors in the initial volumes of oil and gas in place result in erroneous calculations by the material balance equation but do not affect the water influx calculated by the unsteady state equation.

4. Errors in production data or in subsurface sample data will result in erroneous calculations of water influx by the material balance equation, but do not affect results obtained by the unsteady state equation. Water influx by the material balance calculations is equal to withdrawals minus expansions, and in weak water drive reservoirs, this results in one large number being subtracted from another large number to obtain a small number. Thus, relatively small errors in reservoir data will usually result in significant changes in the calculated results.

As a result of these four factors, when agreement is finally reached between water influx calculated by both the material balance and the unsteady state equations, the data will have usually been adjusted with sufficient accuracy to permit reliable predictions of reservoir performance.

Smith[9] examined the sensitivity of some of the variables in the unsteady state equation to determine their effect on reservoir performance predictions. It is usually impossible to accurately define the terms comprising the unsteady state equation. However, some of these terms appear in the denominator of the dimensionless time equation and in the numerator of the equation for calculating the constant B. Thus, it appears that the errors in these terms will not be as important as errors in terms which appear only once in the equations. Changes in net sand thickness, fraction of reservoir periphery open to water influx or boundary pressure will have a direct effect on water influx calculations since these terms appear only once in the equation. Smith found that a ten fold variation in either porosity, or the square of reservoir radius, will result in only a two fold variation in calculated water influx. This is due to these factors being in the denominator of the dimensionless time equations and the numerator of the equation for calculating the constant, B. A ten fold variation in effective water permeability resulted in an approximate five fold variation in water influx. A ten

[9] Smith, P. C., "An Investigation of the Sensitivity of Some of the Variables Affecting the Calculation of Water Influx by the Hurst Unsteady State Method," Master of Petroleum Engineering Thesis, University of Oklahoma, 1958.

fold variation in water viscosity also resulted in approximately a five fold variation in the results.

Limitations in Predicting Reservoir Performance

The use of simultaneous solutions of the unsteady state equation and the material balance equation for predicting performance of water drive reservoirs has certain limitations. As with other methods of forecasting reservoir behavior, the single most important phase of the study is the matching of past performance. If the data can be satisfactorily adjusted so that the past performance of the reservoir can be exactly duplicated, it is reasonable to expect that the match will continue into the future. Several factors which deserve special mention insofar as determining the validity of the method are:

1. Extent of the Aquifer.

Since the extent of the aquifer (in terms of reservoir radius) had to be known in order to effect a solution of the diffusivity equation, it is very important to have some knowledge of the size of the aquifer. The size of the aquifer may be difficult to determine in some cases, but usually sufficient subsurface information will be available to yield an accurate answer. It appears that most aquifers are sufficiently large as compared with their associated hydrocarbon reservoirs that they can be considered to be of infinite extent. Trouble may be encountered with aquifers of unknown size. If an infinite aquifer is assumed with good results when matching past performance, but at some later time the pressure waves reach the extent of aquifer, the rate of water influx may change. Thus, if the extent of the aquifer is unknown, and even though past reservoir performance can be well matched, it is possible that at some later date the expansion of water may reach the limits of the aquifer, in which case, if an infinite aquifer had been assumed, the performance predictions past this date would not be correct.

2. Determining the Magnitude of the Constant B.

The combined use of the material balance and unsteady state equations for the determination of the constant B in the unsteady state equation is a decided weakness in the technique. The material balance equation is not a good tool for calculating water influx. As mentioned previously, water influx by material balance calculations is obtained by subtracting the reservoir fluid expansions from the reservoir fluid production. When reservoir pressure changes, only slightly, small errors in pressure measurement can cause relatively large errors in the fluid expansion term and consequently in the calculated water influx. The use of an average value of B at several different times reduces the magnitude of any potential errors.

3. Selection of Time Intervals in Predicting Performance.

The accuracy of the technique is dependent on the length of time between periods, the shorter the time, the more accurate the calculations. Periods of three or six months are usually sufficiently reliable for most calculations.

Example Calculation-Predicting Reservoir Performance

A water drive reservoir from West Texas will be used to illustrate the procedure used to predict performance of a water drive

Table 6-6
Reservoir Data Water Drive Reservoir D

Type Structure	Elongated Dome
Discovery Date	December 31, 1955
Total Productive Area	1440 acres
Initial oil in place, ST bbls	34,000,000
Initial reservoir temperature	118° F
Initial reservoir pressure	2265 psig
Reservoir saturation pressure	1135 psig
Water viscosity at initial reservoir conditions	0.68 cp
Average porosity in aquifer	20%
Average permeability in aquifer	100 mds
Average radius of field	4500 feet
Ratio of aquifer radius to field radius	4.0
Effective compressibility of reservoir water	144×10^{-6} vol/vol/psi
Initial solution gas-oil ratio, R_{si}	192 SCF/STB

reservoir. This is a limestone reservoir and is an elongated dome, with water influx around the entire periphery of the reservoir. Because of the relatively rapid pressure decline, this reservoir would be classified as having a weak water drive. Table 6-6 and Figures 6-12 through 6-14 show the required reservoir data. The step-by-step solution of the problem is shown in Tables 6-7 and 6-8. Figure 6-15 is a graph showing the best value of the constant B for the reservoir. Early in the producing life of the reservoir, calculated B values may be very erratic due to inaccuracies in data which become magnified due to the small volume of reservoir

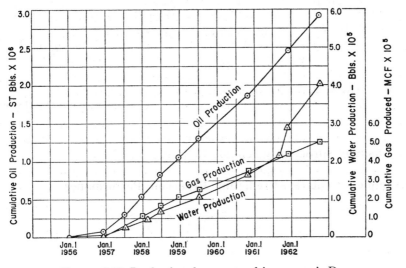

FIGURE 6-12. Production data, water drive reservoir D.

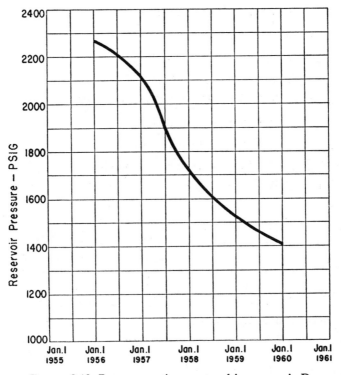

FIGURE 6-13. Pressure vs. time, water drive reservoir D.

withdrawals. For this reason the B value of 250, calculated on January 1, 1957, was not used to obtain the best value of B. Figure 6-16 shows plots of future water influx calculated by both the unsteady state equation and the material balance equation. The intersection of the two curves yields the proper pressure. Only one future prediction has been made. Additional predictions at later dates can be made by utilizing exactly the same procedure used to predict pressure at the end of the first prediction period.

It should be noted that reservoir pressure has not yet declined to the saturation pressure. Once the pressure has declined below the saturation pressure, a material balance equation which is applicable below the saturation pressure will have to be used.

Table 6-7a
Determination of B, Calculation No. 1—Jan. 1, 1957

$$B = \frac{W_{e(mb)}}{\Sigma \Delta_p \times Q_{(t)}}$$

where:

(mb) = material balance equation

Material Balance Equation above p_s:

$$W_e = N_p B_t + W_p - N(B_t - B_{ti})$$

$$p = 2115 \text{ psig (from Fig. 6-13)}$$

A. $W_{e(mb)} = (110,000)(1.1025) + 5000 - 34,000,000(1.1025 - 1.1013)$

$$= 121,300 + 5000 - 40,800$$

$$= 85,500 \text{ Bbls gross water influx}$$

B. $\Sigma \Delta p \times Q_{(t)}$ using time intervals of six months:

Jan. 1, 1957 is the end of the second period:

Period	t	t_d	$Q_{(t)}$	p	Δp	$\Delta p \times Q_{(t)}$
1	365	5.82	4.70[2]	2215	25[3]	117.5
2	182.5	2.91[1]	3.00	2115	75[4]	225.0
						$\Sigma = 342.5$

[1] $t_D = 6.323 \times 10^{-3} \dfrac{kt}{\phi \mu c_e r_w^2} = \dfrac{6.323 \times 10^{-3} \times 100 \times 182.5}{0.20 \times 0.68 \times 14.4 \times 10^{-6} \times (4500)^2}$

$$= 2.91$$

[2] From Table 6-2 where $r_e/r_w = 4.0$ and $t_D = 5.82$

[3] $\Delta p = \frac{1}{2}(p_i - p_1)$

[4] $\Delta p = \frac{1}{2}(p_i - p_2)$ $B = 85,500/342.5 = 250$

Table 6-7b
Determination of B, Calculation No. 2—Jan. 1, 1958

$$p = 1728 \text{ psig}$$

A. $W_{e(mb)} = N_p B_t + W_p - N(B_t - B_{ti})$

$= (650,000)(1.1056) + 45,000 - 34,000,000(1.1056 - 1.1013)$

$= 719,000 + 45,000 - 146,000$

$= 618,000$ Bbls. gross water influx

B. $\Sigma \Delta p \times Q_{(t)}$; Jan. 1, 1958 is the end of the fourth period.

Period	t	t_D	$Q_{(t)}$	p	Δp	$\Delta p \times Q_{(t)}$
1	730	11.64	6.2	2215	25	155
2	547.5	8.73	5.7	2115	75	422
3	365	5.82	4.7	1900	158[1]	743
4	182.5	2.91	3.0	1728	194	582
						$\Sigma = 1902$

[1]. $\Delta p = \frac{1}{2}(P_1 - p_3) = \frac{1}{2}(2215 - 1900) = 158$

$$B = \frac{W_{e(mb)}}{\Sigma \Delta p \times Q_{(t)}} = \frac{618,000}{1902} = 325$$

Table 6-7c
Determination of B, Calculation No. 3—Jan. 1, 1959

$$p = 1525 \text{ psig}$$

A. $W_{e(mb)} = 1,075,000(1.1074) + 83,000 - 34,000,000(1.1074 - 1.1013)$

$= 1,190,000 + 83,000 - 207,000$

$= 1,066,000$

B. $\Sigma \Delta p \times Q_{(t)}$; Jan. 1, 1959 is the end of the sixth period

Period	t	t_D	$Q_{(t)}$	p	Δp	$\Delta p \times Q_{(t)}$
1	1095	17.46	7.0	2215	25	175
2	912.5	14.55	6.75	2115	75	506
3	730	11.64	6.2	1900	158	979
4	547.5	8.73	5.7	1728	194	1106
5	365	5.82	4.7	1600	150	705
6	182.5	2.91	3.0	1525	102	306
						$\Sigma = 3777$

$$B = \frac{W_{e(mb)}}{\Sigma \Delta p \times Q_{(t)}} = \frac{1,066,000}{3777} = 283$$

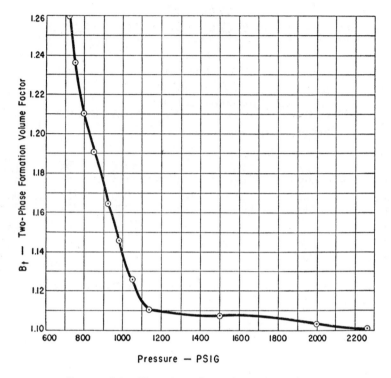

FIGURE 6-14. Two-phase formation volume factor.

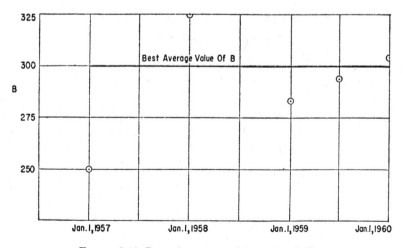

FIGURE 6-15. B vs. time, water drive reservoir D.

Table 6-7d
Determination of B, Calculation No. 4—July 1, 1959

$$p = 1465 \text{ psig}$$

A. $W_{e(mb)} = 1,300,000(1.1078) + 105,000$
$\qquad - 34,000,000(1.1078 - 1.1013)$
$\qquad = 1,440,000 + 105,000 - 221,000$
$\qquad = 1,324,000$

B. $\Sigma\Delta p \times Q_{(t)}$; July 1, 1959 is the end of the seventh period:

Period	t	t_D	$Q_{(t)}$	p	Δp	$\Delta p \times Q_{(t)}$
1	1277.5	20.37	7.15	2215	25	179
2	1095	14.46	7.0	2115	75	525
3	912.5	14.55	6.75	1900	158	1067
4	730	11.64	6.2	1728	194	1203
5	547.5	8.73	5.7	1600	150	855
6	365	5.82	4.7	1525	102	479
7	182.5	2.91	3.0	1465	68	204
						$\Sigma = 4512$

$$B = \frac{W_{e(mb)}}{\Sigma\Delta p \times Q_{(t)}} = \frac{1,324,000}{4512} = 294$$

Table 6-7e
Determination of B, Calculation No. 5—Jan. 1, 1960

$$p = 1405 \text{ psig}$$

A. $W_{e(mb)} = 1,505,000(1.1082) + 130,000$
$\qquad - 34,000,000(1.1082 - 1.1013)$
$\qquad = 1,670,000 + 130,000 - 235,000$
$\qquad = 1,565,000 \text{ Bbls. gross water influx}$

B. $\Sigma\Delta p \times Q_{(t)}$; Jan. 1, 1960 is the end of the eighth period:

Period	t	t_D	$Q_{(t)}$	p	Δp	$\Delta p \times Q_{(t)}$
1	1460	23.28	7.25	2215	25	181
2	1277.5	20.37	7.15	2115	75	536
3	1095	17.46	7.0	1900	158	1106
4	912.5	14.55	6.75	1728	194	1310
5	730	11.64	6.2	1600	150	930
6	547.5	8.73	5.7	1525	102	581
7	365	3.82	4.7	1465	68[1]	320
8	182.5	2.91	3.0	1405	60	180
						$\Sigma = 5144$

[1]. $\Delta p_7 = \frac{1}{2}(p_5 - p_7) = \frac{1}{2}(1600 - 1465) = 68 \text{ psi}$

$$B = \frac{W_{e(mb)}}{\Sigma\Delta p \times Q_{(t)}} = \frac{1,565,000}{5144} = 304$$

Table 6-8a
Predicting Reservoir Performance
Time: July 1, 1960

Trial 1: Assume $p_9 = 1340$ psig

A. $W_{e(mb)} = N_p B_t + W_p - N(B_t - B_{ti})$
   $= (1,705,000)^1(1.1087) + 160,000^1 -$
   $\qquad\qquad\qquad\qquad 34,000,000(1.1087 - 1.1013)$
   $= 1,890,000 + 160,000 - 252,000$
   $= 1,798,000$ Bbls. gross water influx by material balance
   calculations

B. $W_{e(us)} = B \times \Sigma\Delta_p \times Q_t$ (July 1, 1960 is the end of the 9th period.)

1	1642.5	26.19	7.30	2215	25	183
2	1460	23.28	7.25	2115	75	544
3	1277.5	20.37	7.15	1900	158	1130
4	1095	17.46	7.0	1728	194	1358
5	912.5	14.55	6.75	1600	150	1012
6	730	11.64	6.2	1525	102	632
7	547.5	8.73	5.7	1465	68	388
8	365	5.82	4.7	1405	60	282
9	182.5	2.91	3.0	1340	63	189
						$\Sigma = 5718$

---

[1] Future oil and water producing rates assumed on the basis of past production history and anticipated future producing rates.

$W_{e(us)} = 300^* \times 5718 = 1,714,000$ Bbls. gross water influx by unsteady state calculations.

*From Figure 6-15 for best value of B from past production history.

NOTE: The water influx calculated by the two equations are not in agreement; therefore another pressure must be assumed.

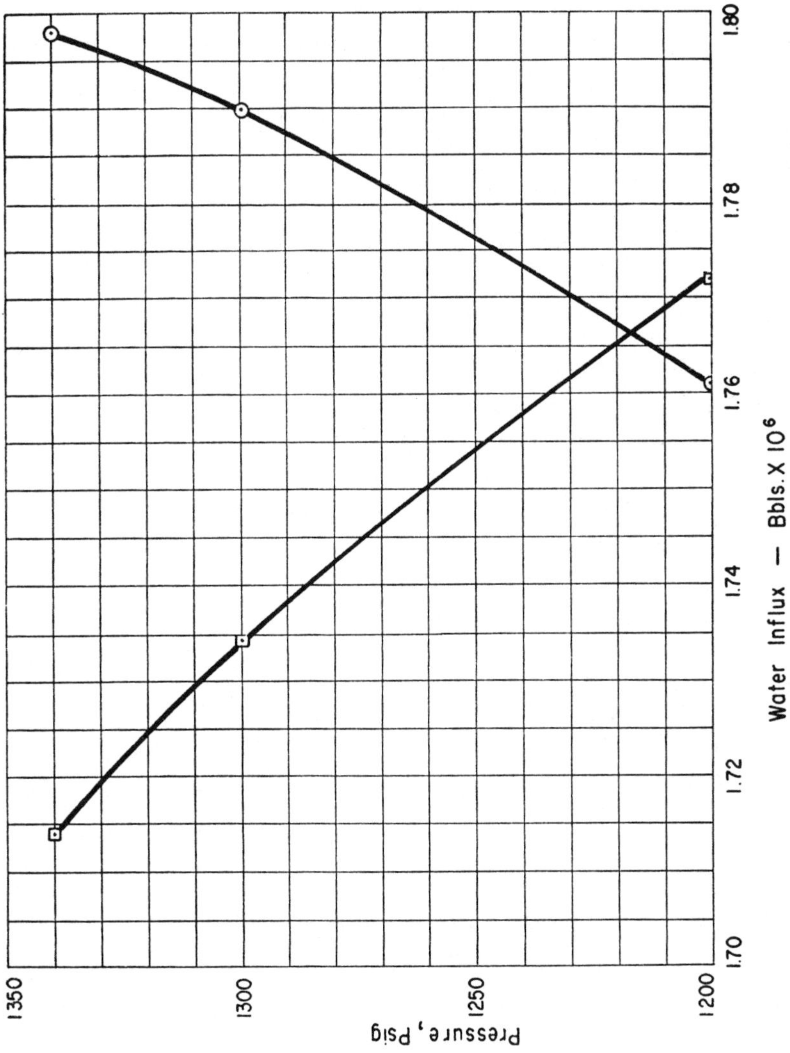

Water Influx — Bbls. X 10^6

FIGURE 6-16. Matching water influx, water drive reservoir D, July 1, 1960. Data from Table 6-8.

Table 6-8b
Predicting Reservoir Performance
Time: July 1, 1960

Trial 2: Assume $p_9 = 1300$ psig

A. $W_{e(mb)} = (1,705,000)(1.1090) + 160,000$
$\qquad - 34,000,000(1.1099 - 1.1013)$
$\qquad = 1,892,000 + 160,000 - 262,000$
$\qquad = 1,790,000$

B. $W_{e(us)} = B \times \Sigma\Delta p \times Q_{(t)}$
$\qquad = 300 \times 5778^* = 1,734,000$

Trial 3: Assume $p_9 = 1200$ psig

A. $W_{e(mb)} = (1,705,000)(1.1099) + 160,000$
$\qquad - 34,000,000(1.1099 - 1.1013)$
$\qquad = 1,893,000 + 160,000 - 292,000$
$\qquad = 1,761,000$ bbls.

B. $W_{e(us)} = B \times \Sigma\Delta p \times Q_{(t)}$
$\qquad = 300 \times 5928 = 1,772,000$

* This calculation is identical to Part B of Trial 1 except for period 9, where pressure is changed from 1340 to 1300. Water influx as calculated by the two equations still does not agree; therefore, another pressure will be assumed.

NOTE: Using the first three trials, plots of pressure versus water influx by both material balance and unsteady state equations, as shown in Figure 6-16, will show the pressure which will result in identical water influx calculations by both methods.

The Material Balance Equation as a Straight Line

The material balance equation can be rearranged to produce a straight line on ordinary Cartesian coordinates.

Rearranging the generalized material balance Equation (3-15):

$$\frac{N_p [B_o + (R_p - R_s) B_g] + W_p B_w}{m B_{ti}\left(\frac{B_g}{B_{gi}} - 1\right) + (B_t - B_{ti})}$$

$$= N + \frac{W_e}{m B_{ti}\left(\frac{B_g}{B_{gi}} - 1\right) + (B_t - B_{ti})}$$

$$(6\text{-}28)$$

Equation (6-28) is a straight line of the form $y = b + k x$, where y is equal to the entire left hand side of Equation (6-28);

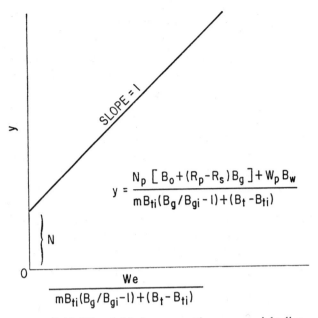

$$y = \frac{N_p \left[B_o + (R_p - R_s) B_g \right] + W_p B_w}{m B_{ti}(B_g / B_{gi} - 1) + (B_t - B_{ti})}$$

$$\frac{W_e}{m B_{ti}(B_g / B_{gi} - 1) + (B_t - B_{ti})}$$

FIGURE 6-17. Material balance equation as a straight line.

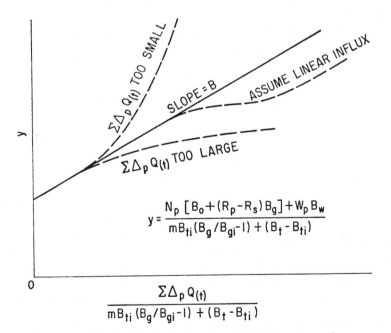

$$y = \frac{N_p \left[B_o + (R_p - R_s) B_g \right] + W_p B_w}{m B_{ti}(B_g / B_{gi} - 1) + (B_t - B_{ti})}$$

$$\frac{\Sigma \Delta_p Q_{(t)}}{m B_{ti}(B_g / B_{gi} - 1) + (B_t - B_{ti})}$$

FIGURE 6-18. Graphical solution of material balance equation.

b, the intercept is equal to N; x is equal to the entire second member of the right hand side of the equation; and k, the slope of the line, is equal to one. Figure 6-17 shows this plot.

In theory, a plot of this nature should be quite useful for estimating N, the initial oil in place, provided W_e, the gross water influx, can be determined independently of the material balance equation. In practice, this plot often has limited value for estimating N because, in an active water drive reservoir, the pressure drop will be small, and the denominator of both sides of Equation (6-28) will also be quite small. Large volumes of water may be produced with the oil, and consequently, the term: $N_p [B_o + (R_p - R_s) B_g] + W_p B_w$ will be large. Dividing a large number by a very small number will produce a much larger number. The actual numbers plotted on the ordinate may be as much as 1,000 times as large as N. In these cases, extrapolating the line back to the y-axis will not result in a reliable estimate of N. However, when pressure drop is substantial and large volumes of water are not produced, this technique may have some application.

The gross water influx, W_e, can be determined by: (1) volumetric calculations, where accurate oil-water contacts can be determined for past periods and where good geologic data are available, and (2) using the Hurst van Everdingen unsteady state water influx Equation (6-21).

An alternate method of plotting the data is to combine Equation (6-21) and (6-28) as follows:

$$\frac{N_p [B_o + (R_p - R_s) B_g] + W_p B_w}{m B_{ti} \left(\frac{B_g}{B_{gi}} - 1\right) + (B_t - B_{ti})}$$

$$= N + \frac{B \Sigma \Delta_p Q_{(t)}}{m B_{ti} \left(\frac{B_g}{B_{gi}} - 1\right) + (B_t - B_{ti})}$$

(6-29)

Equation (6-29) will plot as a straight line and is illustrated by the solid line in Figure 6-18. The slope of the line will be equal to B, the water influx constant in the water influx equation.

Havlena and Odeh[10] have published the results of studies involving the use of straight line material balance relationships. They report that if the term $\Sigma \Delta p Q_{(t)}$ is too small the line will curve upward, while if this term is too large, it will curve downward.

---

[10]Havlena and Odeh, "The Material Balance as an Equation of a Straight Line," *Journal of Petroleum Technology*, August 1963, page 896; and July 1964, page 815.

An S-shaped curve indicates that a better fit could be obtained by assuming linear water influx instead of radial water influx. These concepts are shown by the dotted lines in Figure 6-18. This type of plot can have considerable utility as an aid in determining the proper aquifer size, and other data needed for $Q_{(t)}$ and t_D calculations. Several combinations could be tried, the results plotted and analyzed to determine the best data.

Chapter 7

GRAVITY DRAINAGE RESERVOIRS

The mechanism of gravity drainage occurs in petroleum reservoirs as a result of differences in densities of the reservoir fluids. The effects of gravitational forces can be simply illustrated by placing a quantity of crude oil and a quantity of water in a jar and agitating the contents. After agitation, the jar is placed at rest, and the more dense fluid (normally water) will settle to the bottom of the jar, while the less dense fluid (normally oil) will rest on top of the denser fluid. The fluids have separated as a result of the gravitational forces acting on them.

The fluids in petroleum reservoirs have all been subjected to the forces of gravity, as evidenced by the relative positions of the fluids, i.e. gas on top, oil underlying the gas, and water underlying the oil. The relative positions of the reservoir fluids are shown in Figure 7-1. Due to the long periods of time involved in the petroleum-accumulation-and-migration process it is generally assumed that the reservoir fluids are in equilibrium. If the reservoir fluids are in equilibrium then the gas-oil and oil-water contacts should be essentially horizontal. Although it is difficult to determine precisely the reservoir fluid contacts, best available data indicate that, in most resorvoirs, the fluid contacts actually are essentially horizontal. Hubbert[1] has presented a somewhat different theory of oil accumulation and migration. In this theory, called the "hydrodynamic" theory of oil accumulation, it is postulated that tilted oil-water contacts may be expected as a result of the oil-accumulation process. Figure 7-2 illustrates the hydrodynamic theory of oil accumulation. Hubbert cites several examples to substantiate his theory. It is interesting to note that as early as 1939 essentially the same theory was postulated for the accumulation of oil in the

---

[1] Hubbert, M. K., "Entrapment of Oil Under Hydrodynamic Conditions," *AAPG Bull.*, Vol. XXXVII, No. 8, 1953, p. 1954.

Langham Sand reservoir in the Amelia Field of Jefferson County, Texas.[2]

Gravity segregation of fluids is probably present to some degree in all petroleum reservoirs, but it may contribute substantially to

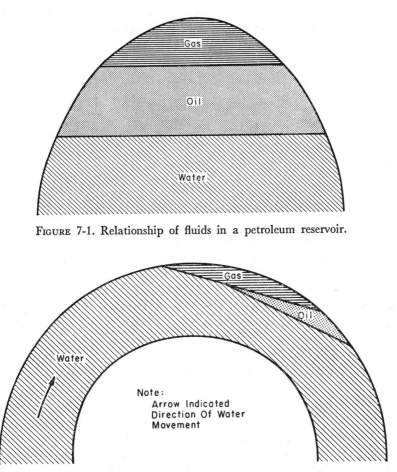

FIGURE 7-1. Relationship of fluids in a petroleum reservoir.

FIGURE 7-2. Hydrodynamic theory of oil accumulation.

oil production in some reservoirs. As one of the principal functions of the reservoir engineer is to forecast the future producing rates of reservoirs under various operating conditions, it would be desirable to be able to calculate the effects on ultimate oil recovery

---

[2] Hamner,. E. J., "Amelia Oil Field, Jefferson County, Texas," *AAPG*, Vol. XXIII, p. 1635.

of various reservoir fluid withdrawal rates. Unfortunately, standard methods for predicting reservoir performance of gravity drainage reservoirs have not yet been developed. Probably the principal reason is that ultimate recovery from gravity drainage reservoirs is rate sensitive, and the material balance equation, the basic tool for predicting reservoir behavior, is not a rate-sensitive equation. However, it is possible to develop methods for studying individual reservoirs and methods for predicting reservoir behavior are discussed later in this chapter.

Reservoirs operating largely under a gravity drainage producing mechanism are characterized by:

1. Low gas-oil ratio from structurally low wells. This is caused by migration of the evolved gas upstructure due to gravitational segregation of the fluids.

2. Formation of a secondary gas cap in reservoirs which initially were undersaturated. Obviously the gravity drainage mechanism does not become operative until reservoir pressure has declined below the saturation pressure, since above the saturation pressure there will be no free gas in the reservoir.

3. Increasing gas-oil ratio from structurally high wells, which is also a result of the upstructure migration of the gas released from solution from the oil.

4. Little or no water production. Water production is indicative of a water drive.

5. Variable rates of pressure decline, depending principally upon the amount of gas conservation. Strictly speaking, where the gas is conserved, and reservoir pressure is maintained, the reservoir would be operating under combined gas-cap drive and gravity drainage mechanisms. Therefore, for the reservoir to be operating solely as a result of gravity drainage, the reservoir would show a rapid pressure decline. This would require the upstructure migration of the evolved gas where it later was produced from structurally high wells, resulting in rapid loss of pressure. Examples of these two

³ Anders, E. L., Mile Six Pool—"An Evaluation of Recovery Efficiency," *Trans.*, *AIME*, Vol. 198, 1953, p. 279.

types of gravity drainage reservoirs are shown in Figures 7-3 and 7-4. Figure 7-3 shows pressure-production and gas-oil ratio production history for the Mile Six Pool in Peru.[3] This reservoir is an excellent example of gravity drainage with effective pressure maintenance by gas injection. Reser-

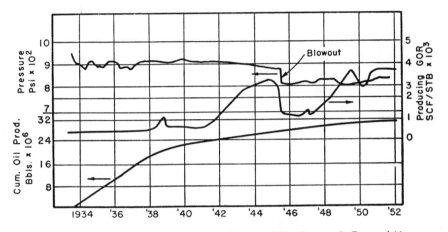

FIGURE 7-3. Reservoir performance history, Mile Six pool, Peru. *(After Anders, AIME Trans., 1953.)*

voir pressure has declined less than 200 psi below its original value. Oil recovery has been exceptionally high, as it is estimated that ultimate recovery will eventually approach 67 percent of the initial oil in place, and that the residual oil saturation at depletion will be approximately 19%. The dip of the reservoir is approximately 20 degrees, and the average air permeability in the direction of dip is about 780 millidarcies.

Figure 7-4 shows reservoir performance of the Wilcox reservoir in the Oklahoma City Field. Reservoir pressure declined to essentially atmospheric pressure within a few years, but even without the benefit of reservoir pressure, in July 1941 the production rate exceeded 75,000 barrels per day from 466 pumping wells, or an average of more than 160 barrels per well per day. All available evidence precluded the presence of a water drive, and in the absence of any reservoir pressure, it must be concluded that gravity drainage was responsible for the high producing rates. The dip of the Wilcox reservoir is approximately 15 degrees, and the average air permeability of the reservoir is about 1000 millidarcies. Thus, the Wilcox reservoir could be classified as a true gravity drainage reservoir.

Ultimate recovery from gravity drainage reservoirs will vary widely, due primarily to the extent of depletion by gravity drainage alone. Where gravity drainage is good, or where producing rates are restricted to take maximum advantage of the gravitational forces, recovery will be high. There are reported cases where recovery from gravity drainage reservoirs has exceeded 80% of

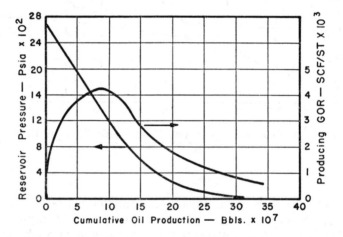

FIGURE 7-4. Reservoir performance, Wilcox Sand, Oklahoma City field. *(After Katz, AIME, 1942.)*

the initial oil in place. In other reservoirs where depletion drive also plays an important role in the oil recovery process, the ultimate recovery will be less.

The most important point to remember in operating gravity drainage reservoirs is that the oil saturation in the vicinity of the well bore must be maintained as high as possible. There are two basic reasons for this: (1) a high oil saturation means a higher oil flow rate, and (2) a high oil saturation means a lower gas flow rate. If the evolved gas migrates upstructure instead of toward the well bore, then a high oil saturation in the vicinity of the well bore can be maintained.

In order to take maximum advantage of the gravity drainage producing mechanism, wells should be located as low structurally as possible. This will result in maximum conservation of the reservoir gas. A typical gravity drainage reservoir is shown in Figure 7-5.

Factors which affect ultimate recovery from gravity drainage reservoirs are: (1) permeability in the direction of dip, (2) dip of the reservoir, (3) reservoir producing rates, (4) oil viscosity, and (5) relative permeability characteristics.

Permeability in the Direction of Dip

Good permeability in the direction of migration of the oil is a prerequisite for efficient gravity drainage. For example, a reservoir with little structural relief which also contained many more or less

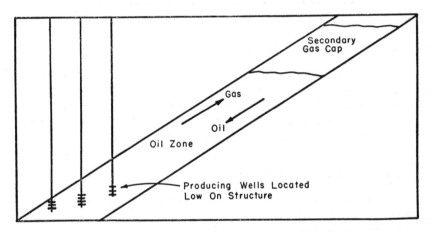

FIGURE 7-5. Typical gravity drainage reservoir.

continuous shale "breaks" could probably not be operated under gravity drainage because the oil could not flow to the base of the structure.

Dip of the Reservoir

In most reservoirs, the permeability in the direction of dip is considerably larger than the permeability transverse to the direction of dip. Therefore, as the dip of the reservoir increases, the oil and gas can flow along the direction of dip (which is also the direction of greatest permeability) and still achieve their desired structural position.

Reservoir Producing Rates

Since the gravity drainage rate is limited, the reservoir producing rates should be limited to the gravity drainage rate, then maximum recovery will result. If the reservoir producing rate exceeds the gravity drainage rate the depletion drive producing mechanism will become more significant with a consequent reduction in ultimate oil recovery. Determination of the gravity drainage rate is discussed later in this chapter.

Oil Viscosity

Oil viscosity is important because the gravity drainage rate is dependent upon the viscosity of the oil. In the fluid flow equations, as the viscosity decreases the flow rate increases. Therefore, the gravity drainage rate will increase as the reservoir oil viscosity decreases.

Relative Permeability Characteristics

For an efficient gravity drive mechanism to be operative, the gas must flow upstructure while the oil flows downstructure. Although this situation involves counterflow of the oil and gas, both fluids are flowing and therefore relative permeability characteristics of the formation are very important.

Fundamental Recovery Process

Recovery by gravity drainage involves two fundamental considerations: (1) the formation of a secondary gas cap, and (2) the gravity drainage rate.

It becomes obvious that a secondary gas cap must be formed when it is remembered that the oil saturation in the vicinity of the well bore must remain high in order to take maximum advantage of gravity drainage. Once the secondary gas cap is formed, it will expand as reservoir pressure continues to decline, provided the gas cap expansion exceeds the gas cap production. The expanding secondary gas cap will then displace oil ahead of it as it expands. Thus, a frontal drive is also operative as gravity drainage proceeds.

Actual determination of the gravity drainage rate is difficult in many cases, due primarily to the lack of needed data. Darcy's Law, which can be used to calculate the steady state flow of oil can be written:

$$q_o = -\frac{k_o A}{\mu_o}\left(\frac{\Delta p}{L} + \rho_o \times \sin \alpha\right) \tag{7-1}$$

where:

q_o = reservoir oil flow rate, cc/sec.
k_o = effective oil permeability, darcys
A = cross-sectional area across which flow occurs, cm^2
μ_o = reservoir oil viscosity, cp.
$\Delta p/L$ = pressure drop per unit length, atm/cm
ρ_o = oil density gradient, atm/cm
α = angle of dip

In a gas-oil system, where there are no applied pressure gradients, the $\Delta p/L$ term is reduced to $\rho_g \times \sin \alpha$ and the resulting equation is:

$$q_o = -\frac{k_o A}{\mu_o}(\rho_g \times \sin \alpha - \rho_o \times \sin \alpha) \tag{7-2}$$

where:

ρ_g = gas density gradient, atm/cm.

Eliminating the minus sign and using oil field units, Equation (7-2) becomes:

$$Q_o = \frac{1.127\, k_o A}{\mu_o B_o}(\Delta \rho \times \sin \alpha) \tag{7-3}$$

where:

Q_o = flow rate, stock tank barrels per day
k_o = effective oil permeability, darcys
μ_o = reservoir oil viscosity, cp.
$\Delta \rho = \rho_o - \rho_g$ = density gradient, psi/ft.
B_o = formation volume factor
1.127 = conversion factor, cgs system to oil field units.

According to Elkins, et al,[4] who originally presented this approach, Equation (7-3) will result in a calculation of maximum gravity drainage. The utility of Equation (7-3) is discussed more fully later in this chapter.

Predicting Reservoir Performance

As was discussed earlier, no single method has yet been found which will always satisfactorily predict performance of gravity drainage reservoirs. However, before a reservoir study is made there will always be some performance history available and this

[4] Elkins, L. F., French, R. W., and Glenn, W. E., "Lance Creek Sundance Reservoir Performance—A Unitized Pressure Maintenance Project," *Trans., AIME*, Vol. 179, 1949, p. 222.

history can be used for determining a satisfactory prediction method. Several methods for forecasting behavior of gravity drainage reservoirs have been presented in the literature, and with these for a background, plus a thorough understanding of the principles of fluid flow through porous media, a satisfactory prediction technique can usually be derived.

There are two basically different approaches which can be used, although these two methods could be combined to form other methods. These two methods can be classified as: (1) the apparent relative permeability method, and (2) the oil saturation method.

Apparent Relative Permeability Method

This method utilizes actual reservoir performance data to calculate relative permeability relationships. The gravity effects result in much lower producing gas-oil ratios than would be expected for reservoirs producing without benefit of gravity drainage. This is due to the upstructure migration of the gas and consequent higher oil saturation in the vicinity of the completion intervals of the wells. Field relative permeability data are calculated using the instantaneous gas-oil ratio equation (discussed in Chapter 3):

$$R = \frac{k_g}{k_o} \times \frac{\mu_o}{\mu_g} \times \frac{B_o}{B_g} + R_s \qquad (7\text{-}4)$$

Equation (7-4) is rearranged to solve for k_g/k_o as follows:

$$\frac{k_g}{k_o} = (R - R_s) \times \frac{\mu_g}{\mu_o} \times \frac{B_g}{B_o} \qquad (7\text{-}5)$$

Oil saturation in the reservoir is then calculated by the equation developed in Chapter 4.

$$S_o = (1 - S_{wi}) \frac{B_o}{B_{os}} \left(1 - \frac{N_p}{N}\right) \qquad (7\text{-}6)$$

Equation (7-6) assumes that the evolved gas is dispersed uniformly throughout the oil zone. This is obviously not the case in a gravity drainage reservoir and will result in the calculation of an abnormally low oil saturation. The field relative permeability data are plotted versus the oil saturations calculated by Equation (7-6). This results in much lower k_g/k_o values than would be calculated by normal depletion drive calculations or laboratory relative permeability data. Figure 7-6 illustrates the differences in k_g/k_o data. It is emphasized that the differences in the two relative permeability curves shown in Figure 7-6 are not the result of non-conformance between laboratory and field relative permeability data but are actually caused by the deliberate misuse of the oil saturation equation for calculating

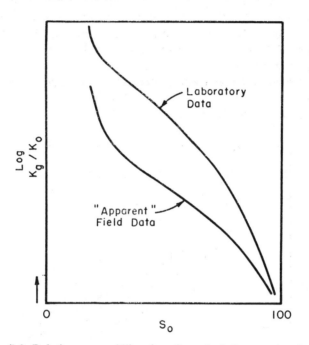

FIGURE 7-6. Relative permeability data for calculating gravity drainage performance.

oil saturation. The oil saturation in the vicinity of the completion intervals is the saturation which will govern the producing gas-oil ratio, and in gravity drainage reservoirs the oil saturation in the lower part of the reservoir is larger than the oil saturation in the upper part of the reservoir due to gas migration upstructure. The calculation of oil saturation by Equation (7-6) results in an "apparent" oil saturation and is satisfactory only if the limitations of the method are known.

To determine the effects of gravity drainage on ultimate recovery, depletion drive calculations are made exactly as outlined in Chapter 4. At least four complete sets of calculations are usually made. One set of calculations is based on laboratory relative permeability data or comparable data which do not include gravity drainage. The other three sets of calculations are based on "apparent" relative permeability data. One of these sets is based on the most reasonable "apparent" data and the other two sets bracket this most reasonable set. Thus, if operating conditions change later in the life of the reservoir and the slope of the "apparent" relative permeability curve is altered the study may still be useful provided the changed conditions are still within the range of the reservoir study. Figure 7-7 shows the relative permeability data which are used in a study and Figure 7-8 shows the results, in graphical form, of the performance predictions.

The performance calculations are prepared exactly as the calculations outlined in Chapter 4, and therefore an example problem will not be worked in this chapter.

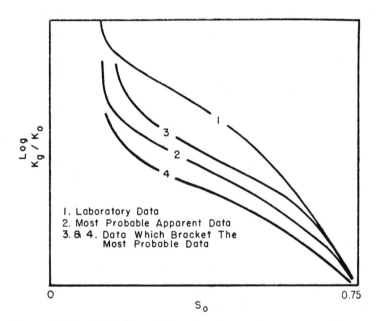

FIGURE 7-7. Relative permeability data for performance predictions.

A serious limitation of this method is that actual reservoir performance data are necessary in order to calculate the "apparent" relative permeability data. Since the complete range of relative permeability-saturation data will never be available, these data must be extrapolated to cover the range of future predictions. Fortunately, a plot of log k_g/k_o vs S_o will usually be a straight line over the saturation range of primary interest, and if enough performance data are available to extend the plot into the straight-line portion, then an extrapolation of the straight line is not too hazardous. However, if the past performance history does not extend into the

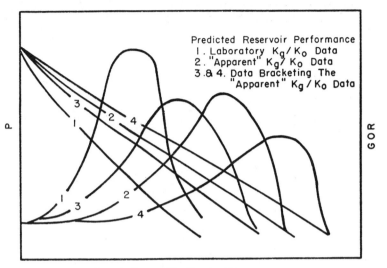

Predicted Reservoir Performance
1. Laboratory K_g/K_o Data
2. "Apparent" K_g/K_o Data
3 & 4. Data Bracketing The "Apparent" K_g/K_o Data

Cumulative Oil Production

FIGURE 7-8. Predicted reservoir performance curves.

straight-line portion of the plot, then extrapolation of such data is extremely hazardous and the validity of any reservoir performance predictions based on these data would be questionable. Examples of these two types of past history are shown in Figure 7-9. Curve A of Figure 7-9 could be extrapolated with reasonable safety as it is apparent that the straight-line portion of the curve has already been reached. On the other hand, curve B has not yet reached the straight-line portion of its plot and several extrapolations are possible. There are insufficient data available to prepare a reasonable reservoir performance prediction using the data from Curve B. Burchaell[5] used a similar technique to reliably predict performance of a reservoir operating under a gravity-drive mechanism.

Oil Saturation Method

Another method for predicting reservoir performance of gravity drainage reservoirs utilizes the Darcy flow Equation (7-3) in con-

[5] Burchaell, E. P., "Reservoir Performance of a High Relief Pool," *Trans. AIME,* Vol. 186, 1949, p. 191.

junction with a properly computed oil saturation.

If the rate of gas migration to the crest of the structure is known, then a formula for calculating oil saturation in that portion of the reservoir where oil is draining can be computed. The oil saturation determined by this method is then used to obtain the proper effective permeability to be placed in Equation (7-3). The

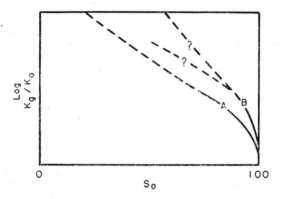

FIGURE 7-9. Extrapolating relative permeability data.

oil saturation equation is based on a material balance of the oil reservoir fluids. Both the size of the secondary gas cap and the rate of change of size of the secondary gas cap must be known before the proper oil saturation equation can be calculated.

Using the proper data, the gravity drainage rate is calculated. This is essentially the method proposed by Elkins, et al,[4] although they did not propose using an oil saturation equation as discussed here. The rate of formation of the secondary gas cap can be estimated by the producing gas-oil ratios of the structurally high wells. In fact, if reliable laboratory relative permeability data are available, the field k_g/k_o data can be calculated, and using this number in the laboratory k_g/k_o data, the oil saturation in the vicinity of the well bore can be read directly from the graph. Of course, this method is fraught with errors, and may have little application in many cases, but it is mentioned here as an example of one of the many methods available for correlating data. The actual producing characteristics of the structurally high wells are probably the best criteria for determining the rate of formation of the secondary gas cap.

Chapter 8

COMBINATION DRIVE RESERVOIRS

Previous chapters have discussed the various forces which expel oil from reservoirs, and methods used to predict behavior from reservoirs being produced by these various drives. Most of the methods outlined are applicable only when the reservoir is being produced almost exclusively by the specific drive being discussed. The driving forces described in previous chapters are: (1) dissolved gas drive (Chapter 4), (2) gas cap drive (Chapter 5), (3) water drive (Chapter 6), and (4) gravity drainage (Chapter 7). Many reservoirs are produced by not one drive alone, but by a combination of two or more of the above forces. Techniques for predicting behavior of these "combination" drive reservoirs must be altered to fit the particular reservoir being studied.

Two combinations of driving forces can be present in combination drive reservoirs. These are: (1) depletion drive and a weak water drive, and (2) depletion drive with a small gas cap and a weak water drive. Then, of course, gravity segregation can play an important role in any of the aforementioned drives. As discussed in Chapter 7, the effects of gravity drainage are often difficult to evaluate and predict in most reservoir engineering studies because the principal tool of the reservoir engineer, the material balance equation, cannot be readily utilized to study gravity drainage effects. Therefore in most combination drive reservoirs where the importance of gravity drainage is relatively minor, the effects of gravity drainage are incorporated in some of the performance data which are being used, as for example, the relative permeability curve. A field relative permeability curve can be used which takes into consideration the effects of gravity drainage. This procedure was outlined in more detail in Chapter 7.

Combination drive reservoirs can be recognized by the occurrence of a combination of some of the following factors:

1. Relatively rapid pressure decline. Water encroachment and/or external gas cap expansion are insufficient to maintain reservoir pressures.

2. Water encroaching slowly into the lower part of the reservoir. Structurally low producing wells will exhibit slowly increasing water producing rates.

3. If a small gas cap is present the structurally high wells will exhibit continually increasing gas-oil ratios, provided the gas cap is expanding. It is possible that the gas cap will shrink due to production of excess free gas, in which case, the structurally high wells will exhibit a *decreasing* gas-oil ratio. This condition should be avoided whenever possible, as large volumes of oil can be lost as a result of a shrinking gas cap. Oil lost due to a shrinking gas cap is discussed more fully in Chapter 13, where methods of calculating oil lost are presented.

4. As a substantial percentage of the total oil recovery may be due to the depletion drive mechanism, the gas-oil ratio of structurally low wells will also continue to increase due to evolution of gas from solution from oil throughout the reservoir as pressure is reduced.

Figure 8-1 shows production history of a typical combination drive reservoir with a weak water drive and no initial free gas cap. Note that the producing gas-oil ratio remains relatively constant for a period of time. This indicates that the reservoir pressure is

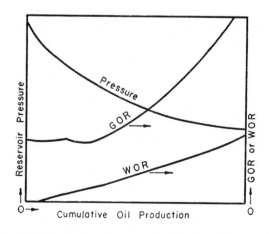

FIGURE 8-1. Production history—combination drive reservoir.

above the saturation pressure. When the gas-oil ratio begins to increase, it is probably due to the fact that reservoir pressure has been reduced below the saturation pressure and the increasing gas-oil ratio is the result of evolution of gas from solution from the oil.

Ultimate recovery from combination drive reservoirs is usually greater than recovery from depletion drive reservoirs but less than recovery from water drive or gas cap drive reservoirs. Actual recovery will depend upon the degree to which it is possible to reduce the magnitude of recovery by depletion drive. In most combination drive reservoirs it will be economically feasible to institute some type of pressure maintenance operation, either gas injection, water injection, or both gas and water injection, depending upon the availability of the fluids.

Indexes of Drives

It is possible to evaluate the efficiency of operation of a combination drive reservoir by rearrangement of the material balance equation. A material balance for a combination drive reservoir can be developed as follows:

$$\text{SCF gas originally} = \text{SCF gas prod.} + \text{SCF gas remaining} \tag{8-1}$$

however:

$$\text{SCF gas originally} = \text{SCF original gas in solution}$$
$$+ \text{ SCF original free gas} = NR_{si} + \frac{mNB_{oi}}{B_{gi}} \tag{8-2}$$

and:

SCF Gas Remaining
$$= \text{SCF Remaining free gas} + \text{SCF Remaining gas in solution.} \tag{8-3}$$

SFC Remaining free gas
= Original reservoir volume — Remaining liquid volume
= Original reservoir volume
  —(remaining oil volume + net water encroachment)
$$= \frac{NB_{oi} + mNB_{oi} - [(N - N_p)B_o + (W_e - W_p)]}{B_g} \tag{8-4}$$

therefore:

SCF Gas Remaining =
$$\frac{mNB_{oi} + NB_{oi} - [(N - N_p)B_o + (W_e - W_P)] + (N - N_p)R_s}{B_g} \tag{8-5}$$

Combining Equations (8-1) through (8-5) yields:

$$= \frac{\left\{ \begin{array}{l} N_p R_p + mNB_{oi} + NB_{oi} \\ - [(N - N_p)\, B_o + (W_e - W_p)] + (N - N_p)R_s \end{array} \right\}}{B_g} \qquad (8\text{-}6)$$

Multiplying both sides of Equation (8-6) by B_g and rearranging results in:

$$NR_{si}B_g - NR_sB_g + NB_o - NB_{oi} + mNB_{oi}\left(\frac{B_g}{B_{gi}}\right) - mNB_{oi}$$
$$= N_p R_p B_g + N_p B_o - N_p R_s B_g - (W_e - W_p) \qquad (8\text{-}7)$$

since $B_t = (R_{si} - R_s)B_g + B_o$, Equation (8-7) reduces to:

$$N(B_t - B_{ti}) + mNB_{oi}\left(\frac{B_g}{B_{gi}} - 1\right)$$
$$= N_p B_o + N_p(R_p - R_s)B_g - (W_e - W_p) \qquad (8\text{-}8)$$

Solving Equation (8-8) for $N_p B_o$, the reservoir oil produced yields the following relationship:

$$N_p B_o = N(B_t - B_{ti}) + mNB_{oi}\left(\frac{B_g}{B_{gi}} - 1\right) + (W_e - W_p)$$
$$- N_p(R_p - R_s)B_g \qquad (8\text{-}9)$$

Before further utilizing Equation (8-9) it is necessary to understand the physical meaning of each of the terms on the right-hand side of the equation. These terms are described briefly:

$N(B_t - B_{ti})$ = The expansion of the original reservoir oil volume with all of its original dissolved gas. After reservoir pressure declines below the saturation pressure, some of the original dissolved gas will be evolved from solution and will occupy space as free gas in the reservoir. Since $B_t = (R_{si} - R_s)B_g + B_o$, this term can be expanded as follows: $N[(R_{si} - R_s)B_g + (B_o - B_{oi})]$. Some of the free gas evolved from solution from the reservoir oil may be produced. Thus in order to determine the *net* expansion of the original reservoir oil with all of its original dissolved gas it is necessary to subtract from $N(B_t -$

B_{ti}) that portion of the original dissolved gas which has been produced. This procedure is discussed later in more detail.

$$mNB_{oi} \left(\frac{B_g}{B_{gi}} - 1 \right) = \text{Expansion of the original free gas cap.}$$

Some of the gas cap gas may be produced, in which case, if the *net* gas cap expansion is desired the gas cap gas production must be subtracted from the gas cap expansion.

$W_e - W_p = $ Net water influx.

$N_p (R_p - R_s) B_g = $ Free gas production. As mentioned previously, this free gas production may be comprised of both gas cap gas and free gas which was originally dissolved in solution in the oil.

Examination of Equation (8-9) reveals that the reservoir oil produced, $N_p B_o$, is a result of (1) expansion of the original reservoir oil with its dissolved gas, plus (2) expansion of the original free gas cap, plus (3) the net encroachment of water into the oil zone, and minus (4) the free gas produced.

The utility of Equation (8-9) can be increased by separating the free gas production into its individual components, gas cap gas production and free dissolved gas production. If "f" is defined as the fraction of produced free gas which comes from the gas cap, then the free gas production can be separated as follows:

Gas Cap Gas Production $= fN_p (R_p - R_s) B_g$

Free Dissolved Gas Production $= (1 - f) N_p (R_p - R_s) B_g$

Rearranging Equation (8-9) as previously discussed yields:

$$N_p B_o = [N(B_t - B_{ti}) - (1 - f) N_p (R_p - R_s) B_g]$$
$$+ \left[mNB_{oi} \left(\frac{B_g}{B_{gi}} - 1 \right) - fN_p (R_p - R_s) B_g \right] + (W_e - W_p) \tag{8-10}$$

The first bracketed term in Equation (8-10) is the *net* expansion of the reservoir oil with its dissolved gas and the second bracketed term is the *net* gas cap expansion. Thus Equation (8-10) shows that the reservoir oil produced is a result of the combined effect of (1) net expansion of the reservoir oil with its original dissolved gas, plus (2) the net gas cap expansion and, plus (3) net water encroachment. Dividing **Equation** (8-10) by $N_p B_o$:

$$1 = \frac{\overset{\text{A}}{[N(B_t - B_{ti}) - (1 - f) N_p (R_p - R_s) B_g]}}{N_p B_o}$$

$$+ \frac{\overset{\text{B}}{\left[mNB_{oi} \left(\frac{B_g}{B_{gi}} - 1 \right) - fN_p (R_p - R_s) B_g \right]}}{N_p B_o} + \frac{\overset{\text{C}}{(W_e - W_p)}}{N_p B_o}$$

$$(8\text{-}11)$$

Term A is the *Depletion Drive Index,* term B is the *Gas Cap Drive Index,* and term C is the *Water Drive Index.*

Determining the fraction of the produced gas which comes from the gas cap may be difficult at times, although usually enough production and reservoir engineering data will be available to satisfactorily determine this number. The usual method of determining f is to determine the change in gas-oil contact from producing wells, after which, with a knowledge of the reservoir size the amount of gas cap gas production can be calculated.

Since the sum of the driving indexes is equal to one, it follows that if the magnitude of one of the index terms is reduced, then one or both of the remaining terms must be correspondingly increased. An effective water drive will usually result in maximum recovery from the reservoir; therefore, if possible, the reservoir should be operated to yield a maximum water drive index and minimum values for the depletion drive index and the gas cap drive index. Maximum advantage should be taken of the most efficient drive available, and where the water drive is too weak to provide an effective displacing force, it may be possible to utilize the displacing energy of the gas cap. In any event, the depletion drive index should be maintained as low as possible at all times as this is normally the most inefficient driving force available.

Equation (8-11) can be solved at any time to determine the magnitude of the various driving indexes. The forces displacing the oil and gas from the reservoir are subject to change from time to time and for this reason Equation (8-11) should be solved periodically to determine whether there has been any change in the driving indexes. Changes in fluid withdrawal rates are primarily responsible for changes in the driving indexes. For example, reducing the oil producing rate could result in an increased water drive index and a correspondingly reduced depletion drive index in a reservoir containing a weak water drive. Also, by shutting in wells producing large quantities of water, the water drive index could be increased, as the net water influx (gross water influx minus water production) is the important factor.

When the reservoir has a very weak water drive, but has a fairly large gas cap, the most efficient reservoir producing mechanism may be the gas cap, in which case a large gas cap drive index is desirable. Theoretically, recovery by gas cap drive is independent of producing rate, as the gas is readily expansible. Low vertical permeability could limit the rate of expansion of the gas cap, in which case the gas cap drive index would be rate sensitive. Also, gas coning into producing wells will reduce the effectiveness of the gas cap expansion due to the production of free gas. Gas coning is usually a rate sensitive phenomenon, the higher the producing rates, the greater the amount of coning.

An important factor in determining the effectiveness of a gas cap drive is the degree of conservation of the gas cap gas. As a practical matter, it will often be impossible, because of royalty owners or lease agreements to completely eliminate gas cap gas production. Where free gas is being produced, the gas cap drive index can often be markedly increased by shutting in high gas-oil ratio wells, and if possible, transferring their allowables to other low gas-oil ratio wells.

Figure 8-2 shows plots of the index of drives for a typical combination drive reservoir. At point A some of the structurally low wells are reworked to reduce water production. This resulted in an effective increase in the water drive index. At point B workover operations are complete, water, gas, and oil producing rates are relatively stable, and the driving indexes show no change. At point C some of the wells which have been producing relatively large, but constant, volumes of water are shut in, which results in an increase in the water drive index. At the same time some of the upstructure high gas-oil ratio wells have been shut in and their allowables transferred to wells lower on the structure producing with normal gas-oil ratios. At point D gas is being returned to the reservoir, and the gas cap drive index is exhibiting a decided increase. The water drive index is relatively constant, although it is decreasing somewhat, and the depletion drive index is showing a marked decline. This is indicative of a more efficient reservoir operation, and if the depletion drive index can be reduced to zero, relatively good recovery can be expected from the reservoir. Of course, to achieve a zero depletion drive index would require the complete maintenance of reservoir pressure, which is often difficult to accomplish. It can be noted from Figure 8-2 that the sum of the various indexes of drive is always equal to one.

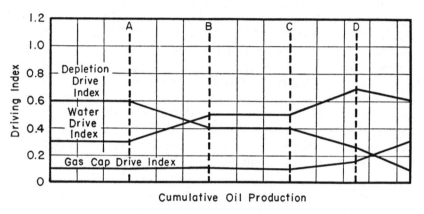

FIGURE 8-2. Indexes of drive.

Equations Used

Combination drive reservoirs can be studied using the conventional Tarner method of predicting reservoir behavior. This method was outlined completely in Chapter 4, *Depletion Drive Reservoirs*, and therefore the Tarner method will not be discussed further in this chapter. However, the equations will have somewhat different forms and these will be developed and discussed.

Material Balance Equations

A material balance equation must be developed for the particular reservoir being considered. By definition a combination drive reservoir is one which has a weak water drive either with or without a small original free gas cap. One of the following balances will be used, depending upon the reservoir drives:

1. Material balance equation which includes both an original free gas cap and water encroachment.

$N_p R_p =$

$$\frac{N(B_t - B_{ti}) + mNB_{oi}\left(\dfrac{B_g}{B_{gi}} - 1\right) + (W_e - W_p) + N_p R_s B_g - N_p B_o}{B_g}$$

(8-12)

2. Material balance equation which includes a weak water drive without an original free gas cap.

A. Equation for pressures above the saturation pressure:

$$N_p/N = \frac{B_o - B_{oi}}{B_o} + \frac{W_e - W_p}{NB_o}$$

(8-13)

B. Equation for pressures below the saturation pressure:

$$N_p R_p = \frac{N(B_t - B_{ti}) + (W_e - W_p) + N_p R_s B_g - N_p B_o}{B_g}$$

(8-14)

3. Oil Saturation Equation.

An equation for calculating oil saturation was developed in Chapter 4, *Depletion Drive Reservoirs*. This equation assumed that all gas in the reservoir was distributed uniformly throughout the oil zone. Although this is a simplification, it can be tolerated in many reservoir studies where gravity segregation is not great.

In combination drive reservoirs where an external gas cap is expanding into the oil zone and where water is encroaching into the oil zone it becomes obvious that the gas and water are never distributed uniformly throughout the reservoir, but are occupying only the upper and lower portions of the reservoir respectively. An oil saturation equation based on the theoretical distribution of the fluids is possible. Figure 8-3 shows the fluid distribution in a combination drive reservoir. The solid line separating the gas cap and the oil zone represents the original gas-oil contact and the solid line separating the oil and water represents the original oil-water contact. The dotted lines represent the respective positions of the gas-oil and water-oil contacts at some later time. That portion of the original oil zone not invaded by expanding gas or encroaching water will be referred to as the remaining oil zone. Since most of the wells will have been completed as far away from both the gas-oil and oil-water contacts as possible, the oil saturation in the remaining oil zone is the oil saturation governing flow into the well bores. As the gas and water move into the oil zone they will displace some oil ahead of them, thus keeping the oil saturation in the remaining oil zone relatively high.

One of the most difficult parts of a reservoir study of a combination drive reservoir is the determination of the proper oil

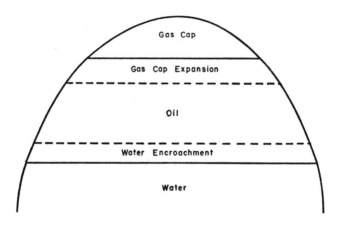

FIGURE 8-3. Fluid distribution—combination drive reservoir.

saturation equation to use. In almost any development certain simplifying assumptions will have to be made, and these simplifications may seriously limit the usefulness of the reservoir study. Two different oil saturation equations will be developed to illustrate the methods used to derive the equations. It is possible that one of these two equations will be found suitable for a particular reservoir study, or it may be necessary to develop still different equations, based on a different set of assumptions.

A general equation for oil saturation is:

$$S_o = \frac{\text{Oil Volume}}{\text{Oil Zone Size}} \tag{8-15}$$

In particular, for a combination drive reservoir, where a gas cap is expanding into the oil zone and water is encroaching into the oil zone, thus effectively reducing the physical size of the remaining oil zone, an equation for calculating oil saturation can be developed as follows:

$$S_o \text{ (at any time)} = \frac{\text{Remaining Oil in the Remaining Oil Zone}}{\text{Remaining Oil Zone Size}}$$

(8-16)

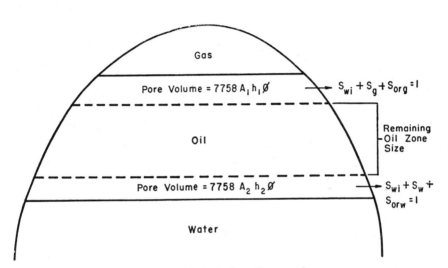

FIGURE 8-4. Calculating oil saturation.

Figure 8-4 shows the remaining oil zone size and the pore volumes of the invaded areas. Examination of Figure 8-4 shows that:

Remaining Oil in the Remaining Oil Zone
= Total Remaining Oil Volume — Oil Volume in the bypassed zones.
= $(N - N_p) B_o - [7758\ A_1 h_1 \phi S_{org} + 7758\ A_2 h_2 \phi S_{orw}]$ (8-17)

where:

A_1 = Average cross-sectional area of the gas-invaded portion of the reservoir, acres.

A_2 = Average cross-sectional area of the water-invaded portion of the reservoir, acres.

h_1 = Thickness of the gas-invaded zone in the reservoir, ft.

h_2 = Thickness of the water-invaded zone in the reservoir, ft.

ϕ = Porosity of the reservoir, fraction

S_{org} = Residual oil saturation in the gas-invaded portion of the reservoir, fraction

S_{orw} = Residual oil saturation in the water-invaded portion of the reservoir, fraction.

Also:

Remaining oil zone size
= Original oil zone size — size of the bypassed zones

$$=\frac{NB_{o1}}{1-S_{w1}} - [7758\,A_1 h_1 \phi + 7758\,A_2 h_2 \phi]$$

$$(8\text{-}18)$$

It may be difficult to evaluate directly the magnitudes of $A_1 h_1$ and $A_2 h_2$ in the above equations. However, other useful information from material balance considerations are available to assist in the solution of the problem. For example, the gas-invaded portion of the reservoir is caused by the expansion of the gas cap. If the assumption is made that none of the gas cap gas is produced, this expansion is equal to:

$$\text{Expansion of the gas cap} = mNB_{o1}\left(\frac{B_g}{B_{g1}} - 1\right)$$

$$(8\text{-}19)$$

From volumetric calculations it is known that:

$$mNB_{o1}\left(\frac{B_g}{B_{g1}} - 1\right) = 7758\,A_1 h_1 \phi S_g$$

$$(8\text{-}20)$$

where:

S_g = Gas saturation in the gas-invaded portion of the reservoir, fraction.

The saturation distribution in the gas-invaded portion of the reservoir is:

$$S_g + S_{org} + S_{w1} = 1 \qquad (8\text{-}21)$$

Rearranging Equation (8-21) to solve for S_g, and substituting this value into Equation (8-20) yields:

$$mNB_{o1} \left(\frac{B_g}{B_{g1}} - 1 \right) = 7758 \, A_1 h_1 \phi \, (1 - S_{wi} - S_{org})$$
(8-22)

The value of $7758 \, A_1 h_1 \phi$ can be computed directly by rearranging Equation (8-22):

$$7758 \, A_1 h_1 \phi = \frac{mNB_{o1} \left(\dfrac{B_g}{B_{g1}} - 1 \right)}{1 - S_{wi} - S_{org}}$$
(8-23)

A similar analysis can be made for the water-invaded portion of the reservoir, where the actual volume of water influx into the water-invaded portion of the reservoir is known from material balance calculations to be equal to $(W_e - W_p)$. Using volumetric calculations the following relationships apply:

$$W_e - W_p = 7758 \, A_2 h_2 \phi S_w$$
(8-24)

where:

S_w = Increase in water saturation, in the water-invaded zone of the reservoir, above the interstitial water saturation, fraction.

The fluid saturation distribution in the water-invaded zone of the reservoir is:

$$S_w + S_{wi} + S_{orw} = 1$$
(8-25)

where:

S_{orw} = Residual oil saturation in the water-invaded zone of the oil reservoir, fraction.

Rearranging Equation (8-25) to solve for S_w, and substituting this term in place of S_w in Equation (8-24) yields:

$$W_e - W_p = 7758 \, A_2 h_2 \phi \, (1 - S_{wi} - S_{orw})$$
(8-26)

The use of Equation (8-26) permits a direct determination of $7758 \, A_2 h_2 \phi$ as follows:

$$7758 \, A_2 h_2 \phi = \frac{W_e - W_p}{1 - S_{wi} - S_{orw}}$$
(8-27)

Combining Equations (8-16), (8-17), (8-18), (8-23), and (8-27) results in:

$$S_o = \frac{(N - N_p)B_o - \left[\dfrac{mNB_{oi}\left(\dfrac{B_g}{B_{gi}} - 1\right)S_{org}}{1 - S_{wi} - S_{org}} + \dfrac{(W_e - W_p)S_{orw}}{1 - S_{wi} - S_{orw}} \right]}{\dfrac{NB_{oi}}{1 - S_{wi}} - \left[\dfrac{mNB_{oi}\left(\dfrac{B_g}{B_{gi}} - 1\right)}{1 - S_{wi} - S_{org}} + \dfrac{W_e - W_p}{1 - S_{wi} - S_{orw}} \right]} \tag{8-28}$$

Before a solution can be obtained for Equation (8-28) the residual oil saturation in the gas-invaded and water-invaded zones of the reservoir must be either known or estimated. If laboratory flood data are available this information can be used to estimate values of S_{org} and S_{orw}. Laboratory flood data will almost always result in lower residual oil saturations than can be obtained in the field, because in the laboratory the core sample is much more homogeneous than the total reservoir. In the reservoir, considerable bypassing of oil may occur, resulting in a higher residual oil saturation than obtained in flooding the more homogeneous core samples.

Since displacement of oil by water is normally more efficient than displacement of oil by gas, the residual oil saturation in the water-invaded zone is usually less than the residual oil saturation in the gas-invaded zone.

After the residual oil saturation values have been determined the oil saturation at any time can be calculated using Equation (8-28).

Equation (8-28) has one severe limitation. It assumes that none of the gas cap gas is produced. This seldom occurs in actual reservoir operations as it is usually impossible to completely eliminate the production of gas cap gas. This limitation becomes more critical when the size of the gas cap size is several times as large as the oil zone size, as a relatively small pressure drop will result in an expansion of the gas cap to the extent that it will expand into the entire oil zone. If none of the gas cap gas is produced, then when the gas cap expansion is equivalent to the size of the original oil zone, the economic limit has been reached and the reservoir can no longer be produced as an oil reservoir.

If the amount of gas cap gas which is produced is either known, or can be assumed, then Equation (8-28) can be modified to take this into consideration. The modified equation is shown here:

$$S_o =$$

$$\frac{(N - N_p)B_o - \left[\dfrac{(1-f)\ mNB_{oi}\left(\dfrac{B_g}{B_{gi}} - 1\right)S_{org}}{1 - S_{wi} - S_{org}} + \dfrac{(W_e - W_p)S_{orw}}{1 - S_{wi} - S_{orw}}\right]}{\dfrac{NB_{oi}}{1 - S_{wi}} - \left[\dfrac{(1-f)\ mNB_{oi}\left(\dfrac{B_g}{B_{gi}} - 1\right)}{1 - S_{wi} - S_{org}} + \dfrac{W_e - W_p}{1 - S_{wi} - S_{orw}}\right]} \tag{8-29}$$

where:

f = fraction of gas cap expanded volume which is produced.

Where all of the expanded gas cap gas is produced Equation (8-29) reduces to:

$$S_o = \frac{(N - N_p)B_o - \dfrac{(W_e - W_p)S_{orw}}{1 - S_{wi} - S_{orw}}}{\dfrac{NB_{oi}}{1 - S_{wi}} - \dfrac{W_e - W_p}{1 - S_{wi} - S_{orw}}} \tag{8-30}$$

It is very important to select the proper oil saturation equation as the relative permeability relationships are critical functions of oil saturation. Therefore, determination of the correct oil saturation equation is an important step in a reliable prediction of reservoir performance.

The oil saturation equations developed in this chapter are subject to limitations which in many cases may be very severe. The principal difficulty with these equations is the problem of determining the fraction of the gas cap expansion which will be produced. However, the oil saturation equation developed in Chapter 4, *Depletion Drive Reservoirs,* is also subject to several limitations, the principal one being the assumption that all of the free gas in the oil zone portion of the reservoir is distributed uniformly throughout the oil zone.

Instantaneous Gas-Oil Ratio Equation

The third equation used in the prediction of behavior of combination drive reservoirs is the instantaneous producing gas-oil ratio, described and developed in Chapter 3, *Oil Reservoirs.*

Example Problem 8-1

The Tarner method will be used to predict behavior of a reservoir which has an original gas cap and water influx. Basic data required for the performance prediction are shown in Table 8-1. Figure 8-5 shows relative permeability ratio data. Tables 8-2 through 8-6 and Figures 8-6 through 8-8 summarize the calculation.

Table 8-1
Basic Data—Reservoir Y

Initial stock tank oil in place = 60,000,000 bbls.
Ratio of original gas zone size to original oil zone size, m = 0.5
Net water influx per barrel of stock tank oil prod. = 0.2
Original Reservoir Pressure = 3,500 psia
Formation Temperature = 195° F.
Interstitial water saturation = 25%
Specific gravity of produced gas = 0.75
Residual oil saturation in gas-invaded and water-invaded portions of reservoir, S_{or} = 40%

Table 8-2
Summary of Reservoir Performance Predictions Reservoir Y

Pressure Psia	N_p/N	R SCF/St Bbl.	N_p Bbls $\times$ 10⁶
3500 (p_i)			
3000	0.101	1430	6.06
2700	0.195	1560	11.70
2400	0.294	2220	17.64
2100	0.341	12600	20.46
1800	—	—	—

Table 8-3
Basic Data—Combination Drive Reservoir Y

Pressure Psia	Z	R_s SCF/ST Bbl.	B_o	B_t	B_g	μ_o/μ_g
3500	0.869	1500	1.550	1.550	0.000821	
3000	0.848	1430	1.518	1.583	0.000930	
2700	0.822	1360	1.486	1.627	0.001020	7.30
2400	0.816	1280	1.450	1.710	0.001140	8.70
2100	0.796	1180	1.414	1.850	0.001270	10.00
1800	0.832	1070	1.375	2.075	0.001550	

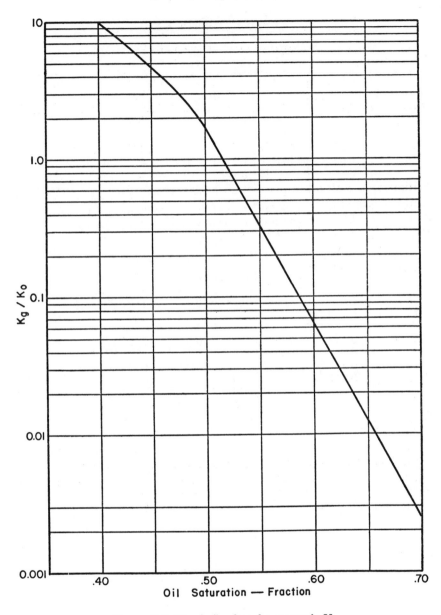

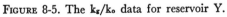

FIGURE 8-5. The k_g/k_o data for reservoir Y.

Table 8-4
Summary of Calculations—Prediction of Reservoir Performance—Reservoir Y

Pressure Psia	N_p/N Assumed	G_{mb}	S_o	k_g/k_o	R	G_{gor}	G Actual
3500 (p_i)							
3000	0.05[1]	147.0 N	0.745	0	1,430	73.25 N	
	0.03	146.8 N	0.770	0	1,430	43.95 N	
	0.10	148.5 N	0.716	0	1,430	146.50 N	
(Actual)	0.101				1,430		148.5 N
2700	0.10[2]	120.5 N	0.746	0	1,360	0	
	0.15	125.5 N	0.693	0.0035	1,397	69.4 N	
	0.20	130.5 N	0.637	0.0200	1,572	138.5 N	
(Actual)	0.195				1,560		130.5 N
2400	0.25	170.0 N	0.651	0.013	1,424	76.6 N	
	0.30	178.0 N	0.586	0.100	2,385	196.5 N	
	0.32	183.0 N	0.571	0.170	3,159	282.0 N	
(Actual)	0.294				2,220		177.0 N
2100	0.32	186.0 N	0.621	0.031	4,555	122.0 N	
	0.35	198.0 N	0.547	0.40	5,530	255.0 N	
	0.36	201.0 N	0.519	1.00	12,060	542.0 N	
(Actual)	0.341				12,600		192.0 N
1800	0.35		Nega-tive[3]				

[1] See Figure 8-7 for a plot of these data, and Table 8-5 for sample calculations.

[2] See Figure 8-8 for a plot of these data, and Table 8-6 for sample calculations.

[3] A negative oil saturation indicates that the gas cap and enroached water have invaded the oil zone to such an exten that there is no remaining oil zone. Therefore the abandonment pressure is between 2100 psia and 1800 psia.

Table 8-5

Example Calculations—First Period—p = 3,000 psia
Combination Drive Reservoir Y

Trial 1: Assume $N_p = 0.05\ N$

$$G_{mb1} = N_{p1}\ R_{p1} =$$

$$= \frac{N\left[(B_t - B_{ti}) + m\ B_{ti}\left(\dfrac{B_g - B_{gi}}{B_{gi}}\right)\right] - N_p\ (B_t - R_{si}\ B_g) + (W_e - W_p)}{B_g}$$

$$= \frac{\left[N\left[(1.583 - 1.550) + 0.5 \times 1.550\left(\dfrac{0.000930 - 0.000821}{0.000821}\right)\right]\right.}{\left. - 0.05\ N\ (1.583 - 1500 \times 0.000930) + [(0.2)\ (.05\ N) - 0]\right]}{0.000930}$$

$$= \underline{147.0\ N}$$

$$S_o = \frac{(N - N_p)\ B_o - \left[\dfrac{m\ N\ B_{ti}\left(\dfrac{B_g}{B_{gi}} - 1\right)\ S_{or}}{1 - S_{wi} - S_{or}} + \dfrac{(W_e - W_p)\ S_{or}}{1 - S_{wi} - S_{or}}\right]}{\dfrac{N\ B_{oi}}{1 - S_{wi}} - \left[\dfrac{m\ N\ B_{ti}\left(\dfrac{B_g}{B_{gi}} - 1\right)}{1 - S_{wi} - S_{or}} + \dfrac{(W_e - W_p)}{1 - S_{wi} - S_{or}}\right]}$$

$$= \frac{\left[(N - 0.05\ N)\ 1.518 - \left[\dfrac{(0.5)\ (N)\ (1.55)\left(\dfrac{0.000930}{0.000821} - 1\right)(0.4)}{1 - 0.25 - 0.4} + \dfrac{(0.2)\ (0.05\ N)\ (0.4)}{1 - 0.25 - 0.4}\right]\right]}{\dfrac{N\ (1.550)}{1 - 0.25} - \left[\dfrac{0.5 \times 1.55 \times N\left(\dfrac{0.00930}{0.00821} - 1\right)}{1 - 0.25 - 0.40} + \dfrac{0.2 \times 0.05\ N}{1 - 0.25 - 0.40}\right]}$$

$$= 0.745$$

$$k_g/k_o = 0 \quad \text{(from Fig. 8-7 where } S_o = 0.745)$$

$$R = \frac{k_g}{k_o} \times \frac{\mu_o}{\mu_g} \times \frac{B_o}{B_g} + R_s = 0 \times \frac{\mu_o}{\mu_g} \times \frac{B_o}{B_g} + 1430 = 1{,}430$$

$$G_{gor1} = \left(\frac{R_1 + R_{si}}{2}\right) N_{p1} = \left(\frac{1430 + 1500}{2}\right) 0.05\ N = 73.25\ N$$

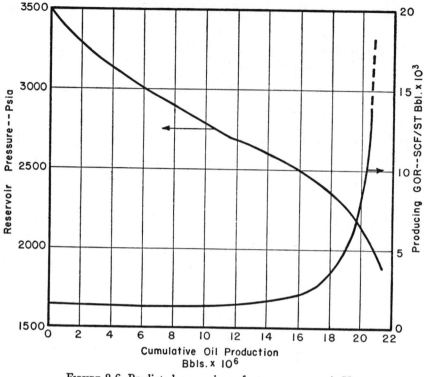

FIGURE 8-6. Predicted reservoir performance, reservoir Y.

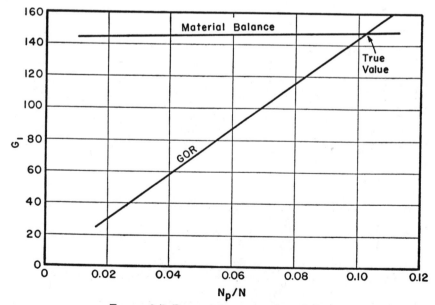

FIGURE 8-7. Determining true value of G_1.

Table 8-6
Example Calculations—Second Period—p = 2700 psia
Combination Drive Reservoir Y

Trial 1: Assume $N_p = 0.15 N$

$$N_{p2} R_{p2} = \frac{\left[N\left[(1.627 - 1.550) + 0.5 \times 1.550\left(\frac{0.00102 - 0.000821}{0.000821} \right) \right] \atop -0.15 N [1.627 - 1500 \times 0.00102] + (0.2 \times 0.15 N - 0) \right]}{0.00102}$$

$$= 274.0 N$$

$$G_{mb2} = N_{p2} R_{p2} - G_1 = 274.0 N - 148.5 N = \underline{125.5 N}$$

$$S_o = \frac{\left[(N - 0.15 N) 1.486 - \left[\frac{0.5 N \times 1.550\left(\frac{0.00102}{0.000821} - 1 \right) 0.40}{1 - 0.25 - 0.40} + \frac{0.2 \times 0.15 N \times 0.40}{1 - 0.25 - 0.40} \right] \right]}{\frac{N \times 1.550}{1 - 0.25} - \left[\frac{0.5 N \times 1.550\left(\frac{0.00102}{0.00821} - 1 \right)}{1 - 0.25 - 0.40} + \frac{0.2 \times 0.15 N}{1 - 0.25 - 0.40} \right]}$$

$$= 0.693$$

$$k_g/k_o = 0.0035$$

$$R_2 = \frac{k_g}{k_o} \times \frac{\mu_o}{\mu_g} \times \frac{B_o}{B_g} + R_s = 0.0035 \times 7.30 \times \frac{1.486}{0.00102} + 1360$$

$$= 1{,}397$$

$$G_{gor2} = \left(\frac{R_1 + R_2}{2} \right)(N_{p2} - N_{p1}) = \left(\frac{1397 + 1430}{2} \right)(0.15 N - 0.101 N)$$

$$= 69.4 N$$

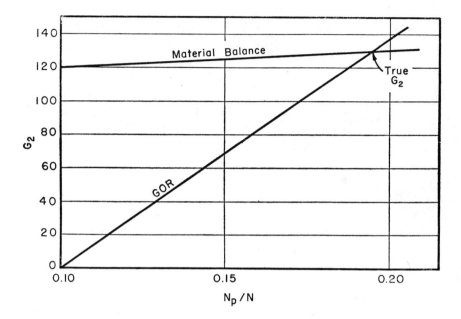

FIGURE 8-8. Determining true value of G_2.

Chapter 9

PRESSURE MAINTENANCE

Ultimate recovery from oil reservoirs can often be substantially increased by augmenting the natural reservoir energy. This increased recovery is due primarily to one or both of the following factors: (1) decreasing the depletion drive index by maintaining reservoir pressure the maximum possible amount, or (2) replacing the natural displacing forces with a more efficient displacing force, as for example, replacing a gas cap drive with an artificial water drive. Returning gas to the reservoir to maintain reservoir pressure and displace the oil from the reservoir by an expanding artificial gas cap could be classified in both of the above categories, since the depletion drive index will be reduced, and the expanding external gas drive is certain to be more efficient than the dissolved gas drive.

Pressure maintenance operations can be divided into four distinct categories: (1) gas injection, (2) water injection, (3) miscible fluid injection, or (4) combinations of the aforementioned fluids. Each of these methods is discussed in this chapter.

The installation of pressure maintenance facilities often requires the expenditure of large sums of money, and although additional oil recovery is almost assured, this additional oil recovery must more than pay the cost of installing and operating the pressure maintenance facilities. Thus it is of the utmost importance to be able to accurately predict the amount of the increased production and also the volume of injected fluid required to recover this additional oil. Three different techniques are commonly used to predict recovery from a pressure maintenance operation, (1) conventional material balance prediction methods, (2) frontal drive prediction methods, and (3) models. Any of these methods, if used with the proper precautions, and with accurate data, will usually provide reasonably accurate information for the reservoir study. By the same token, if either technique is carelessly used, without making

199

the necessary adjustments in the data, then little weight can be given to the calculated results.

There are two severe limitations of the conventional material balance method of predicting reservoir performance under pressure maintenance operations. One of these limitations is the difficulty of developing a usable oil saturation equation. The development of various oil saturation equations was discussed at length in Chapter 8, *Combination Drive Reservoirs*. Therefore, the discussion of oil saturation equations in this chapter will be limited.

The injected fluid must be assumed to either effectively reduce the size of the oil zone, or else be distributed uniformly throughout the oil zone. The latter assumption is entirely incorrect, but if the first assumption is used, then some method must be devised for determining the fraction of injected fluid which will be produced. In any pressure maintenance project, substantial quantities of the injected fluids will be produced and these produced fluids will have quite an effect on the oil saturation equation.

The other principal limitation of the material balance method of predicting reservoir behavior is the difficulty in determining a representative relative permeability curve. If it is possible to shut in wells producing substantial quantities of injected fluids then the actual relative permeability curve may follow quite closely the trend expected as a result of extrapolating the past field relative permeability behavior. However, if these wells cannot be shut in, because of royalty considerations or otherwise, then these produced fluids will drastically alter the slope of the relative permeability curve.

Unfortunately, petroleum reservoirs are heterogeneous in nature and generally exhibit rather wide variations in permeability within a single reservoir. Thus many reservoirs are actually comprised of a large number of beds of varying permeability in communication with the respective underlying and overlying beds within the unit. Since each of these beds may behave more or less as an independent unit, the use of "average" relative permeability will often fail to accurately describe reservoir performance. This is especially true early in the life of a pressure maintenance program, where the injected fluid may move quite rapidly through a highly permeable zone resulting in premature breakthrough of the injected fluid at a producing well.

However, the value of the prediction technique can still be preserved if proper precautions are taken, as the predicted results can still yield accurate information concerning the ultimate recovery and the gross reservoir behavior.

The relative permeability curve and the oil saturation equation are actually so closely related to each other that it is impossible to separate the two. Careful consideration should be given to the potential effects on the reservoir study of future variations in these two factors.

Oil recovery as calculated by the frontal drive method is characterized by a high oil producing rate before water breakthrough, and then, simultaneously with water breakthrough, a drastic reduction in oil producing rate with a very large water producing rate. Very little oil is calculated to be recovered after water breakthrough in the frontal drive method. This type of reservoir performance is seldom seen in actual reservoirs, and this discrepancy is due primarily to the assumption normally made in frontal drive calculations that the reservoir is one single homogeneous bed. Thus the displacing fluid, whether it be water or gas, is assumed to move through the reservoir in the form of a single "front," and production will change from all oil to almost all displacing fluid within a relatively short period.

However, few petroleum reservoirs encountered in actual practice are comprised of a single bed of uniform permeability. Most actual reservoirs will have a wide variation, both laterally and vertically, in permeability, although permeability variations are often reasonably uniform in a lateral direction. It is not uncommon in a reservoir to encounter a highly permeable zone which can be mapped in the same relative structural position throughout the reservoir. It can be proved in a very simple manner that the advance of a displacing fluid in a bed is proportional to the permeability of the bed. For example, consider two horizontal beds of the same cross-sectional area and length, but having different permeabilities, as shown in Figure 9-1. Using the linear flow model shown in Figure 9-1, the flow rate of a displacing phase through the beds, which are assumed to be isolated from each other, can be calculated from Darcy's law as follows:

$$q_1 = \frac{k_1 A_1 \Delta p}{\mu L} \tag{9-1}$$

and

$$q_2 = \frac{k_2 A_2 \Delta p}{\mu L} \tag{9-2}$$

where the subscripts 1 and 2 refer to conditions in beds 1 and 2 respectively.

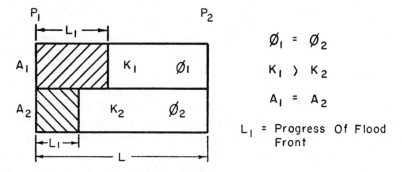

FIGURE 9-1. Effect of permeability on flood front velocity.

The velocity of travel of the displacing phase can be found by dividing the flow rate by the cross-sectional area exposed to flow, which is:

$$v = q/\phi A \qquad (9\text{-}3)$$

Substituting Equation (9-3) into Equations (9-1) and (9-2) results in:

$$q_1 = v_1\phi_1 A_1 = \frac{k_1 A_1 \Delta p}{\mu L}$$

or:

$$v_1 = \frac{k_1 \Delta p}{\mu L} \qquad (9\text{-}4)$$

and:

$$q_2 = v_2\phi_2 A_2 = \frac{k_2 A_2 \Delta p}{\mu L} \qquad (9\text{-}5)$$

or:

$$v_2 = \frac{k_2 \Delta p}{\mu L} \qquad (9\text{-}6)$$

If the velocity ratio $\bar{v} = \dfrac{v_1}{v_2}$, then combining Equations (9-6) and (9-7) will determine this velocity ratio:

$$\bar{v} = \frac{v_1}{v_2} = \frac{k_1 \Delta p}{\mu L} \ \bigg/ \ \frac{k_2 \Delta p}{\mu L} \qquad (9\text{-}7)$$

The Δp, ϕ, μ, and L values in beds 1 and 2 are identical, and therefore they can be cancelled from Equation (9-7), resulting in:

$$\overline{v} = \frac{v_1}{v_2} = \frac{k_1}{k_2} \tag{9-8}$$

which shows that the velocity of flow through each bed is proportional only to the permeability of the bed.

Maintaining reservoir pressure at a high level offers several advantages: (1) oil viscosity is reduced because of the larger amount of gas retained in solution, (2) effective permeability to oil is increased, also as a direct result of the decreased liberation of gas from the oil, and (3) the flowing life of the reservoir is extended, which will materially reduce lifting costs. In many cases this last factor alone will almost pay the cost of the pressure maintenance facilities, and when the economics of pressure maintenance facilities are being studied, it definitely should be included as an important economic factor.

Pressure Maintenance by Gas Injection

Gas has been a widely-used fluid for pressure maintenance operations. There are several reasons for this: (1) gas is readily available in many areas, either from the reservoir being produced, or from extraneous sources, (2) since the gas is nonreactive with the reservoir rock it can be injected into the reservoir with a minimum amount of trouble, (3) it may be desirable to conserve the produced gas for a future gas market, and the gas can be returned to the reservoir where it will not only be stored for future use, but where it will also displace some oil from the reservoir, or (4) state regulatory agencies may force the return of gas as a conservation measure.

Determining the gas requirements for a pressure maintenance operation is a major consideration in the overall economics of a gas injection project. Conventional material balance studies, as outlined in the latter part of this chapter will provide most of the basic information required for the economy study. Elkins and Cooke[1] have presented some useful information concerning the gas requirements for nine different gas injection projects. This information

[1] Elkins, L. F. and Cooke, J. T., "Pilot Gas Injection—Its Conduct and Criteria for Evaluation," *Trans.* AIME, 1949, Vol. 186, p. 180.

is reproduced in Table 9-1 and Figure 9-2. Elkins and Cooke used gas replacement volume instead of injected gas volume as the oil recovery is a result of both injected gas volume and solution gas expansion. None of the fields, with the possible exception of Reservoir F exhibited any indications of gravity drainage. The authors concluded from this study that oil recovery appeared to be primarily dependent on oil viscosity and total gas volume, and independent of reservoir pressure.

Due to the low viscosity of gas, the permeability variations in a reservoir are very important, as early breakthrough of injected gas may occur where there are continuous zones of unusually higher

Table 9-1

Data Pertaining to Gas Injection Projects
(After Elkins and Cooke, Trans. AIME, Vol. 186, 1949, p. 180)

Field[1]	μ_o Cp.	Formation Pressure During Injection Psia	Shrinkage of Formation Oil from Initial Condition to Last Point Shown[2] Percent
A	0.57-0.80	1750- 800	11.5
B	0.5	2400-2100	9.0
C	1.4	300- 50	10.0
D	1.5	400- 40	12.0
E	0.9-1.1	900- 75	13.0
F	1.6	175- 30	20.0
G	1.8	1200-1080	2.0
H	0.52	1020- 960	2.5
I	2.6-3.0	625- 200	3.0

[1] Letters conform with curves shown in Figure 9-2.
[2] Based on formation oil at initial conditions as 1.00.

permeability than the average permeability of the reservoir. Therefore, it is important to know something about the permeability variations in the reservoir so that the proper precautions can be taken to reduce early breakthrough of injected gas. Where the injected gas has "broken through" the permeable zones, it is necessary to continue recycling the gas through these depleted, high-permeability zones if they cannot be isolated by squeeze cementing or other remedial operations. This may seriously affect the economics of the entire operation and cause premature shutdown of the pressure maintenance project, as each MCF of injected gas will cost a specific amount.

An excellent example of the benefits of pressure maintenance has been described by Justus,[2] et al for the Brookhaven Field in Mississippi. Reservoir pressure was declining rapidly before initiation of the pressure maintenance program. The authors estimate that approximately 25% additional oil (10 million barrels) will be recovered by the gas injection operations. Figure 9-3 shows the pressure production history of the field. The Brookhaven Field produces from the Basal Tuscaloosa formation which is Upper Cretaceous in age. Average depth of the producing section is about 10,300 feet subsurface. It is a sandstone reservoir with an average permeability of 256 millidarcies, an interstitial water saturation of approximately 45 percent, and an average porosity of about 25 percent.

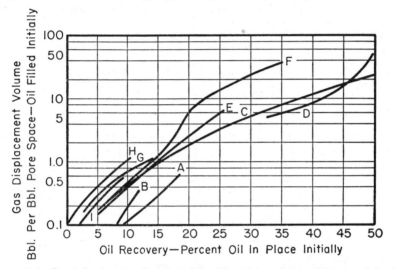

FIGURE 9-2. Gas injection requirements for oil recovery. (After Elkins and Cooke, Trans. AIME, Vol. 186, 1949)

In addition to the future producing gas-oil ratios predicted by material balance methods, production data can often be extrapolated to yield valuable information concerning future gas requirements. Figure 9-4 shows plots of cumulative gas injected and injected gas-oil ratios plotted versus cumulative oil production. A semi-logarithmic plot of these data is an essentially straight line, which lends itself to extrapolation. There is some mathematical justification for this straight-line semi-logarithmic plot. It should be noted that a

[2] Justus, J. B., Cassingham, R. W., Blomberg, C. R., and Ashby, W. H., "Pressure Maintenance by Gas Injection in the Brookhaven Field, Mississippi," Trans. AIME, 1954, Vol. 201, p. 97.

change in operating conditions, such as reducing the volume of injected gas, or shutting in high gas-oil ratio wells would change the slope of the plots in Figure 9-4.

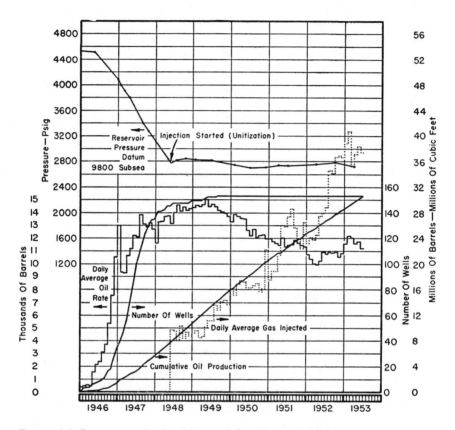

FIGURE 9-3. Pressure production history of Brookhaven field, Lincoln County, Miss. *(Justus, Cassingham, Blomberg and Ashby, Trans. AIME, Vol. 201, 1954.)*

Condensing Gas Drive

Laboratory studies have shown that extremely high recoveries, sometimes approaching 100 percent, can be obtained by using a condensing gas as the injected fluid. A condensing gas is defined as a gas which is appreciably soluble in the reservoir oil. The reservoir oil volume is increased considerably by the condensing gas phase going into solution in the oil, which materially increases the

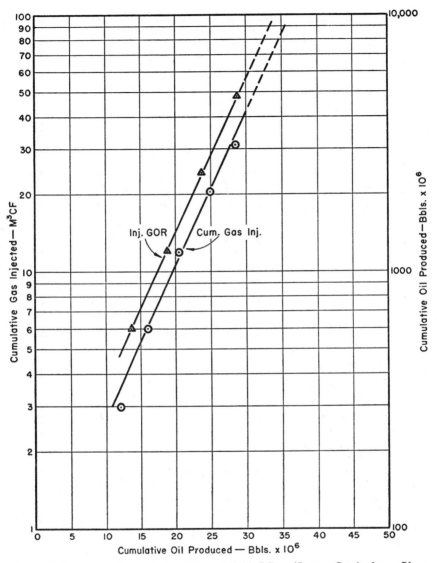

FIGURE 9-4. Gas requirements, Brookhaven field, Miss. (*Justus, Cassingham, Blomberg and Ashby, Trans. AIME, Vol. 201, 1954*)

effective oil permeability. Stone and Crump[3] have presented laboratory data which show the effects of several variables on ultimate oil recovery by a condensing gas drive. Figure 9-5 summarizes their

[3] Stone, H. L. and Crump, J. S., "The Effect of Gas Composition Upon Oil Recovery by Condensing Gas Drive," *Trans. AIME*, 1956, Vol. 207, p. 105.

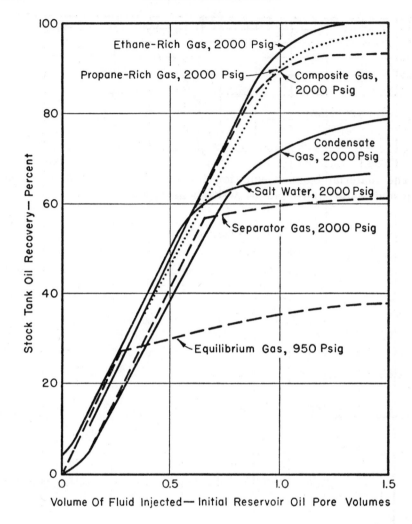

FIGURE 9-5. Oil recovery as a function pf volume of fluid injected (light oil experiments).

results when using a high-gravity crude oil as the displaced phase. Stone and Crump conclude that "This increased recovery is believed to result from solution of the injected gas both at the invading gas front and behind this front. Gas condensation at the front tends to retard invasion of the oil-saturated portion of the reservoir by the displacing gas, since it swells the oil phase at that point, and also dissolves the leading fingers of the gas phase. At the same time the swelling of the oil lowers the viscosity of that phase, and this effect favors more efficient displacement of the oil."

Predicting Performance by Gas Injection

A. Tarner Method

The conventional Tarner method can usually be applied with good results provided reliable data are available, and the proper precautions, outlined in Chapter 3, *Oil Reservoirs*, are taken.

The material balance equation for an oil reservoir with a gas cap and water drive can be written as follows:

$$N_p [B_o + (R_p - R_s) B_g] = m N B_{gi} \left[\frac{B_g}{B_{gi}} - 1 \right]$$
$$+ N (B_t - B_{ti}) + (W_e - W_p B_w)$$

$$(9-9)$$

Equation (9-9) is quite interesting, as the left side of the equation is equal to the reservoir oil and gas produced. The first term on the right side of the equation is the expansion of the gas cap; the second term on the right side is the expansion of the oil zone with its dissolved gas; and the third term is the net water influx (or net expansion of water into the oil zone). Thus, the material balance equation states that the oil and gas produced is equal to the sum of the expansion of gas, oil, and water. If gas is injected into the reservoir, then the injected gas would be an additive term on the right side of Equation (9-9). For example, if, at any time G_i SCF of gas has been injected into the reservoir, Equation (9-9) becomes:

$$N_p [B_o + (R_p - R_s) B_g] = m N B_{gi} \left[\frac{B_g}{B_{gi}} - 1 \right]$$
$$+ N [B_t - B_{ti}] + [W_e - W_p B_w] + G_i B_g$$

$$(9-10)$$

where:

G_i = Cumulative gas injected, SCF.

Sometimes the volume of gas injected can be expressed as some fraction of the cumulative gas produced, $N_p R_p$, or $G_i = f (N_p R_p)$. If gas injection is commenced at some time later than initial conditions, which is usually the case. and some fraction of the produced gas is injected, then:

$$G_i = F \left[N_p R_p - (N_p R_p)_g \right] \qquad (9\text{-}11)$$

where:

F = Fraction of produced gas which is injected.

$(N_p R_p)_g$ = Cumulative gas produced prior to commencing gas injection operations.

Combining Equations (9-11) and (9-10):

$$N_p \left[B_o + (R_p - R_s)\, B_g \right] = m\, N\, B_{gi} \left(\frac{B_g}{B_{gi}} - 1 \right) + N\, (B_t - B_{ti})$$
$$+ (W_e - W_p\, B_w) + F \left[N_p R_p - (N_p R_p)_g \right]$$
$$(9\text{-}12)$$

It should be noted that if gas injection begins immediately on producing the reservoir, then the term $(N_p R_p)_g$ is zero.

Rearranging Equation (9-12) to solve for $N_p R_p$, cumulative gas produced, which is the way the equation will be used in the Tarner method results in:

$$N_p R_p = \frac{\left[\begin{array}{l} m N B_{ti} \left(\dfrac{B_g}{B_{gi}} - 1 \right) + N\,(B_t - B_{ti}) \\ + (W_e - W_p\, B_w) + N_p\,(R_s\, B_g - B_o) - F\,(N_p R_p)_g\, B_g \end{array} \right]}{(1 - F)\, B_g}$$
$$(9\text{-}13)$$

Equation (9-13) is used with the instantaneous gas-oil ratio equation and the oil saturation equation to study the effects of a gas-injection pressure maintenance program. An example problem will be worked at the end of the chapter to more clearly illustrate the method.

Injected Gas Drive Index

The relative efficiency of the gas injection pressure maintenance operations can be determined by arranging Equation (9-10) to solve for $N_p B_o$, the produced reservoir oil:

$$N_p B_o = N(B_t - B_{ti}) + mNB_{ti}\left(\frac{B_g}{B_{gi}} - 1\right)$$
$$+ G_i B_g + (W_e - W_p B_w) - N_p(R_p - R_s)B_g$$

$$(9\text{-}14)$$

Rearranging Equation (9-14) to solve for the index of drives, as discussed in Chapter 8, *Combination Drive Reservoirs*, results in:

$$1 = \frac{[N(B_t - B_{ti}) - (1 - f)N_p(R_p - R_s)B_g]}{N_p B_o}$$

$$+ \frac{\left[mNB_{ti}\left(\frac{B_g}{B_{gi}} - 1\right) - fN_p(R_p - R_s)B_g\right]}{N_p B_o} + \frac{G_i B_g}{N_p B_o} + \frac{W_e - W_p}{N_p B_o}$$

$$(9\text{-}15)$$

where:

f = fraction of produced free gas which comes from the gas cap.

The term $\dfrac{G_i B_g}{N_p B_o}$ is the injected gas drive index. When this term is large with respect to the other terms the recovery from the reservoir is due primarily to the injected gas, but if this term is small compared to the other terms, then the injected gas is ineffective insofar as oil recovery is concerned. The evaluation of this term for a depletion drive reservoir is very important, as the only other producing mechanism is the solution gas. For a depletion drive reservoir the gas cap and water influx terms are zero, and Equation (9-15) reduces to:

$$1 = \overset{A}{\frac{N(B_t - B_{ti}) - N_p(R_p - R_s)B_g}{N_p B_o}} + \overset{B}{\frac{G_i B_g}{N_p B_o}} \qquad (9\text{-}16)$$

Part A of Equation (9-16) is the depletion drive index and part B is the injected gas drive index. Since recovery by depletion drive is usually very poor, it is essential to maintain a high injected gas drive index. If the reservoir pressure can be maintained constant, then the B_t values do not change and the depletion drive index will be zero. Theoretically, the greatest recovery would occur at constant reservoir pressure. However, economic factors may dictate some pressure reduction, as it may be uneconomic, or physically impossible, to return enough gas to the reservoir to maintain a constant pressure. Therefore, in practice, the reservoir pressure declines continuously in most pressure maintenance operations. A periodic check on the index of drives will show the efficiency of gas injection operations.

B. Frontal Drive Methods

The frontal drive technique can be used to predict reservoir behavior under gas injection operations. The technique is discussed more fully and an example problem worked in Chapter 10, *Improving Oil Recovery,* and since the fundamental principles involved are identical, the frontal drive method will not be discussed in this chapter.

Pressure Maintenance by Water Injection

Pressure maintenance by water injection has all the inherent advantages of pressure maintenance by gas injection, and also has the additional advantages of a more efficient displacing fluid. Residual oil saturations following a water drive are usually considerably smaller than when followed by a gas drive. This is due primarily to the more favorable mobility ratio $\left(\dfrac{k_w}{k_o} \; \dfrac{\mu_o}{\mu_w} \right)$ of the water drive and also to the wetting characteristics of most reservoir rocks, which are believed to be predominantly water-wet. The displacing water travels more uniformly through the whole reservoir with less oil-bypassing.

The injection of water into the reservoir poses several problems not encountered with gas injection, the principal problems being the reaction of the injected water with the reservoir rock and the corrosion of both surface and subsurface mechanical equipment by corrosive materials in the water. These latter two problems are discussed more fully in Chapter 10.

Water is usually injected at the base of the reservoir, while the producing wells are located upstructure. The objective in water injection operations is to achieve a uniform frontal advance of the water. This can best be achieved by carefully studying the geologic aspects of the reservoir and planning the injection program accordingly. For example, water injection into a domal-type structure is probably best accomplished by using wells distributed uniformly throughout the reservoir, with injection being in the base of the reservoir.

In an oil wet reservoir, particularly where gravity segregation has a significant influence on reservoir performance, gas injection may result in more efficient oil recovery than water injection. This has been observed in several field cases where it was possible to compare oil recovery efficiency in the same reservoir from an expanding gas cap and from natural water influx. In fact some recent case histories have shown that some gas injection projects have recovered as much as 75 percent of the initial oil in place.

Predicting Performance by Water Injection

Performance of a reservoir under water injection can be predicted by either the conventional Tarner method or by the frontal drive method. If the Tarner method is used, a material balance equation must be developed to take into consideration the effects of water injection. The equation can be developed as follows:

$$\text{SCF Gas Originally} = \text{SCF Gas Produced} + \text{SCF Gas Remaining} \tag{9-17}$$

The balance can be developed in the same manner as outlined in Chapter 8, *Combination Drive Reservoirs*, except that where water is being injected, the SCF of gas remaining will be defined as follows:

$$\text{SCF Gas Remaining} = \text{Original Total Volume} - \text{Rem. Liquid Vol.} \tag{9-18}$$

The remaining liquid volume is equal to the sum of the remaining oil volume plus the net water encroachment, plus the water injected, or:

SCF Gas Remaining

$$= \frac{(NB_{oi} - mB_{oi}) - [(N - N_p)B_o + (W_e - W_p B_w) + W_i]}{B_g} \tag{9-19}$$

where:

W_i = gross water injected, barrels.

The resulting material balance equation is:

$$N \left[(B_t - B_{ti}) + mB_{ti} \left(\frac{B_g}{B_{gi}} - 1 \right) \right]$$
$$= N_p [(R_p - R_s) B_g + B_o] - (W_e - W_p B_w) - W_i$$
$$(9\text{-}20)$$

If there is no gas cap present in the reservoir, Equation (9-20) reduces to:

$$N (B_t - B_{ti}) = N_p [(R_p - R_s) B_g + B_o] - (W_e - W_p B_w) - W_i$$
$$(9\text{-}21)$$

If there is no water drive in the reservoir, a sightly different material balance is required, since W_i is defined as the gross water injected:

$$N (B_t - B_{ti}) = N_p [(R_p - R_s) B_g + B_o] - (W_i - W_p B_w)$$
$$(9\text{-}22)$$

where W_p still is the water production from the reservoir as previously defined. Equations (9-20) and (9-21) make no attempt to distinguish between produced injected water and produced influx water as it is usually impossible to do so in actual operations.

The proper material balance equation is used with the instantaneous gas-oil ratio equation and the oil saturation equation to predict reservoir performance by the Tarner method. An example problem will not be worked using water injection since the techniques for reinjection are very similar, whether the injected fluid be gas or water. Very often the future injection of water can be described in the material balance equation as some fraction of the oil production. This is especially convenient, and reliable, if the past history of water injection operations shows a straight line relationship when plotted versus cumulative oil production. Figure 9-6 shows such a plot from data presented by Torrey[4] on the Midway Field in Arkansas. Net water injected is defined as gross water injected minus water produced. Examination of Figure 9-6 will show that approximately 1.4 barrels of water have been injected for each barrel of oil produced. Since the plot is essentially a straight line, the future water injection rates could be expressed in terms of the oil production, which for the Midway Field would be as follows:

---

[4] Torrey, Paul D., "A Review of Some Important Water-Injection Projects," API Drilling and Production Practice, 1951, p. 286.

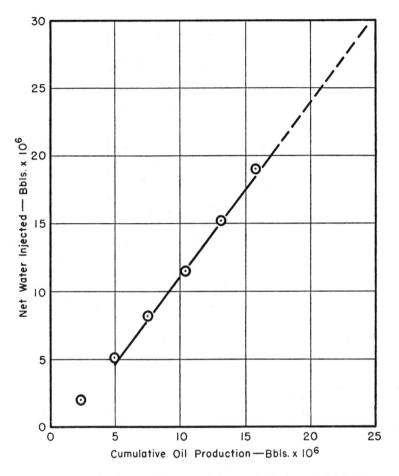

FIGURE 9-6. Water injection requirements, Midway field, Ark. *(API Drilling and Production Practices, 1951, p. 301)*

$$(W_i - W_p B_w) = 1.4 N_p \qquad (9\text{-}23)$$

Expressing the net water injection in terms of N_p cumulative oil production, would result in a simplification of Equation (9-22), as follows:

$$N(B_t - B_{ti}) = N_p[(R_p - R_s) + B_o] - fN_p \qquad (9\text{-}24)$$

where:

f = barrels of net water injected per barrel of oil produced.

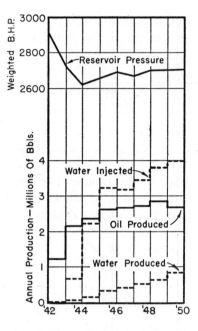

FIGURE 9-7. Production data, Midway field, Ark. *(After Torrey, API Drilling and Production Practices, 1951, p. 286)*

Index of Injected Water Drive

Equation (9-20) can be rearranged to solve for the various indexes of drive as follows:

$$1 = \frac{N(B_t - B_{ti}) - (1 - f) N_p (R_p - R_s) B_g}{N_p B_o}$$

$$+ \frac{\left[mNB_{ti}\left(\frac{B_g}{B_{gi}} - 1\right) - fN_p(R_p - R_s) B_g \right]}{N_p B_o} + \frac{W_e - W_p B_w}{N_p B_o} + \frac{W_i}{N_p B_o}$$

$$(9\text{-}25)$$

The term $\dfrac{W_i}{N_p B_o}$ is the index of injected water drive, and the magnitude of this number will indicate the importance of the injected water as a recovery agent.

Control of the Gas Cap

Where water is being injected into a reservoir which contains a gas cap, the problem of gas cap shrinkage quite often becomes a problem of considerable significance in reservoir operations. This problem was discussed briefly in Chapter 6, *Water Drive Reservoirs*, and is also discussed more fully in Chapter 13, *Economics*, where various economic aspects of reservoir operations are considered. However, the problem is especially important in water drive pressure maintenance operations for two reasons: (1) the gas cap can expand only as a result of a decrease in reservoir pressure, and in pressure maintenance operations the decrease in reservoir pressure per unit of oil production is usually quite low, and (2) it is usually almost impossible to eliminate the production of gas cap gas from the reservoir due to the random location of producing wells. Therefore, it is obvious from a consideration of these two factors that shrinkage of the gas cap is a distinct possibility. It will be necessary to eliminate gas cap shrinkage by either shutting in the wells producing the gas cap gas or returning fluid to the gas cap to replace the gas which has been produced. It may be impossible to shut in those wells producing the gas cap gas, either because of royalty considerations or because of rules of state regulatory bodies, in which case if gas cap shrinkage is to be eliminated, some fluid must be returned to the reservoir to replace the space voided by the produced gas.

It is common practice to return some fraction of the produced gas to the reservoir in order to maintain the size of the gas cap, however, in some cases it has been more economical to return water instead of gas to the gas cap. This may be feasible when there are no facilities readily available for compressing the gas for its return to the reservoir, and the water, of course, is readily available, since it is already being injected into the base of the structure. This particular technique has been successfully applied in several cases, although the possibility of gravity segregation has to be considered.

Typical Water Injection Pressure Maintenance Operations

The Midway Field in Arkansas is an excellent example of the benefits to be derived by a water-injection pressure maintenance program. Figure 9-7 shows the production history of this reservoir. The Midway Field produces from the Smackover lime. The reservoir contained approximately 150 million barrels of stock tank oil in place originally, but was apparently being produced by depletion drive, as evidenced by the initial rapid pressure decline. Full-scale water injection operations were initiated approximately two years after discovery of the reservoir, and as a result of the water injec-

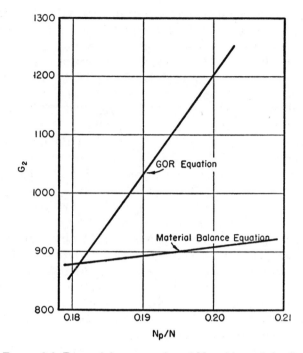

FIGURE 9-8. Determining true value of N_{p2} with gas injection.

tion program, the reservoir pressure actually increased slightly before levelling off. For several years thereafter pressure remained fairly constant. As a result of the pressure maintenance program, ultimate oil recovery is expected to be approximately 75 million barrels, compared to only about 25 million barrels expected to be recovered by depletion drive.

Example Problem 9-1

Reservoir X, which was used in Chapter 4 to illustrate the Tarner method for predicting behavior of depletion drive reservoirs, will also be used to show the calculated effects of pressure maintenance by gas injection. The conventional Tarner method will also be used for the gas injection study. The necessary data are shown in Tables 4-1 and 4-2 and in Figures 4-2, 4-3, and 4-4 of Chapter 4, so this information will not be repeated here. Beginning at 1,800 psia reservoir pressure, seventy-five percent of the produced gas is to be returned to the reservoir. In order to simplify the calculations it will be assumed that 75% of all of the gas which has been

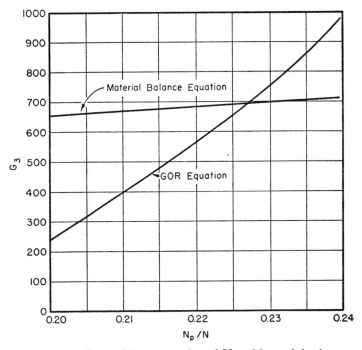

FIGURE 9-9. Determining true value of N_{p_3} with gas injection.

produced from the saturation pressure, 2,100 psia, down to 1,800 psia, will be returned, the material balance equation will be:

$$N_p R_p = \frac{N\ (B_t - B_{ti}) - N_p\ (B_t - R_{ss}B_g)}{(1 - 0.75)\ B_g}$$

A simplified oil saturation equation will be used wherein the assumption will be made that the injected gas is distributed uniformly throughout the oil zone. The oil saturation equation then will reduce to:

$$S_o = \left(1 - \frac{N_p}{N}\right)\frac{B_o}{B_{os}}\ (1 - S_{wi})$$

Table 9-2 shows the calculated results obtained by injecting 75% of the produced gas, beginning at 1,800 psia. Table 9-3 shows a summary of the calculations for the performance prediction, while Tables 9-4 and 9-5 show example calculations for gas injection. The predicted additional recovery as a result of returning 75% of the produced gas to the reservoir is shown in Figure 9-10.

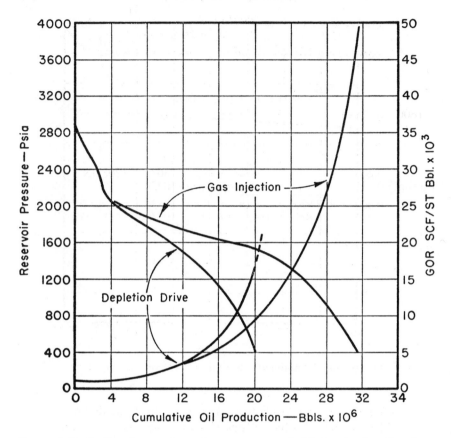

FIGURE 9-10. Predicted reservoir performance, reservoir X, showing benefits of gas injection.

Table 9-2
Summary of Results of Gas Injection — Reservoir X

Pressure Psia	N_p/N	R SCF/ST Bbl.	N_p Bbls. $\times 10^6$	N_{pt}[1] Bbls. $\times 10^6$
1800	0.0393	1936	3.795	7.240
1500	0.1810	10470	17.476	20.921
1200	0.2265	20085	21.870	25.315
1000	0.2475	27460	23.897	27.342
700	0.2709	39112	26.157	29.602
400	0.2894	47465	27.943	31.388

[1] Includes oil produced above the saturation pressure.

Table 9-3
Summary of Calculations. Predicted Reservoir Performance by
Injecting 75% of Produced Gas — Reservoir X

P	N_p/N (Assumed)	G_{mb}	S_o	k_g/k_o	R	G_{gor}	G (Actual)
1800 (actual)	0.0393				1936		64.34N
1500	0.180	878.06N	0.678	0.278	10300	860.2N	
	0.182	879.66N	0.676	0.286	10590	895.0N	
	0.200	907.66N	0.662	0.362	13070	1205.0N	
(actual)	0.181				10470		878.86N
1200	0.200	652.8N	0.643	0.474	14635	238.5N	
	0.220	684.8N	0.627	0.610	18545	565.0N	
	0.240	716.8N	0.611	0.765	22985	988.0N	
(actual)	0.2265				20085		694.8N
1000	0.245	496.0N	0.590	1.000	26110	427.5N	
	0.2475	502.0N	0.588	1.050	27460	500.0N	
	0.250	504.0N	0.586	1.065	27860	563.0N	
(actual)	0.2475				27460		502.0N
700	0.260	768.0N	0.547	1.830	35362	393.0N	
	0.270	778.0N	0.539	1.980	38162	739.5N	
	0.272	780.0N	0.537	2.080	40062	826.0N	
(actual)	0.2709				39112		778.8N
400	0.280	785.2N	0.497	3.585	44765	381.5N	
	0.289	797.2N	0.491	3.805	47565	785.0N	
	0.290	799.2N	0.490	3.830	7865	830.0N	
(actual)	0.2894				47465		800.0N

Table 9-4
Example Calculations — Gas Injection
First Period — p = 1500 psia
Reservoir X

Trial 1: Assume $N_p = 0.20$ N

$$N_{p2}R_{p2} = \frac{N(B_t - B_{ts}) - N_p(B_t - R_{ss}B_g)}{(1 - 0.75) B_g}$$

$$= \frac{N(1.792 - 1.480) - 0.20 N(1.792 - 1340 \times 0.001853)}{0.25 \times 0.001853} = 972.0 \text{ N}$$

$$G_{mb2} = N_{p2}R_{p2} - N_{p1}R_{p1} = 972.0 \text{ N} - 64.34 \text{ N} = \underline{907.66 \text{ N}}$$

$$S_o = \left(1 - \frac{N_p}{N}\right) \frac{B_o}{B_{os}} (1 - S_{wi}) = (1 - 0.20)(0.973)(0.85) = 0.662$$

$$k_g/k_o = 0.362 \text{ (from Fig. 4-4 at } S_o = 0.662)$$

$$R = \frac{k_g}{k_o} \times \frac{\mu_o}{\mu_g} \times \frac{B_o}{B_g} + R_s = 0.362 \times 42.4 \times 777 + 1150 = 13070$$

$$G_{gor2} = \left(\frac{R_2 + R_1}{2}\right)(N_{p2} - N_{p1}) = \left(\frac{13070 + 1936}{2}\right)(0.20\ N - 0.0393\ N)$$

$$= 1205\ N$$

Trial 2: Assume $N_p = 0.18\ N$

$$N_{p2}R_{p2} = \frac{N(1.792 - 1.480) - 0.18\ N(1.792 - 1340 \times 0.001853)}{0.25 \times 0.001853}$$

$$= 942.4\ N$$

$$G_{mb2} = 942.4\ N - 64.34\ N = \underline{878.06\ N}$$

$$S_o = 0.82 \times 0.973 \times 0.85 = 0.678$$

$$k_g/k_o = 0.278$$

$$R_2 = 0.278 \times 42.4 \times 777 + 1150 = 10,300$$

$$G_{gor2} = \left(\frac{10,300 + 1936}{2}\right)(0.18\ N - 0.0393\ N) = \mathbf{860.8\ N}$$

Trial 3: Assume $N_p = 0.182\ N$

$$N_{p2}R_{p2} = \frac{N(1.792 - 1.480) - 0.182\ N(1.792 - 1340 \times 0.001853)}{0.25 \times 0.001853}$$

$$= 944.0\ N$$

$$G_{mb2} = 944.0\ N - 64.34\ N = 879.66\ N$$

$$S_o = 0.818 \times 0.973 \times 0.85 = 0.676$$

$$k_g/k_o = 0.286$$

$$R_2 = 0.286 \times 42.4 \times 777 + 1150 = 10590$$

$$R_{gor2} = \left(\frac{10590 + 1936}{2}\right)(0.182\ N - 0.0393\ N) = \mathbf{895.2\ N}$$

Table 9-5
Example Calculations — Gas Injection
Second Period — p = 1200 psia — Reservoir X

Trial 1 : Assume $N_p = 0.20\ N$

$$N_{p3}R_{p3} = \frac{N(B_t - B_{ts}) - N_p(B_t - R_{ss}B_g)}{(1 - 0.75)\ B_g}$$

$$= \frac{N(2.239 - 1.480) - 0.2\ N(2.239 - 1340 \times 0.002365)}{0.25 \times 0.002365}$$

$$= 1596.0N$$

$$G_{mb3} = N_{p3}R_{p3} - (G_2 + G_1) = 1596.0 \text{ N} - (878.86 \text{ N} + 64.34 \text{ N})$$
$$= \underline{652.8 \text{ N}}$$

$$S_o = \left(1 - \frac{N_p}{N}\right)\frac{B_o}{B_{os}}(1 - S_{wi}) = (1 - 0.20)\frac{1.399}{1.480}(1 - 0.15) = 0.643$$

$$k_g/k_o = 0.474 \text{ (from Fig. 4-4 at } S_o = 0.643)$$

$$R = \frac{k_g}{k_o} \times \frac{\mu_o}{\mu_g} \times \frac{B_o}{B_g} + R_s = 0.474 \times 48.8 \times 590 + 985 = 14635$$

$$G_{gor3} = \left(\frac{R_3 + R_2}{2}\right)(N_{p3} - N_{p2}) = \left(\frac{14635 + 10470}{2}\right)(0.20 \text{ N} - 0.181 \text{ N})$$
$$= 238.5 \text{ N}$$

Trial 2: Assume $N_p = 0.22$ N

$$N_{p3}R_{p3} = \frac{N(2.239 - 1.480) - 0.22 \text{ N}(2.239 - 1340 \times 0.002365)}{0.25 \times 0.002365}$$

$$= 1628.0 \text{ N}$$

$$G_{mb3} = N_{p3}R_{p3} - (G_2 + G_1) = 1628.0 \text{ N} \ (878.86 \text{ N} + 64.34 \text{ N})$$
$$= \underline{684.8 \text{ N}}$$

$$S_o = 0.78 \times 0.945 \times 0.85 = 0.627$$

$$k_g/k_o = 0.61$$

$$R_3 = 0.61 \times 48.8 \times 590 + 985 = 18545$$

$$G_{gor3} = \left(\frac{18545 + 10470}{2}\right)(0.22 \text{ N} - 0.181 \text{ N}) = \underline{555.0 \text{ N}}$$

Trial 3: Assume $N_p = 0.24$ N

$$N_{p3}R_{p3} = \frac{N(2.239 - 1.480) - 0.24 \text{ N}(2.239 - 1340 \times 0.002365)}{0.25 \times 0.002365}$$

$$= 1660 \text{ N}$$

$$G_{mb3} = N_{p3}R_{p3} - (G_2 + G_1) = 1660 \text{ N} - (878.86 \text{ N} + 64.34 \text{ N})$$
$$= \underline{716.8 \text{ N}}$$

$$S_o = 0.76 \times 0.945 \times 0.85 = 0.611$$

$$k_g/k_o = 0.765$$

$$R_3 = 0.765 \times 48.8 \times 590 + 985 = 22985$$

$$G_{gor3} = \left(\frac{22985 + 10470}{2}\right)(0.24 \text{ N} - 0.181 \text{ N}) = 988.0 \text{ N}$$

Chapter 10

IMPROVING OIL RECOVERY

Using presently-known technology a substantial amount of oil remains unrecoverable by primary recovery. Various methods of improving oil recovery have been developed, all of which involve the injection of some fluid into the reservoir. Improving oil recovery by pressure maintenance, using gas or water, was discussed in Chapter 9.

The following factors are important in determining the optimum reservoir pressure (or time) at which a fluid injection project should be commenced:

1. Reservoir oil viscosity—minimum oil viscosity which occurs at the bubble point pressure, is desirable.
2. Free gas saturation in the oil zone.
   a. Water Injection Project: It is desirable to have an equilibrium gas saturation, possibly as much as 10%. This will occur at a pressure which is below the bubble point pressure.
   b. Gas Injection Project: A zero gas saturation in the oil zone is desired. This occurs while reservoir pressure is at or above bubble point pressure.
3. Cost of injection equipment. This is related to reservoir pressure, and at higher pressures, the cost of injection equipment increases. Therefore a low reservoir pressure at initiation of injection is desirable.
4. Productivity of producing wells. A high reservoir pressure is desirable to increase the productivity of producing wells, which prolongs the flowing period of the wells, decreases lifting costs, and may shorten the overall life of the project.
5. Effect of delaying investment on the time value of money. A delayed investment in injection facilities is desirable from this standpoint.
6. Overall life of the reservoir. Because operating expenses are an important part of total costs, it is desirable to begin the fluid injection as early as possible.

Some of the six previously listed factors act in opposition to others. Thus the actual pressure at which a fluid injection project should be initiated will require optimization of the various factors in order to develop the most favorable overall economics.

The principal requirement for a successful fluid injection project is that sufficient oil must remain in the reservoir after primary operations have ceased to render economic the secondary recovery operations. This high residual oil saturation after primary recovery is essential not only because there must be a sufficient volume of oil left in the reservoir, but also because of relative permeability considerations. A high oil relative permeability, i.e. high oil saturation, means more oil recovery with less production of the displacing fluid. On the other hand, a low oil saturation means a low oil relative permeability with more production of the displacing fluid at a given time.

Depletion drive reservoirs will usually be more susceptible to successful fluid injection operations than reservoirs operating under other driving forces because of the lower recovery from this type of reservoir.

Gas cap drive reservoirs present a problem, particularly in water flooding and miscible flooding, as the possibility of moving oil and/or the displacing fluid into the depleted gas cap is always present. Many water flooding projects have been unsuccessful primarily because it was impossible, or uneconomic, to restrict the migration of fluids to the gas cap. Natural permeability barriers can often be used to restrict the migration of fluids to the gas cap and it may be possible to use selective plugging of input wells to restrict the loss of input fluid to the gas zone.

Water drive reservoirs usually are poor secondary recovery prospects because of the better oil recoveries as a result of the water drive, there being less oil remaining after the end of primary operations.

Improving Oil Recovery by Fluid Injection

In addition to supplying energy to the reservoir to assist in oil recovery, one of the principal objectives of a fluid injection project is literally to push the oil to the producing wells. To accomplish this objective the injected fluid must pass through those pore spaces where the remaining oil saturation is located. Since capillary forces play an important role in oil recovery, a knowledge of the capillary forces is requisite to achieve maximum oil recovery.

The principal methods used to improve oil recovery will be discussed briefly, and methods of predicting recovery will be developed.

Immiscible Gas

Immiscible gas was one of the first methods used to improve oil recovery. In pattern-type injection projects immiscible gas is usually a very inefficient fluid for additional oil recovery. This poor recovery efficiency is principally the result of three factors: (1) The gas is non-wetting to the reservoir rocks. Therefore, the gas will move preferentially through the larger pore spaces of the reservoir rock, bypassing much of the reservoir oil. Some gas saturation will usually be present, and the preexisting gas saturation, again because of its non-wetting nature, will occupy the larger pore spaces. Thus the injected gas may be displacing mostly gas and not oil. (2) Due to the low viscosity of gas, its mobility is quite high, which results in excessive channelling and bypassing of the oil. (3) Since gas is non-wetting and occupies the larger pore spaces where flow occurs the easiest, a high effective permeability to gas is developed at relatively low gas saturations. This high effective gas permeability increases the gas mobility, further aggravating the channelling problem mentioned previously.

For these three reasons, gas is seldom injected in a pattern well arrangement. Crestal gas injection, often referred to as an external gas drive, is usually more efficient than pattern gas injection, particularly when gravity segregation aids oil recovery. Excellent recoveries from crestal gas injection projects have been reported. Methods of predicting performance of gas injection projects were presented in Chapter 9, "Pressure Maintenance," and additional methods will be presented later in this chapter.

Water

At the present time water is the most widely used injection fluid. Water is usually more efficient than gas as a displacing fluid because: (1) It is more wetting to the reservoir rock than gas, and will therefore enter a larger number of pores in the reservoir rock. (2) The viscosity of water is greater than the viscosity of gas, which will also improve oil recovery. (3) In a water wet reservoir the effective water permeability is usually low, except at very large water saturations, which also reduces the mobility of the water phase, thereby improving displacement efficiency. In an oil wet reservoir, water is the non-wetting phase, and effective water permeability will be higher at a given water saturation. Also, in an oil wet reservoir the water will preferentially pass through the larger pore spaces. If there is little oil remaining in these large pore spaces as a result of an existing gas saturation, then recovery by water injection may be relatively poor. For these reasons, the wetting conditions of the reservoir will have an important influence on the ultimate oil recovery obtained from a water injection project.

It has been observed that recovery from pattern type water injection projects may be substantially less than recovery from natural water drives. Since the fundamental mechanism of displacement must be the same for both cases, the reasons for these often substantial differences in recovery deserve some discussion. If the fundamental displacement mechanism is the same, then any difference in recovery must be due to the fact that in the pattern water injection projects, the coverage, or sweep efficiency, of pattern injection systems is less than that for natural water drives. Sweep efficiencies for various injection patterns have been studied extensively. Figures 10-20 and 10-21 show examples of some of the studies which have been reported.

The improvement in sweep efficiencies is a field of study where immediate improvements in oil recovery are possible. The use of mathematical models is particularly useful in this respect, where the entire reservoir can be modelled and variations in reservoir properties can be included. It is these variations in reservoir rock and fluid properties which affect sweep efficiencies to the greatest extent. Some inexpensive yet mathematically precise models are available for studying this problem.[1]

Methods of predicting performance of water injection projects were presented in Chapter 9, "Pressure Maintenance," and additional methods will be discussed in more detail later in this chapter.

In an effort to improve water injection recovery efficiency, various modifications have been developed. Some of the more important developments will be briefly discussed.

1. Carbonated Water Flooding. The use of carbon dioxide and water will often improve recovery as much as 50 percent over conventional water flooding. In this process a mixture of carbon dioxide and water, equivalent to approximately 20 percent of one pore volume, is injected. This slug of carbonated water is followed by plain water. Carbon dioxide is highly soluble in oil, and it appears that most of the carbon dioxide will leave the water phase and enter the oil phase. Thus, the carbon dioxide performs two functions, (1) it materially reduces the viscosity of the reservoir oil, and (2) it swells the reservoir oil. Both of these factors will increase oil recovery.

Another important consideration is that the carbon dioxide will often substantially improve water injection rates by reducing bac-

[1] Cole, Frank W, "Front Tracking Mathematical Model," Private Report, 1965

teria formation in the injected water, and by an acidization effect on the formation. This latter effect may substantially reduce the operating life of a project, thereby materially improving the overall economics.

At the present time there are a number of these projects in operation, and the process has been extensively reported in petroleum literature.[2, 3]

In order to predict the performance of carbonated water floods, it is necessary to determine the residual oil saturation resulting from carbonated water injection, and then the standard methods used to predict performance of conventional water floods can be utilized.

2. Polymer Water Flooding. It is well known that oil recovery by water injection can be improved by increasing the viscosity of water. Over the years a large number of patents have been issued which were related to increasing the viscosity of water. However, until recently, most of these methods have been too expensive to be economically usable in practice. At the present time a polymer is available, which although still relatively expensive, appears to economical for many applications.[4] Approximately 5 percent by weight of this polymer will increase the apparent viscosity of water to about 20 centipoises, a 20-fold increase in viscosity. The increase in viscosity is apparently a function of the shearing rate of the fluid, as the viscosity measured in a conventional viscometer tube shows a substantially smaller viscosity increase.

In practice, because of the high cost of the polymer, a slug of polymerized water, possibly as much as 30 percent of a pore volume, is injected, followed by plain water. The objective is to inject enough polymerized water so that, at breakthrough, a maximum reservoir volume will have been contracted by the polymerized water. Laboratory tests, plus a careful study of reservoir inhomogeneties, are requisite prior to initiating a field test of the material.

The polymer water flooding technique may have application in high viscosity oil reservoirs where ordinary water would bypass most of the reservoir oil. A major limitation of this technique is that water injectivity is reduced to the same degree that apparent water viscosity is increased, i.e. a 20-fold increase in apparent water viscosity will result in a 20-fold reduction in water injectivity

[2] Dunlop, D.D., and Welker, J. R., "Physical Properties of Carbonated Oils," *Trans. AIME*, (1963) p. I-873.

[3] "How Carbon Dioxide Floods Stack Up With Conventional-Type Water Floods," *Oil & Gas Journal*, July 1962, p. 106.

[4] Jones, M. A., "Waterflood Mobility Control: A Case History," Journal of Petroleum Technology, Sept. 1966, p. 1151.

during the time the polymerized water is being injected into the reservoir. After conventional water injection has been resumed, injectivity should gradually increase as the high viscosity slug is moved away from the well bore.

There are a relatively large number of these field projects in operation, and experience has indicated that fewer pore volumes of water may be required than for conventional water floods, while recoveries may be as much as twice that obtained from conventional water floods. To predict the performance of polymer water floods, it would first be necessary to determine by laboratory tests the residual oil saturation to be expected. Then the performance predictions used for conventional water floods would be applicable.

3. Alternate Gas-Water Injection. Laboratory studies have shown that the injection of gas into a large-diameter core, where the oil has previously been displaced by a miscible fluid followed by a water flood, will recover substantial additional oil, possible as much as 10 percent more oil. (See references 2 and 3, Chapter 6). The additional oil recovery is believed to be the result of the gas moving through pores bypassed by the water.

This injection method may have good application in very low permeability reservoirs, where injectivity is a major problem. Because of its low viscosity it may be possible to inject as much as 20 times the volume of gas, as is possible with water. Therefore, project life can be materially reduced. This technique is still in the experimental stage, although there are several field tests underway at the present time.

In order to predict performance of this technique, it is first desirable to conduct laboratory experiments to determine residual oil saturations. Then conventional frontal advance or other flood performance prediction techniques can be modified to predict performance.

4. Wettability Reversal. This oil recovery method utilizes the fact that the injected water displaces the formation water ahead of the injected water bank because the two fluids are miscible, and the capillary forces holding the formation water are eliminated. Therefore, oil is displaced from the reservoir by the advancing formation water bank which is built up ahead of the injected water bank. The formation water displaces a certain amount of the reservoir oil, the residual oil saturation being a function of the wetting characteristics of the reservoir rock. If a chemical can be added to the injected water which will alter the wettability of the reservoir rock, then the injected water may pass through a different set of pores than did the advancing formation water. The result will be some

additional oil recovery.[5] For example, in an oil wet reservoir sodium hydroxide added to the injected water will usually convert the rock to a water wet condition. In a reservoir which is initially water wet it would be necessary to inject a chemical with the water which would convert the reservoir rock to an oil wet condition.

This oil recovery technique is relatively new, and there are only a few small-scale field trials in operation.

In order to predict performance of this technique, it is first necessary to determine the native wettability of the reservoir rock and then find a chemical which could be used to economically reverse the wettability. Laboratory tests should be run to determine the residual oil saturations resulting from the two types of displacements. Conventional water flood prediction techniques could be used to predict performance.

Miscible Fluid Injection

The capillary forces holding the oil in the reservoir rocks can be eliminated if an injection fluid is used which is miscible with the reservoir oil.[6]

Although these miscible fluids will displace 100 percent of the oil which they contact, recovery is actually substantially less because of the low viscosity and low density of the injected fluid. The low viscosity causes channelling and bypassing, and the low density promotes gravity segregation and consequent over-running of the oil. Because of these two factors, this method works best in low viscosity, high API gravity oil reservoirs.

This method has more limited application than water injection, but it will be economic for specific reservoir and operating situations. Laboratory data are essential to predict performance, and a thorough analysis of the phase relationships of all the fluids is necessary.

Thermal Oil Recovery

The use of heat to recover oil, particularly low API gravity oil, has been studied for many years. Underground combustion, hot water, and steam have been used.[7]

Underground combustion is still in the experimental stages. Although theoretical oil recoveries are quite high when this technique

---

[5] Leach, R. O., et al, "A Laboratory and Field Study of Wettability Adjustment in Water Flooding," *Journal of Petroleum Technology*, February 1962, p. 206.

[6] Walker J. W., and Turner, J. L., "Performance of Seeligson Zone 20B-07 Enriched-Gas-Drive Project," *Journal of Petroleum Technology*, April 1968, page 369.

[7] Gates, C. F. and Ramey, H. J., Jr., "Better Technology Opens Way for More Thermal Projects," *Oil and Gas Journal*, July 13, 1964, page 72-80.

is used, the high temperatures resulting from combustion cause very low densities and viscosities of the displacing phase, with the consequent problems of channelling and over-running. In addition, the high temperatures cause many operating problems which require special training of the field operating personnel.

The use of steam to increase recovery from high viscosity oil reservoirs is increasing. At the present time there are a relatively large number of these projects in operation throughout the world, although the process is still in the experimental stage.

Two entirely different methods of utilizing the steam are being practiced. First there is the steam soak, or huff-and-puff, process, whereby steam is injected into a producing well for approximately two weeks. The well is then shut in for about two days, after which it is placed back on production. This is essentially a well-bore stimulation technique, but it may be economically possible to stimulate the same well several times. However, in general, oil recovery declines with each succeeding stimulation.

Second, there is the steam displacement technique, where steam is injected into injection wells and the oil is displaced to surrounding producing wells as in conventional fluid injection operations.[8, 9]

In steam injection operations the cost of steam will be a major factor in the overall costs. Therefore, it is desirable to terminate steam injection at some optimum time, after which the steam bank in the reservoir will be pushed to the producing wells by cold water injection. It is first necessary to determine the desired maximum temperature at the producing wells, and then determine the time at which steam injection is terminated and cold water injection commenced. Mathematical models of this type have been programmed for computer usage and are available for use.[10]

Predicting Recovery from Fluid Injection Projects

Several more or less standard methods have been developed for predicting behavior of gas and water injection projects. However, laboratory data, coupled with field experience must be used for predicting behavior of miscible floods or thermal floods. The technique developed by Stiles" is probably the most commonly-used

[8] Van Dijk, C., "Steam-Drive Project in the Schoonebeek Field, The Netherlands," *Journal of Petroleum Technology*, March 1968, page 295.

[9] Ramey, H. L., "How to Calculate Heat Transmission in Hot Fluid Injection," *Petroleum Engineer*, November 1964, page 110.

[10] Cole, Frank W., "Mathematical Model for Predicting the Performance of Steam Injection Projects," Private Report, 1966.

[11] Stiles, Wm. E., "Use of Permeability Distribution in Water Flood Calculations," *Trans.* AIME, Vol. 186, 1949, p. 9.

method of predicting performance of pattern water floods. In addition to providing usually reliable information, the method has the advantage of being straightforward in its approach and requiring few laborious calculations.

Stiles's Method of Water Flood Predictions

The method presented by Stiles takes into account the effect of permeability variations in predicting the performance of water floods.

From an analysis of Darcy's Law, in this case linear flow will be assumed, it can be shown that the fluid flow will be proportional to the permeability of the medium.

Consider the case of several beds in parallel as shown in Figure 10-1:

$$q_1 = \frac{k_1 A_1 \Delta p}{\mu L} \tag{10-1}$$

$$q_2 = \frac{k_2 A_2 \Delta p}{\mu L} \tag{10-2}$$

and:

$$q_t = q_1 + q_2 + q_3 + \ldots q_n \tag{10-3}$$

$$\text{Total permeability capacity} = \Sigma_o^n kh \tag{10-4}$$

At any time t_1, the distance of fluid travel, x_1, is proportional to k_1 (h_1, h_2, h_3 and h_4 being numerically equal).

Basic assumptions used in this method:

1. Uniform water and oil saturation.
2. The reservoir can be divided into a number of beds of varying permeability.
3. Linear flow is the basic flow mechanism.
4. The distance water has travelled through each segment of the reservoir is proportional to the permeability of the segment.
5. Individual permeabilities variations do not change from input to producer.

If the permeability of the reservoir can be subdivided into various zones, the injected water will sweep the zones of higher permeability first, and it will be in these zones that water breakthrough will first occur.

This method is unique in its approach in its use of the permeability distribution. As a basis for the study of fluid flow in a bed of irregular permeability, the irregularities are represented by a

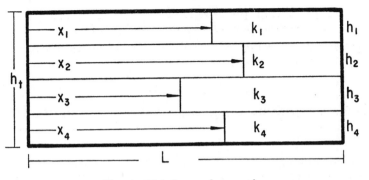

FIGURE 10-1. Layered reservoir

permeability distribution curve and a capacity distribution curve. In obtaining the curves, the permeability values regardless of their structural position in the formation, are arranged in order of decreasing permeability. If these permeability values so arranged are plotted versus the cumulative thickness, a permeability distribution curve is obtained. Rather than use actual permeability values in this curve, Stiles found it more convenient to state the permeabilities in terms of the ratio of the actual permeability values to the average permeability of the formation, or:

$$K' = \frac{k_1}{k_{avg}} \qquad (10\text{-}5)$$

This term is called *dimensionless permeability* and is used throughout the paper.

The capacity distribution curve, which is the first step in the method, is a plot of the cumulative capacity (starting with the highest permeabilities) versus the cumulative thickness. Mathematically, the capacity distribution is the integration of the permeability distribution curve. In practice it is convenient to first obtain the capacity distribution curve and derive from it a smoothed dimensionless permeability curve. To obtain the capacity distribution curve, divide the reservoir into unit thicknesses of permeability. A permeability profile should be plotted in order to obtain a more representative permeability distribution. The calculation of cumulative capacity from typical permeablity data is shown in Table 10-1. The basic permeability data were taken from the core analysis data shown in Figure 10-2.

The cumulative capacity C is next plotted against h, the cumulative thickness fraction, to obtain a curve as shown in Figure 10-3.

Table 10-1
Calculation of Capacity Distribution

(1)	(2)	(3)	(4)	(5)	(6)
Cum. Thickness Feet	h Fraction of Cum. Thickness $\Sigma_o{}^n$①$/\Sigma_o{}^t$①	k Perme- ability Mds.	kh Perme- ability Capacity	ΔC Increment of Total Capacity ④$/\Sigma_o{}^t$④	C Cumulative Capacity Fraction $\Sigma_o{}^n$⑤
1	0.03226	195	195	0.1489	0.1489
2	0.06452	120	120	0.0917	0.2406
3	0.09677	115	115	0.0878	0.3285
4	0.12903	80	80	0.0611	0.3896
5	0.16129	80	80	0.0611	0.4507
6	0.19355	62	62	0.0474	0.4981
7	0.22581	58	58	0.0443	0.5424
8	0.25807	54	54	0.0413	0.5837
9	0.29033	45	45	0.0344	0.6181
10	0.32259	44	44	0.0366	0.6517
11	0.35485	42	42	0.0321	0.6838
12	0.38711	30	30	0.0306	0.7144
13	0.41937	35	35	0.0267	0.7411
14	0.45163	32	32	0.0244	0.7655
15	0.48389	31	31	0.0237	0.7892
16	0.51615	30	30	0.0229	0.8121
17	0.54841	29	29	0.0222	0.8343
18	0.58067	25	25	0.0191	0.8534
19	0.61293	25	25	0.0191	0.8725
20	0.64519	21	21	0.0160	0.8885
21	0.67745	20	20	0.0153	0.9038
22	0.70971	17	17	0.0130	0.9168
23	0.74197	17	17	0.0130	0.9298
24	0.77423	15	15	0.0115	0.9413
25	0.80649	14	14	0.0107	0.9520
26	0.83875	14	14	0.0107	0.9627
27	0.87101	13	13	0.0099	0.9726
28	0.90327	12	12	0.0091	0.9817
29	0.93553	11	11	0.0084	0.9901
30	0.96779	8	8	0.0061	0.9962
31	1.00000	5	5	0.0038	1.0000

where:

$$C = \frac{\Sigma_o{}^n kh}{\Sigma_o{}^t kh} \qquad (10\text{-}6)$$

and:

n = any number of beds.

t = total number of beds.

It has already been established that:

$$k_{avg} = \frac{\Sigma_o{}^t kh}{\Sigma_o{}^t h} \qquad (10\text{-}7)$$

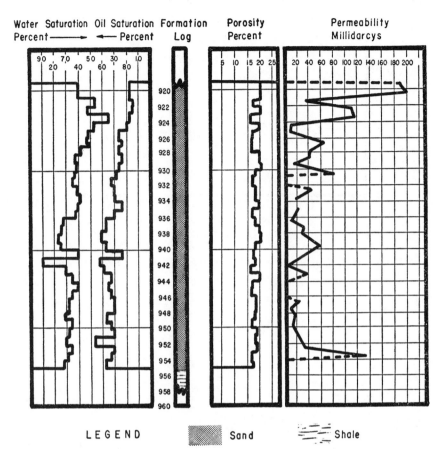

FIGURE 10-2. Analysis of Bartlesville sand core from Delaware Consolidated Oil Co., Delaware District unit well No. DW-61, Delaware-Childers field, Nowata County, Okla., Oct., 1954. *(After U.S. Bureau of Mines Report of Investigation No. 5134)*

also:

$$h = \frac{\Sigma_o^n h}{\Sigma_o^t h} \qquad (10\text{-}8)$$

$$slope = \frac{\Delta C}{\Delta h} \qquad (10\text{-}9)$$

$$\frac{\Delta C}{\Delta h} = \frac{C_1 - C_2}{h_1 - h_2} \qquad (10\text{-}10)$$

$$= \frac{\dfrac{\Sigma_o^{n_1} kh}{\Sigma_o^t kh} - \dfrac{\Sigma_o^{n_2} kh}{\Sigma_o^t kh}}{\dfrac{\Sigma_o^{n_1} h}{\Sigma_o^t h} - \dfrac{\Sigma_o^{n_2} h}{\Sigma_o^t h}} \qquad (10\text{-}11)$$

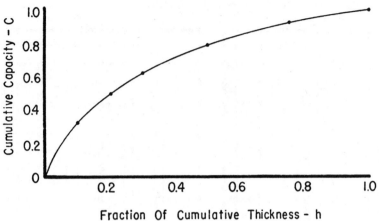

FIGURE 10-3. Cumulative capacity vs. fraction of cumulative thickness.

since:

$$k_{avg} = \frac{\Sigma_o{}^t\, kh}{\Sigma_o{}^t\, h} = \frac{\Sigma_o{}^t\, kh}{h_t}$$

or:

$$\Sigma_o{}^t\, kh = k_{avg}\, h_t$$

Equation (10-11) can be simplified as follows:

$$slope = \frac{\dfrac{\Sigma_o{}^{n_1}\, kh - \Sigma_o{}^{n_2}\, kh}{k_{avg}\, h_t}}{\dfrac{\Sigma_o{}^{n_1}\, h - \Sigma_o{}^{n_2}\, h}{h_t}}$$

$$= \frac{\Sigma_o{}^{n_1}\, kh - \Sigma_o{}^{n_2}\, kh}{k_{avg}\, (\Sigma_o{}^{n_1}\, h - \Sigma_o{}^{n_2}\, h)} \qquad (10\text{-}12)$$

however:

$$\Sigma_o{}^{n_1}\, kh - \Sigma_o{}^{n_2}\, kh = kh \qquad (10\text{-}13)$$

and:

$$\Sigma_o{}^{n_1}\, h - \Sigma_o{}^{n_2}\, h = h \qquad (10\text{-}14)$$

Therefore:

$$slope = \frac{kh}{k_{avg}\, h} = \frac{k}{k_{avg}} = K' \qquad (10\text{-}15)$$

Table 10-2
Calculation of Permeability Distribution

(1) Fraction of Cum. Thickness h	(2) Increment of Cum. Thickness Δh $(h_n - h_{n-1})$	(3) Cumulative Capacity, Fraction C (from Fig.10-3)	(4) Increment of Cum. Capacity ΔC $(C_n - C_{n-1})$	(5) Dimen-sionless Permeability K' ④ ÷ ②	(6) Average Cumulative Thickness, Fraction h' $[(h_n + h_{n-1}) \div 2]$
0.01	0.01	0.045	0.045	4.50	0.005
0.02	0.01	0.083	0.038	3.80	0.015
0.05	0.03	0.180	0.097	3.23	0.035
0.10	0.05	0.310	0.130	2.60	0.075
0.20	0.10	0.500	0.190	1.90	0.150
0.30	0.10	0.640	0.140	1.40	0.250
0.40	0.10	0.735	0.095	0.95	0.350
0.50	0.10	0.800	0.065	0.65	0.450
0.60	0.10	0.861	0.061	0.61	0.550
0.70	0.10	0.910	0.049	0.49	0.650
0.80	0.10	0.950	0.040	0.40	0.750
0.90	0.10	0.978	0.028	0.28	0.850
0.95	0.05	0.990	0.012	0.24	0.925
1.00	0.05	1.000	0.010	0.20	0.975

The differentiation of the capacity distribution curve to obtain the permeability distribution curve is shown in Table 10-2.

Due to the way K' was obtained, it is necessary to plot K' versus h', the average value, rather than h.

A plot of K' versus h' is then made. The area under the curve is equal to 1.0.

Proof that: $W + X + Y = 1$

$$W + X + Y = \Sigma K'h \qquad (10\text{-}16)$$

$$K' = \frac{k}{k_{avg}} \qquad (10\text{-}15)$$

$$h = \frac{h'}{\Sigma h'} \qquad (10\text{-}17)$$

$$k_{avg} = \frac{\Sigma k h'}{\Sigma h'} \qquad (10\text{-}18)$$

Combining Equations (10-15) and (10-18):

$$K' = \frac{k}{\frac{\Sigma k h'}{\Sigma h'}} = \frac{k \Sigma h'}{\Sigma k h'} \qquad (10\text{-}19)$$

Combining Equations (10-16), (10-17), and (10-19):

$$W + X + Y = \Sigma K'h = \Sigma \left[\frac{k\Sigma h'}{\Sigma kh'} \left(\frac{h'}{\Sigma h'} \right) \right] = \Sigma \frac{kh'}{kh'} = 1 \qquad (10\text{-}20)$$

Derivation of Water Cut and Recovery Equations

The derivations of the water cut and recovery equations are based on two principal assumptions:

1. Fluid flow is linear.

2. The distance of penetration of the flood front is proportional to permeability.

With these assumptions, the front of advancing water would have the same shape as the Permeability Distribution Curve. A water flood of a block of formation would then have a shape as shown in Figure 10-4. For clarity, assume that the line cd represents the producing well and the line ab represents the injection well. Rotation of Figure 10-4 clockwise 90° will also assist in visualizing the reservoir conditions. The position of the flood front after h_1 beds have been flooded out will be cfb. At any time t_1, when the fraction of the beds flooded would be h_1, the volume of the reservoir which has been flooded is obtainable directly from Figure 10-4. The oil recovery will be equivalent to $X + Y$. The total reservoir volume will be $X + Y + Z$. Therefore, the fraction of oil recovery will be:

$$\text{Recovery} = \frac{X + Y}{X + Y + Z} \qquad (10\text{-}21)$$

It is pertinent now to define the various parts of Figure 10-4 in more concrete terms:

    1. $W + X + Y = 1$

    2. $X + Y + Z = k'h$; as $h = 1.0$ then $X + Y + Z = K'$

    3. $W + X = \Sigma K'h = C$

    4. $X = K'h$

If: $W + X + Y = 1$

         $Y = 1 - (W + X) = 1 - C$

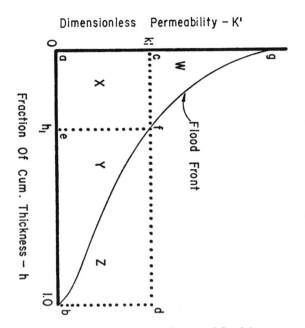

FIGURE 10-4. Theoretical advance of flood front.

The recovery equation then becomes:

$$\text{Recovery} = \frac{X + Y}{X + Y + Z} = \frac{K'h + (1 - C)}{K'} \qquad (10\text{-}22)$$

This yields an equation which can be solved from data available in the tables previously prepared. In the producing well it has been assumed that all premeabilities greater than K' are flowing only water. The capacity flowing water is therefore C. $(C = \Sigma\ K'h)$. The capacity flowing oil is $(1 - C)$.

The water and oil production rates can now be calculated using these capacities and by including relative permeability and viscosity data. Also, in the case of oil, the formation volume factor must be determined.

$$\text{Rate of water production} = C\left(\frac{k_{rw}}{\mu_w}\right) \qquad (10\text{-}23)$$

$$\text{Rate of oil production} = 1 - C\left(\frac{k_{ro}}{\mu_o}\right)\frac{1}{B_o} \qquad (10\text{-}24)$$

$$\text{Water cut or \% water} = \frac{C\left(\dfrac{k_{rw}}{\mu_w}\right)}{C\left(\dfrac{k_{rw}}{\mu_w}\right) + (1-C)\left(\dfrac{k_{ro}}{\mu_o}\right)\dfrac{1}{B_o}} \times 100$$

$$(10\text{-}25)$$

Dividing both numerator and denominator by $\left(\dfrac{k_{ro}}{\mu_o}\right)\left(\dfrac{1}{B_o}\right)$ yields:

$$\% \ H_2O = \frac{C\dfrac{k_{rw}}{k_{ro}}\dfrac{\mu_o}{\mu_w}B_o}{C\dfrac{k_{rw}}{k_{ro}}\dfrac{\mu_o}{\mu_w}B_o + (1-C)} \times 100 \qquad (10\text{-}26)$$

$$\text{let } A = \frac{k_{rw}}{k_{ro}}\frac{\mu_o}{\mu_w}B_o \qquad (10\text{-}27)$$

then:

$$\% \ \text{Water} = \frac{CA}{CA + (1-C)} \times 100 \qquad (10\text{-}28)$$

Example Problem 10-1

An example problem will be worked to illustrate the method. Permeability data for the problem were obtained from Figure 7, page 16 of the U. S. Bureau of Mines R. I. 5134, "Recent Developments in Water Flooding in Nowata County, Oklahoma, Oil Fields, 1954-55," by J. L. Eakin, published in May, 1955. This information is reproduced as Figure 10-2. Table 10-3 lists other pertinent data concerning the problem. Tables 10-4 through 10-6 and Figures 10-5 through 10-8 show a step-by-step solution of the problem.

Frontal Advance Technique for Predicting Results of Either Water or Gas Injection

The frontal advance method of calculating flood behavior, developed in Chapter 2, can be used for studying the results of either water floods or gas floods. The following data are required in order to predict performance by the frontal advance method:

1. Relative permeability data.

2. Reservoir fluid viscosity data.

3. Interstitial water saturation.

Table 10-3
Pertinent Data — Stiles's Problem

Porosity, $\phi = 0.181$
Gas saturation, $S_g = 0.10$
Interstitial water saturation, $S_{wi} = 0.25$
Oil saturation, $S_o = 0.65$
Oil formation volume factor, $B_o = 1.00$
Reservoir water viscosity, $\mu_w = 0.90$ cp.
Reservoir oil viscosity, $\mu_o = 10.0$ cp.
Relative permeability to water, $k_{rw} = 0.05$
Relative permeability to oil, $k_{ro} = 0.40$
Residual oil saturation, $S_{or} = 0.30$
Five-spot flooding pattern
Ten acres per five spot
Water injection rate $= 100$ Bbls/day
Areal sweep efficiency $= 100\%$

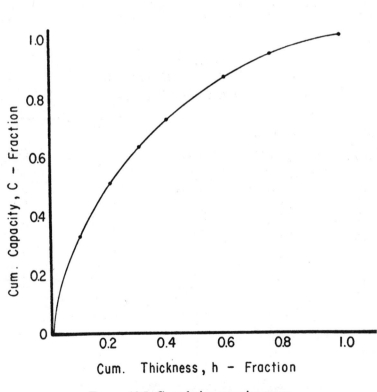

FIGURE 10-5. Cumulative capacity curve.

Table 10-4
Stiles's Problem — Example 10-1

(1) Fraction of Cum. Thickness h	(2) Dimen- sionless Permeability K'	(3) Cumulative Capacity, Fraction C	(4) K'h	(5) K'h + (1 — C)	(6) Recovery, Fraction of Total ⑤ ÷ ②
0.00	5.50	0.000	0.0000	1.000	0.1818
0.01	4.50	0.045	0.0450	1.000	0.2222
0.02	3.80	0.083	0.0760	0.993	0.2613
0.05	3.23	0.180	0.1615	0.982	0.3040
0.10	2.60	0.310	0.2600	0.950	0.3654
0.20	1.90	0.500	0.3800	0.880	0.4632
0.30	1.40	0.640	0.3750	0.735	0.5250
0.40	0.95	0.735	0.3800	0.645	0.6789
0.50	0.65	0.800	0.3250	0.525	0.8077
0.60	0.61	0.861	0.3660	0.505	0.8279
0.70	0.49	0.910	0.3430	0.433	0.8837
0.80	0.40	0.950	0.3200	0.370	0.9250
0.90	0.28	0.975	0.2520	0.277	0.9893
0.95	0.24	0.990	0.2280	0.238	0.9917
1.00	0.20	1.000	0.2000	0.200	1.0000

Table 10-5
Stiles's Problem — Example 10-1
Calculation of Water Cut

(1) Fraction of Cum. Thickness h	(2) Cumulative Capacity, Fraction C	(3) CA*	(4) CA + (1 — C)	(5) Water Cut, Fraction ③ ÷ ④
0.00	0.000	0.0000	1.0000	0.0000
0.01	0.045	0.0625	1.0175	0.0614
0.02	0.083	0.1153	1.0323	0.1117
0.05	0.180	0.2500	1.0700	0.2336
0.10	0.310	0.4306	1.1121	0.3843
0.20	0.500	0.6945	1.1945	0.5814
0.30	0.640	0.8889	1.2489	0.7118
0.40	0.735	1.0209	1.2859	0.7939
0.50	0.800	1.1112	1.3112	0.8475
0.60	0.861	1.1959	1.3349	0.8959
0.70	0.910	1.2640	1.3540	0.9335
0.80	0.950	1.3196	1.3696	0.9635
0.90	0.975	1.3543	1.3793	0.9819
0.95	0.990	1.3751	1.3851	0.9928
1.00	1.000	1.3890	1.3890	1.0000

$$*A = \frac{k_{rw}}{k_{ro}} \times \frac{\mu_o}{\mu_w} \times B_o = \frac{0.05}{0.40} \times \frac{10}{0.9} \times 1.0 = 1.389$$

Table 10-6
Calculations — Example 10-1

(1) Cum. Oil Recovery Fraction of Total	(2) Δ Oil Recovery, Bbls. $(①_n - ①_{n+1})^* \times 129,500^*$	(3) Cum. Oil Recovery, Bbls. $\Sigma②$	(4) Water Cut Fraction (Fig. 10-7)	(5) Average Water Cut Fraction $\frac{④_n + ④_{n-1}}{2}$	(6) Average Oil Prod. Rate B/D $100(1-⑤)$	(7) Time to Prod. Oil Recovery at Avg. Rate Days $②÷⑥$	(8) Cum. Time After Fillup Days $\Sigma⑦$	(9) Cum. Water Injected Bbls. $43530^{**} + 100⑧$	(10) Cum. Time Including Fillup Days $⑨÷100$	(11) Cum. Water Produced Bbls. $⑨ - (43530 + ③)$
0.0	0	0	0	0	100.00	0	0	43530	435.3	0
0.1818	23543	23543	0	0	100.00	235.4	235.4	67070	670.7	0
0.20	2357	25900	0.015	0.0075	99.25	23.8	259.2	69450	694.5	20
0.25	6475	32375	0.100	0.0575	94.25	68.7	327.9	76320	763.2	415
0.30	6475	38850	0.215	0.1575	84.25	76.9	404.8	84010	840.1	1630
0.35	6475	45325	0.330	0.2725	72.75	89.0	493.8	92910	929.1	4055
0.40	6475	51800	0.445	0.3875	61.25	105.7	599.5	103480	1034.8	8150
0.45	6475	58275	0.555	0.5000	50.00	129.5	729.0	116430	1164.3	14625
0.50	6475	64750	0.660	0.6075	39.25	165.0	894.0	132930	1329.3	24830
0.55	6475	71225	0.735	0.6975	30.25	214.0	1108.1	154340	1543.3	39585
0.60	6475	77700	0.795	0.7650	23.50	275.5	1383.6	181890	1818.8	60660
0.65	6475	84175	0.840	0.8175	18.25	354.8	1738.4	217370	2173.6	89665
0.70	6475	90650	0.875	0.8575	14.25	454.4	2192.8	262810	2628.0	128630
0.75	6475	97125	0.905	0.8900	11.00	588.6	2781.4	321670	3216.6	181015
0.80	6475	103600	0.930	0.9175	8.25	784.9	3566.3	400160	4001.5	253030
0.85	6475	110075	0.948	0.9390	6.10	1061.5	4627.8	506310	5063.0	352705
0.90	6475	116550	0.956	0.9520	4.80	1349.0	5976.8	641210	6412.0	481130
0.95	6475	123025	0.970	0.9630	3.70	1750.0	7726.8	816210	8162.0	649655
0.99	5180	128205	0.990	0.9800	2.00	2590.0	10316.8	1075210	10752.0	903475
1.00	1295	129500	1.000	0.9950	0.50	2590.0	12906.8	1334210	13342.0	1161180

* Total Recoverable Oil $= 7758 \, Ah\phi \left(\dfrac{S_o}{B_o} - \dfrac{S_{or}}{B_{or}}\right) = 7758 \times 10 \times 31 \times 0.181 \times \left(\dfrac{0.65}{1.00} - \dfrac{0.30}{1.00}\right) = 129,500$ bbls.

** Fillup Volume $= 7758 \, Ah\phi \cdot S_g = 7758 \times 10 \times 31 \times 0.181 \times 0.10 = 43,530$ bbls.

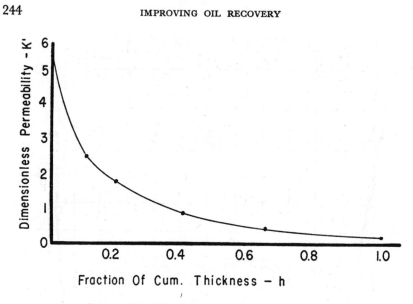

FIGURE 10-6. Dimensionless permeability curve.

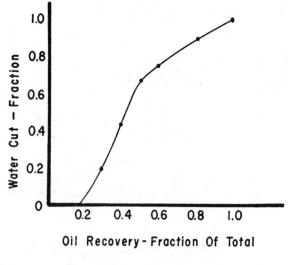

FIGURE 10-7. Water cut curve.

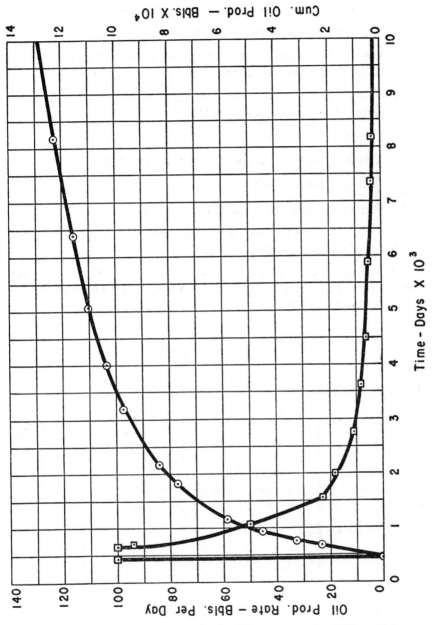

FIGURE 10-8. Predicted oil production history, example problem 10-1.

4. Oil saturation at the beginning of the flood.

5. Gas saturation at the beginning of the flood.

6. Water saturation at the beginning of the flood.
(if different from the interstitial water saturation.)

7. Size of the reservoir, and in particular, the cross-sectional area across which flow occurs.

8. Porosity of the reservoir.

9. Distance between input and producing wells.

10. Rate of fluid injection.

11. Degree of inclination of the reservoir.

A step-wise procedure for predicting behavior of a water flood or a gas flood is as follows:

1. Calculate F_D, the fraction of displacing fluid flowing, by using Equation (10-29) for a horizontal reservoir and Equation (10-30) for an inclined reservoir.

$$F_D = \frac{1}{1 + \dfrac{k_o}{k_D} \dfrac{\mu_D}{\mu_o}} \qquad (10\text{-}29)$$

or

$$F_D = \frac{1 - \dfrac{0.044\, k_o\, A\, \Delta\rho\, \text{Sin}\, \alpha}{q_t} \dfrac{\mu_o}{\mu_D}}{1 + \dfrac{k_o}{k_D} \dfrac{\mu_D}{\mu_o}} \qquad (10\text{-}30)$$

A complete range of displacing phase saturations are assumed, and an F_D value is calculated for each assumed saturation.

2. Plot F_D vs. S_D.

3. From the plot of F_D vs. S_D, obtain the slope $\left(\dfrac{d\,F_D}{d\,S_D}\right)$ at various S_D's.

4. Plot $\dfrac{d\,F_D}{d\,S_D}$ vs. S_D

5. For a given volume of fluid injected, Q_t, select a complete range of S_D's and calculate the distance of flood front travel, Δx, using the continuity equation:

$$\Delta x = \frac{Q_t}{\phi A} \left(\frac{d F_D}{d S_D} \right) \qquad (10\text{-}31)$$

6. Prepare a plot of S_D vs. Δx. The area under this curve is equal to $(S_D) (\Delta x)$.

$$\phi A \Delta x S_D \qquad (10\text{-}32)$$

Equation (10-32) is the familiar volumetric equation and is equal to the volume of water injected, or:

$$Q_t = \phi A \Delta x S_D \qquad (10\text{-}33)$$

Equation (10-33) can be rearranged to solve for a term which is needed for the final solution of Δx.

Equation (10-33) is rearranged to solve for $S_D \Delta x$:

$$\text{Area Under Curve} = S_D \Delta x = \frac{Q_t}{\phi A} \qquad (10\text{-}34)$$

Since the volume of fluid injected, Q_t, is known, the area under the S_D vs. Δx curve can be calculated from Equation (10-34). The position of the cut-off line, Δx, can be determined by a trial-and-error procedure of measuring the area under the curve for various values of Δx, and when a value of Δx is found which yields an area under the curve which is equal to that calculated from Equation (10-34), then the proper Δx has been found. This procedure was developed by Hocott,[12] and represents a simplification of the procedure originally developed by Buckley and Leverett.

When the flood front reaches the producing well, then breakthrough occurs. The time required for breakthrough of the displacing phase can be determined using the procedure previously described for calculating the position of the flood front, except that the position of the flood front is now known, and the only unknown is Q_t, the volume of input fluid required. Since the injection rate is known, the time required for the injection of Q_t volumes of fluid is:

$$\Delta t = \frac{Q_t}{q_t} \qquad (10\text{-}35)$$

where:

Δt = cumulative time, days
Q_t = cumulative fluid injected, bbls. (or SCF)
q_t = fluid injection rate, bbls/day (or SCF/day)

---

[12] Hocott, C. R., "Mechanics of Fluid Injection Water," *Producers Monthly,* Vol. 21, No. 1, September 1957.

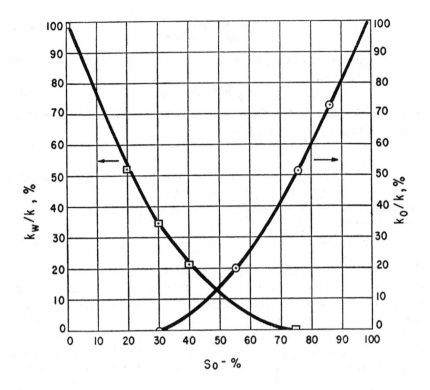

FIGURE 10-9. Relative permeability data, example problem 10-2.

7. To calculate recovery after breakthrough, the same procedure described in Steps 1 through 6 is used, except that the cut off line is now the distance between input and producing wells. The area under the S_D vs. Δx curve is still equal to the cumulative oil produced.

The rate of oil recovery after breakthrough is sharply reduced, and the rate of production of the displacing fluid is sharply increased. The ratio of displacing fluid injected to oil produced (injected water-oil ratio or injected gas-oil ratio) can be easily determined from the preceding calculations, since oil recovery is equal to the area under the S_D vs. Δx curve. The area between two of the curves is equal to the oil recovery for the period of time which has elapsed between the two times.

An example problem using the frontal advance method for predicting performance of a water-flood will be shown, using the same data as used in the Stiles method, also worked in this chapter. Pre-

Table 10-7
Determining $\dfrac{dF_w}{dS_w}$ — Example 10-2

(1) S_o a	(2) K_o/K a	(3) K_w/K a	(4) K_o/K_w ② ÷ ③	(5) F_w b	(6) dF_w/dS_w c
0.75	0.495	0	—	—	—
0.65	0.327	0.015	21.80	0.338	6.50
0.60	0.260	0.030	8.67	0.562	4.00
0.55	0.200	0.068	2.94	0.790	2.33
0.50	0.148	0.110	1.35	0.892	1.43
0.45	0.102	0.149	0.68	0.942	0.75
0.40	0.064	0.213	0.31	0.973	0.33
0.35	0.032	0.277	0.12	0.998	0.11
0.30	0	0.350	0	1.000	0

a. data from Figure 10-9.

b. $F_w = \dfrac{1}{1 + \dfrac{K_o}{K_w}\dfrac{\mu_w}{\mu_o}}$

c. data from slope of Figure 10-10.

dicting reservoir performance by these two different techniques also allows a comparison of the advantages of the two techniques.

Example Problem 10-2

An example problem using the frontal advance method will be worked with the same data used for Example 10-1 (Stiles's method). Figure 10-9 shows the relative permeability data used to work the problem. Tables 10-7 through 10-10 and Figures 10-10 through 10-13 show the step-by-step procedure and the results.

Table 10-8
Calculating Δx — Example 10-2

S_w	dF_w/dS_w	100 Days Δx	500 Days Δx	1037 Days Δx	2000 Days Δx	5000 Days Δx	10,000 Days Δx
0.35	6.50	69.6	348	722	1392	3480	6960
0.40	4.00	43.0	215	446	860	2150	4300
0.45	2.33	26.0	130	270	520	1300	2600
0.50	1.43	15.4	77	160	308	770	1540
0.55	0.75	8.0	40	83	160	400	800
0.60	0.33	3.6	18	37	72	180	360
0.65	0.11	1.0	5	10	20	50	100
0.70	0	0	0	0	0	0	0

Example Calculation for Table 10-8

$\theta = 100$ days; $S_w = 0.25$.

$Q_t = 100$ days $\times$ 100 bbls/day $\times$ 5.62 ft^3/bbl = 56,200 ft.^{3}

Vol. of 10 acre 5-spot = $43,560 \times 10 \times 31 = 13,504,000$ ft.^{3}

$$A = \frac{V}{X} = \frac{13,504,000}{467} = 28,934 \text{ ft.}^2$$

where:

V = Vol. of 10-acre 5-spot.
X = distance between producing and injection wells.
A = average cross-sectional area across which the front moves.

$$\Delta x = \frac{Q_t}{\phi A}\left(\frac{dF_w}{dS_w}\right) = \frac{56,200}{0.181 \times 28,934} \ (6.50) = 69.6$$

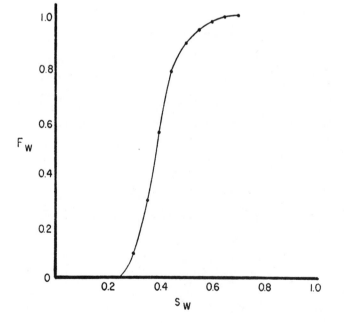

FIGURE 10-10. f_w vs. S_w, example problem 10-2.

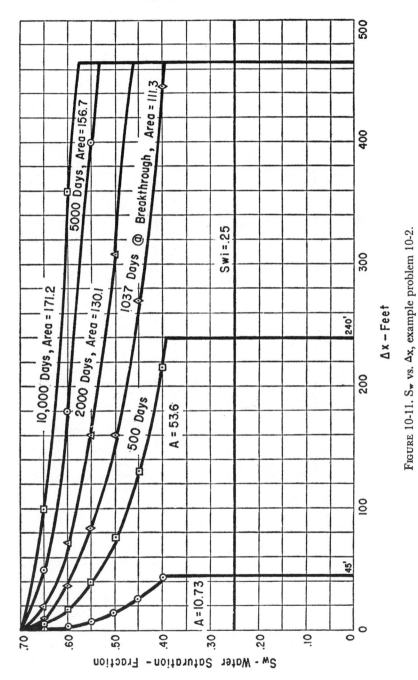

FIGURE 10-11. S_w vs. Δx, example problem 10-2.

Table 10-9

Cumulative Production — Oil and Water

Example 10-2

Time Days	Area Under Curve (Fig. 10-11)	Reservoir Vol. Displaced ft.³	Cum. Oil Prod. S.T. Bbls.	Cum. Water Inj. Bbls.	Cum. Water Prod. Bbls.
100	10.7	56193	10000	10000	0
500	53.6	280703	50000	50000	0
1037	111.3	582880	103700	103700	0
2000	130.1	681133	121300	200000	78700
5000	156.7	820638	146150	500000	353850
10000	171.2	896574	159670	1000000	840330

Table 10-10

Oil and Water Producing Rates — Example 10-2

(1) Cum. Time Days	(2) Time During Interval Days $(①_n - ①_{n-1})$	(3) Cum. Oil Prod. S.T. Bbls. (Table 10-9)	(4) Oil Prod. During Period S.T. Bbls. $(③_n - ③_{n-1})$	(5) Avg. Oil Prod. Rate Bbls./Day $(④ \div ②)$	(6) Cum. Water Prod. Bbls. (Table 10-9)	(7) Water Prod. During Period Bbls. $(⑥_n - ⑥_{n-1})$	(8) Avg. Water Prod. Rate Bbls./Day $(⑦ \div ②)$	(9) Avg. Water Cut Fraction $[⑧ \div (⑤ + ⑧)]$
100	100	10000	10000	100.0	0	0	0	0
500	400	50000	40000	100.0	0	0	0	0
1037	537	103700	53700	100.0	0	0	0	0
2000	963	121300	17600	18.3	78700	78700	81.7	0.82
5000	3000	146150	24850	8.3	353850	275150	91.7	0.92
10000	5000	159670	13520	2.7	840330	486480	97.3	0.97

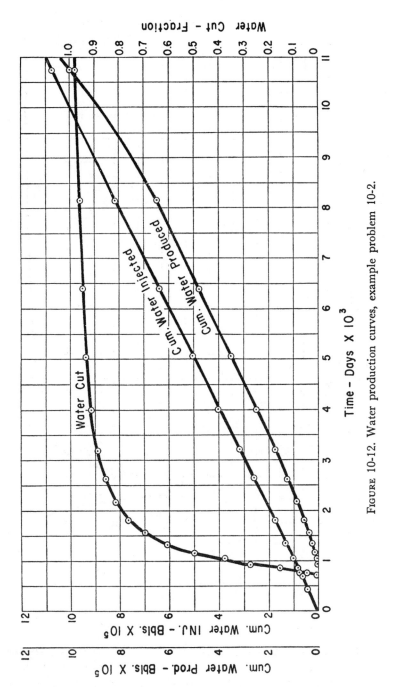

FIGURE 10-12. Water production curves, example problem 10-2.

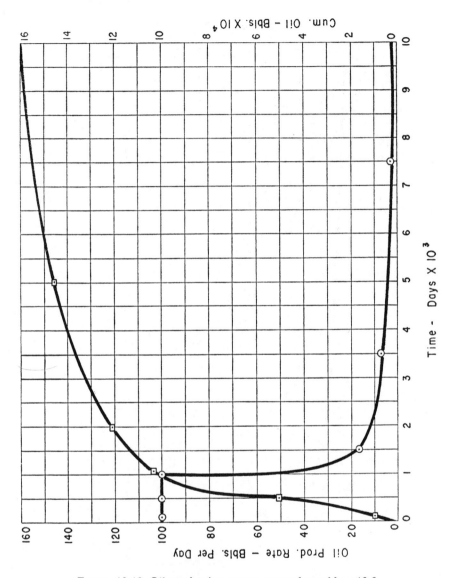

FIGURE 10-13. Oil production curves, example problem 10-2.

Well Arrangements

In fluid injection operations some of the wells in the reservoir must be used for injection of the displacing fluid. In some cases producing wells can be converted to injection wells while in

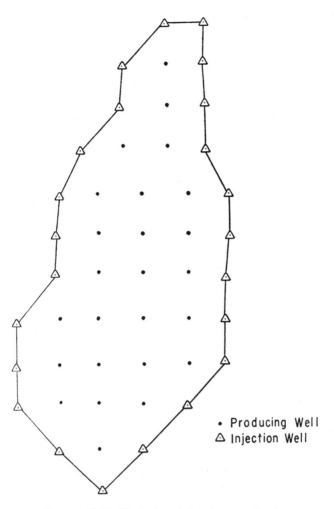

Figure 10-14. Typical peripheral water flood.

other cases it may be necessary or desirable to drill new injection wells.

One of the basic objectives in a fluid injection project is to contact as much of the reservoir as possible with the displacing phase. In order to achieve this objective various patterns or well arrangements have been devised. Four basic types of well arrangements are used in fluid injection projects: (1) crestal injection, (2) basal injection, (3) peripheral injection, and (4) pattern injection.

In crestal injection, as the name implies, the injection is through wells located at the top of the structure. Gas injection programs typically use crestal gas injection patterns.

In basal injection, the fluid is injected at the bottom of the structure. Many water injection projects use basal injection systems. In water injection, additional benefits from gravity segregation of the fluids are obtained when a basal injection pattern is used.

In peripheral flooding, the injection wells are located at the external boundary of the reservoir and the oil is displaced toward the interior of the reservoir. Figure 10-14 shows a typical peripheral-type well arrangement.

Conventional patterns which have been used are the 4-spot, 5-spot, 7-spot, 9-spot, direct line drive, and staggered line drive.

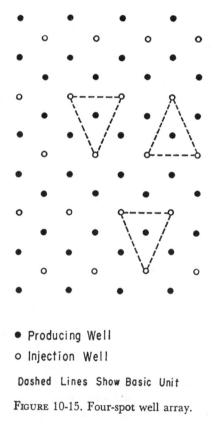

● Producing Well

o Injection Well

Dashed Lines Show Basic Unit

FIGURE 10-15. Four-spot well array.

These patterns are shown in Figures 10-15 through 10-19. The 4-spot and 7-spot patterns are identical except that the producing and injection wells are reversed. These various flooding patterns are characterized by slightly different *sweep efficiencies*. Sweep efficiency is defined as that fraction of the total area, of a two-dimensional reservoir model, contacted by the displacing phase at the time of displacing phase breakthrough. Figure 10-20 shows calculated sweep efficiencies for staggered line drive and direct line drive networks. The five-spot pattern is merely a special arrangement of a staggered line drive pattern. The calculated sweep efficiency at breakthrough for a five-spot is 0.715, for unity mobility ratio.

Where actual reservoirs are being studied not only the two dimensions, width and length, must be considered, but consideration

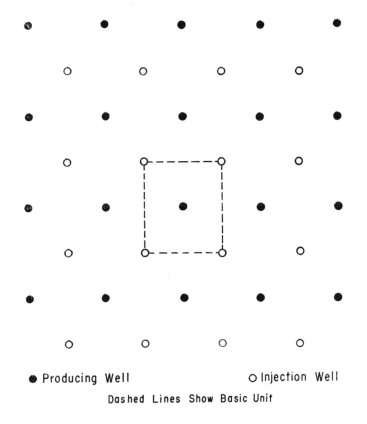

● Producing Well   ○ Injection Well

Dashed Lines Show Basic Unit

FIGURE 10-16. Five-spot well array.

must also be given to the third dimension, the reservoir thickness. Thus three distinct sweep efficiency terms have evolved. These are:

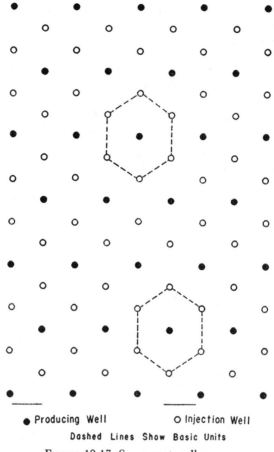

● Producing Well   O Injection Well
Dashed Lines Show Basic Units
FIGURE 10-17. Seven-spot well array.

(1) horizontal, or areal, sweep efficiency, (2) vertical sweep efficiency, and (3) volumetric sweep efficiency. The areal, or horizontal
sweep efficiency is the two-dimensional sweep efficiency term previously described. Vertical sweep efficiency is that fraction, or percentage of a two-dimensional model of the reservoir (considering
only thickness and length) contacted at displacing phase breakthrough. Permeability variations in the reservoir are largely responsible for variations in vertical sweep efficiency. Volumetric
sweep efficiency is a three-dimensional term and is defined as the
product of areal and vertical sweep efficiency. This latter sweep
efficiency factor is of considerable interest to those concerned with
the prediction of water flood behavior. It is not uncommon for
actual water floods to have volumetric sweep efficiencies of 5% or

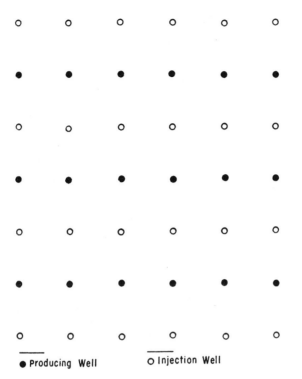

● Producing Well   ○ Injection Well

FIGURE 10-18. Direct-line drive well array.

less at initial water breakthrough. This is caused by thin, high permeability zones within the reservoir. Injected water moves rapidly through these high-permeability zones and water breaks through to the producing well quite early. Where such conditions are present it should be realized that the flood is not behaving abnormally, but is reacting as the permeability capacity (kh) profile of the reservoir dictates. If methods cannot be devised to reduce either injection into or production from these high-permeability zones, then provisions will have to be made for handling larger volumes of water throughout the life of the flood in order to deplete the reservoir.

Sweep efficiency continues to improve after water breakthrough and if enough pore volumes of water can be passed through the reservoir, the sweep efficiency would eventually approach 100 percent. Dyes, Caudle and Erickson[13] have shown the effect of mobility ratio on oil production after breakthrough. Figure 10-21 is repro-

---

[13] Dyes, A. B., Caudle, B. H., and Erickson, R. A., "Oil Production after Breakthrough—as Influenced by Mobility Ratio," *Trans.* AIME, Vol. 201, 1954, p. 81.

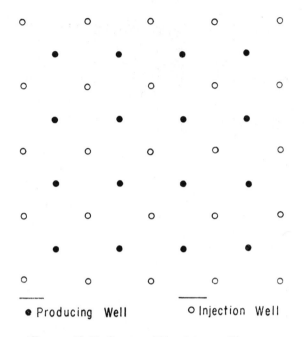

● Producing Well   ○ Injection Well

FIGURE 10-19. Staggered-line-drive well array.

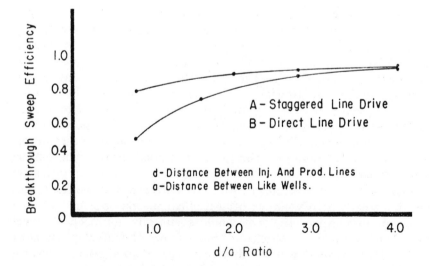

FIGURE 10-20. Variation of sweep efficiency at breakthrough. *(After Muskat and Wyckoff, Trans. AIME, Vol. 107, 1934.)*

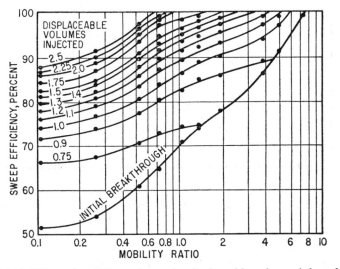

FIGURE 10-21. Effect of mobility ratio on the displaceable volumes injected for the five-spot pattern.

duced from their paper. These data show that areal sweep efficiency at breakthrough is dependent to a large extent on mobility ratio. Mobility ratio is defined by Dyes, et al. as the mobility of the fluids ahead of the front divided by the mobility of the fluids behind the front, or:

$$M = \frac{\left[\left(\dfrac{k}{\mu}\right)_1 + \left(\dfrac{k}{\mu}\right)_2\right] \text{ahead of front}}{\left[\left(\dfrac{k}{\mu}\right)_1 + \left(\dfrac{k}{\mu}\right)_2\right] \text{behind front}} \qquad (10\text{-}37)$$

where:

M = mobility ratio

subscripts 1 and 2 refer to different fluids flowing in the reservoir.

It can be seen from **Figure 10-21** that for the five spot pattern studied, a mobility ratio of 0.5 will yield an areal sweep efficiency at breakthrough of approximately 70%, while at a mobility ratio of 7.5, areal sweep efficiency approaches 100%.

Areal sweep efficiency continues to improve as more pore volumes of water are injected into the reservoir. For example, according to Dyes, et al., for a mobility ratio of 0.5, areal sweep efficiency is approximately 96 percent after injecting 2.0 displaceable volumes of water. Displaceable volume is defined as the product of the pore

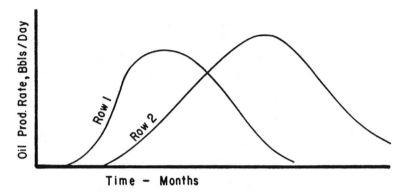

FIGURE 10-22. Typical oil producing history, peripheral water flood.

volume of the unit pattern and the displacement efficiency (the change in oil saturation which occurs in the swept region).

Peripheral Water Flooding

Predicting behavior of peripheral type water floods involves several problems not encountered in pattern water floods, such as the conventional five-spot well arrangement. The principal difference is that in a peripheral water flood, "fill-up" is never achieved until very late in the producing life of the flood. Referring to Figure 10-14, which shows the injection and producing well arrangement for a typical peripheral water flood, it can be seen that where a more or less uniform gas saturation is present at the initiation of the flood, the first row of producing wells will respond prior to response in the second row of producing wells. Fill-up of the gas space in the first row will also take place prior to fill-up of the gas space in the second row.

The producing characteristics of each row of wells in a peripheral flood will be similar to the overall behavior of a pattern flood. Figure 10-22 shows the oil production histories of the first two rows of a peripheral flood. There is a time lag of several months between the response of the first-row producers and the second-row producers. However, once the first row producers have responded to water injection, the total production from the unit may remain relatively constant for a long period of time, for as the first row production begins to decline, the second row has started to respond, maintaining the overall producing rate.

The oil producing rate in a fluid injection project is a direct function of the amount of fluid being injected into the reservoir.

Thus in a peripheral flood, where there are usually fewer injection wells than in a pattern flood, the peak producing rate will be lower. This lower peak producing rate is offset by the smaller number of injection wells, with consequent reduced investment in injection facilities.

One of the principal operating problems which arises in a peripheral water flood is deciding when to shut in producing wells which have been passed by the flood front. It becomes immediately apparent that if all wells are continued on production, then after the flood front has moved past several rows so much of the injected water will have been withdrawn from these wells behind the flood front that the net advance of the flood front will have been reduced to zero. In other words, as much water is removed from producing wells behind the flood front as is being injected into the reservoir through the injection wells. However, due to reservoir inhomogeneities and to sweep efficiencies peculiar to the particular well layout, all of the oil recoverable from the first row of producing wells may not be recovered if these first row wells are shut in and the oil is displaced to succeeding rows. For each reservoir there is some optimum water cut for shutting in producing wells behind the flood front. This optimum water cut is that water cut where the additional oil recovered by continued production of wells behind the flood front is exactly balanced by the additional expenses incurred by this continued production. The additional expenses are comprised not only of the cost of lifting and handling the produced water from behind the flood front, but also the cost of prolonging the overall flood life by removing part of the injected water from the wells behind the front. These factors must be evaluated for each flood, and then a program can be formulated for shutting in the wells behind the flood front when they reach the optimum water cut.

Predicting Behavior of Peripheral Water Floods

Since peripheral water floods never actually reach the fill-up stage until late in the life of the flood, the conventional Stiles and frontal advance techniques cannot be used with any accuracy for predicting flood behavior. Prediction methods which can take into consideration the delayed fill-up times of the various rows must be used. The method developed by Suder and Calhoun[14] offers a reasonable method of predicting peripheral water flood behavior. In

---

[14] Suder, F. E., and Calhoun, J. C., Jr., "Water Flood Calculations," API *Drilling and Production Practice, 1949* p. 260.

this technique the time required for fill-up is included as an integral part of the method, and the reservoir can be divided into any number of "layers" to simulate the actual permeability distribution of the reservoir.

Mathematical models have considerable utility in predicting performance of peripheral injection projects. Front tracking models are particularly useful in this regard.[15]

Special Considerations Involved in Water Flooding

Water flooding presents some unique problems, which although not within the scope of this manual, require brief mention. Probably the most important single problem associated with water flooding is the handling and treatment of the injection water. Physical plugging of the injection sand face is an ever-present problem when the injection water contains insoluble compounds, as all waters do in some quantities. In addition to this physical plugging which can occur from scale, dirt particles, and chemical precipitates, most producing formations contain varying amounts of clay, which may hydrate, or swell, when it comes into contact with certain waters which are not in ionic balance with the reservoir clays.

Thorough planning and engineering are required to properly design a water injection system for a water flood. Basically, there are three different types of water systems for water flooding, (1) open systems, (2) closed systems, and (3) semi-closed systems. In the open system the water is thoroughly aerated in an attempt to attain all oxidation reactions on the surface. After aeration and chemical treatment the water is passed through settling basins where the precipitates are allowed to settle.

In the closed system, every effort is made to exclude oxygen from the system. Subsurface source waters must be used in the closed system, the basic precept of the closed system being that since the injection water in its original state was stable, if oxygen and other contaminants can be excluded the water will remain stable as it is returned to the formation. At the present time, most systems which use water from a subsurface source are of the closed type, since less chemical treatment is usually required. The principal problem in closed water systems is that it is very difficult to completely exclude oxygen from the system. Semi-closed systems are used where it is impractical to completely eliminate oxygen from the system, but where a completely open system is undersirable because of the additional chemical treatment required.

---

[15] Cole, Frank W., "Front Tracking Mathematical Models," Private Report, 1965.

The following report[16] illustrates the design and installation of a typical water injection system.

Water Flood Case History

Most full-scale water floods are preceded by a pilot operation, which is a water flood on a small portion of the reservoir. Normally, the most favorable part of the reservoir is selected for the pilot operation and when the pilot flood has progressed to the point where conclusions can be drawn regarding the flood operations, the flood is then either discontinued or expanded to other portions of the reservoir, depending upon the result of the pilot operation. A pilot water flood is usually desirable regardless of the amount of reservoir data available, because in addition to uncertainties in at least some of the reservoir data, the pilot operation is also an ideal time to determine the most desirable method of treating and handling the injection water. As in the analysis of reservoir data, regardless of the amount of laboratory testing which is done prior to actual water injection operations, there are some parts of the water injection operations which cannot be duplicated in the laboratory. For example, the amount of iron which will be picked up by the water as it passes through the equipment and lines can only be estimated, and this estimate is subject to considerable error.

The water flood operation which will be discussed is an excellent example of a case where the operator has taken maximum advantage of a pilot water flood operation to determine not only the feasibility of a full-scale water flood but at the same time to determine the most economical method of handling and treating the water for a full-scale water flood program.

This pilot water flood, located in the Mid-Continent area, utilized four different types of injection-water systems during the 18-month period of pilot operations. The operator, who will have a very large flood if the pilot flood is expanded to cover the entire reservoir, has taken advantage of this small-scale operation to determine the most economical method of handling the injection water. Since very large volumes of water, compared to most other water floods, will be required, a small unit savings in water treating and handling costs will result in substantial savings. Complete records were maintained during this period in order that a proper evaluation of the various types of water-treating systems could be made.

Water for the operation was to be obtained from two separate sources: (1) produced water from another oil-producing horizon in

[16] Cole, Frank W., "Water Flood Case History," Proceedings of Water Quality Control for Subsurface Injection, University of Oklahoma, Dec. 10-11, 1957, p. 79.

the field, and (2) water from a water-bearing formation which, although oil-productive in the same general area, was not oil-productive in this field. Chemical analyses of the two sources of water are shown in Table 10-11. As shown by the chemical analyses, the two

Table 10-11
Supply Water Chemical Analysis

Test	Water Supply A	Water Supply B
Specific Gravity	1.120	1.117
pH	6.2	6.6
Total Alkalinity (as CA CO_2), ppm..............	180.	107.
Calcium, ppm	10,600.	9,700.
Magnesium, ppm	2,400.	2,300.
Sodium, ppm	49,000.	49,000.
Barium, ppm	0	0
Sulfate, ppm	515.	475.
Chloride, ppm	100,000.	100,000.
Silica, ppm	10.	15.
Total Iron, ppm	1.3	2.0
Aluminum, ppm	—	0.1
Turbidity (as SiO_2), ppm.....................	oily	6.
Total Dissolved Solids, ppm....................	163,000.	162,000.
CO_2, ppm	250.	105.
H_2S, ppm	150.	4.6
Dissolved Oxygen, ppm	0	0

waters are similar in nature except that Water Supply A contains much more dissolved H_2S and more dissolved CO_2 than Water Supply B. The high NaCl, H_2S, and CO_2 content of the supply waters indicated that, at least potentially, the corrosion rate could be severe.

The two sources of supply water were compatible, as evidenced by their similarity in chemical composition and also a simple mixing test which showed that no precipitates were formed when the two waters were combined. Although H_2S was present, as there was apparently no dissolved oxygen in the water the operator felt that if he could preclude oxygen from the system the relatively high H_2S content could be tolerated.

The principal objective in a water flood operation is to recover a maximum amount of oil at a minimum cost. As the water flood operation involves the injection of large volumes of water, compared to the oil recovered, the cost of injection water is always a major consideration in the overall economics. The most desirable objective would be to pump the injection water directly from the source of supply to the injection well without performing any intermediate operations on the water. The operator did essentially this on the first system he tried. This system was a semi-closed system wherein the two sources of water were collected in a raw water tank on which a crude oil seal was maintained. From the raw water tank the water was delivered by a gravity system to the injection pumps, where the water was then pumped to the injection wells.

Table 10-12
Injection Water Chemical Analysis (From Injection Well)

Test	Semi-Closed	Type Water System Mod. Open	Full Open	Closed
Specific Gravity	1.119	1.126	1.119	1.118
pH	6.5	7.6	7.6	6.9
Total Alkalinity (as CA CO_3), ppm..	130.	134.	76.	140.
Calcium, ppm	10,300.	10,600.	10,200.	10,505.
Magnesium, ppm	2,200.	2,400.	2,400.	2,300.
Sodium, ppm	51,000.	50,000.	49,000.	51,400.
Barium, ppm	0	0	0	0
Sulfate, ppm	550.	600.	610.	530.
Chloride, ppm	103,000.	103,000.	100,000.	104,000.
Silica, ppm	15.	7.	7.	8.5
Total Iron, ppm	5.9	0.3	2.2	2.1
Aluminum, ppm	0.1	0.1	0.1	0.2
Turbidity (as SiO_2), ppm......	>50.	3.6	5.8	3.2—4.2
Total Diss. Solids, ppm	167,000.	167,000.	162,000.	169,000.
CO_2, ppm	140.	0	10.	106.
H_2S, ppm	93.	0.2	0.7	88.
Dissolved Oxygen, ppm	0	0.2	0	0

No chemical treatment or filters of any kind were used. This of course, is an ideal system, and if it had been successful, would have resulted in substantial savings. Unfortunately, it was not successful. Injection rates soon began to decrease, obviously indicating that plugging was occurring at the injection sand face. The second column in Table 10-12 shows the chemical analysis of a typical sample of injection water taken at the injection well during this period. The H_2S was apparently reacting with the iron to form iron sulfide. There was also some carry-over of oil with the injection water as evidenced by the unusually high turbidity. The iron sulfide, which is oil wet, will readily adsorb these small droplets of oil, and this mucky material will plug the injection face of the well. It became obvious that this particular semi-closed system, although desirable, would not be satisfactory.

After less than four months of operation the wells were acidized, and a new water treating system was initiated. Believing that the hydrogen sulfide was the principal cause of the trouble, and again with the desire to retain the simplest possible treating system, a modified-open type of water system was tried. The water passed through blower-type aerating towers and then went directly to filters. Settling ponds were not used with the hope of reducing chemical treatment and maintaining a low oxygen content by incomplete aeration. Due to the constantly changing quantities of the two different supply waters, the H₂S and oxygen content were constantly changing. Filters plugged very frequently, and the water injection rates began to decrease. This was not altogether unexpected, and in order to allow some of the insoluble compounds such as iron sulfide and ferric hydroxide to settle out of the water, a settling pond, complete with baffles was installed in the system. After completion of the retention pond the injection wells were again acidized, which restored them to full injection capacity.

Laboratory tests were run on the aerated water to determine the optimum retention period. Figure 10-23 is a graph showing Residual Hydrogen Sulfide content versus Retention Time. Using the laboratory data as a guide a retention time of two days was selected in designing the retention pond.

The modified open system was in operation less than three months, including the time required to install the retention pond.

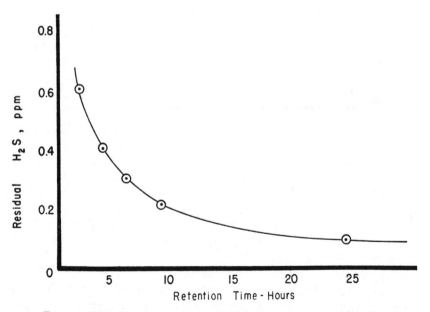

FIGURE 10-23. Residual hydrogen sulfide content vs. retention time.

Even in this open system, chemical treatment was not used, except for very short test periods, as the end objective of minimum water treating costs was still paramount. In this completely open system the aeration was still limited in order to keep the dissolved oxygen to a minimum. The operator believed that if the amount of oxygen admitted to the system was controlled such that the oxidation processes would react with all of the oxygen present, then the additional oxygen picked up by the water in the retention pond would be small, thus minimizing the additional oxidization processes which could take place on the downstream side of the retention pond.

Injection rates began to decrease almost immediately, even with the use of the full open system. In addition to the sand face plugging, the corrosion rate was excessive and it became obvious that some system of corrosion mitigation would have to be installed. Corrosion test coupons and test nipples had been in use since the inception of the pilot program. The test coupons and nipples were removed periodically and visually inspected to determine the degree of corrosion. Typical hydrogen sulfide corrosion was evidenced in the form of deep isolated pits, rather than general corrosion over the entire test sections.

Due to the frequent plugging of filters and serious reduction of injection rates, it was obvious that chemical treatment would have to be initiated or else some other water system would have to be used.

At this time a decision was made to try a fully closed system, still without chemical treatment of any kind. While the closed system was being installed, the surface lines were cement coated to reduce corrosion and the tubing was plastic coated on the surface, with a pliable section of plastic inserted in the collars of the tubing joints as joints were made up before running in the hole. This plastic insert provided, at least theoretically, a leak-proof seal between adjacent plastic-coated joints of tubing.

A diagram of the fully closed system is shown in Figure 10-24. The supply water is collected in the raw water tank, on which a diesel oil seal of approximately 18 inches is maintained. The water from the raw water tank is then picked up by a centrifugal pump in order to keep the entire system under pressure from this point forward, thus decreasing the possibility of getting air into the system. The water then passes through filters to the clear water tank where a diesel oil seal is again maintained. A float valve on the clear water tank is used to retain a minimum head of water in the tank.

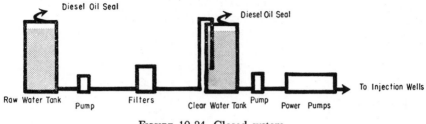

FIGURE 10-24. Closed system.

A centrifugal pump delivers the water from the clear water tank to the injection pumps, where the water is then delivered through headers to the injection wells.

The supply water is apparently reasonably stable, even though it has been brought from reservoir conditions to atmospheric conditions, as evidenced by the longer operating periods before filter backwashing becomes necessary.

When the closed system was inaugurated the injection wells were again acidized to restore original injection rates. The fully closed system has been in operation approximately seven months and injection rates are still satisfactory. Although some fall-off in injection rate is occurring, most of the decrease is believed due to the gradual fillup of the reservoir, rather than to injection sand face plugging.

The corrosion rate has been reduced, as evidenced by both visual examination of test pieces and coupon weighing.

Figure 10-25 depicts the changes in turbidity throughout the totally closed system. It is noted that the filters reduce the turbidity to a minimum, but that by the time the water has reached the injection well it has increased a small amount, possibly due to some hydrogen sulfide reactions.

Table 10-13 presents some interesting comparisons between certain important chemical analyses for the various treating systems. These data are all from samples taken at an injection well. For example, in the semi-closed and closed systems, the hydrogen sulfide and carbon dioxide content are high, essentially equal to their magnitudes in the original supply water. In both the modified open

FIGURE 10-25. Changes in turbidity closed system.

Table 10-13
Effect of Type System on Important Chemical Analyses

Type System	Turbidity, ppm, SiO_2	CO_2 ppm	H_2S ppm	Total Iron, ppm
Semi-Closed	50	140	93	5.9
Modified Open	3.6	0	0.2	0.3
Full Open	5.8	10	0.7	2.2
Closed	3.5	106	88	2.1

and open systems they have been reduced to low values, evidencing the results of aeration. Turbidity is high in the semi-closed system, as there was no filter. In the other three systems, the turbidity was markedly reduced due principally to the filters which were in use in these systems. The total iron content was high in the semi-closed system but lower in the other three systems. This is due to the oxidation of iron in the modified open and open systems, and due to the filters in the closed system.

In summary, in a period of less than 18 months a satisfactory water treating system was found which required no chemical treatment. This was accomplished during the period of pilot water flooding operations without seriously retarding the progress of the flood. Although close supervision and control of the program was required during this period, including frequent water analyses, this program will reap substantial dividends in the future, as the anticipated size of the flood is quite large and the cost of any water treatment would be large when considered for the entire flooding operation. The actual cost of trying the various systems was not large as the most simple system was attempted first.

This is a case where full advantage was taken of the pilot flood to determine, not only whether the formation could be successfully flooded, but also the most economic method of handling the supply water. It has paid off in the form of large dollar savings to the operator.

Predicting the Results of Water Flooding

In addition to the conventional Stiles, Frontal Advance, and Suder-Calhoun methods of predicting water-flood recovery, core analysis and statistical methods can also be used to advantage as an aid in determining the reasonableness of the predictions. Also, statistical data on similar reservoirs are invaluable when sufficient data on the reservoir under study are unavailable.

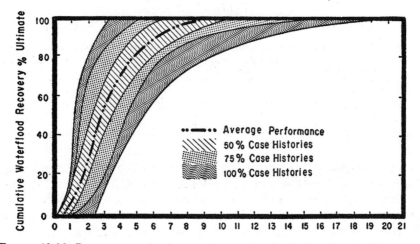

FIGURE 10-26. Percent waterflood recovery vs. time in shallow Bartlesville sandstone fields. (*After Smith and Worrell, Ref. 17.*)

Laboratory flooding tests provide useful information concerning both the floodability of a reservoir and the oil recovery to be expected. Since laboratory tests are run on a small, relatively homogeneous core sample, the oil recovery is usually greater than that actually achieved in the reservoir because the sweep efficiency in a reservoir is always less than 100%.

Smith and Worrall[17] have presented statistical data on 21 depleted Bartlesville sandstone water floods. Their analysis of these floods resulted in some very useful correlations. Figure 10-26 shows graphically the results of their study. It is interesting to note that more than 50% of the reservoirs studied showed very little variation in recovery. Tables 10-14 and 10-15 also show some of the statistical data developed by Smith and Worrall.

---

[17] Smith, O. L. and Worrall, K. E., "Prediction from Performance of Depleted Shallow Water Floods," Petroleum Conference on Production and Reservoir Engineering, Tulsa, Oklahoma, March 20-21, 1958, AIME Paper No. 1050-G.

Table 10-14

Completed Waterflood Data—Bartlesville Sandstone

Curve No.	Acres Flooded	Thickness Feet	Bbl. Oil Recovered by Waterflood			Water Injected Bbl	Wtr. Inj. Cumulative Oil Prod.	Flood Life Months
			Total	Per Acre	Per Ac-Ft			
1	97	30	207,536	2,140	71.3	6,623,000	32	139
2	37	30	80,975	2,189	73.0	907,360	11	119
3	60	18	125,109	2,085	116.0	2,681,325	21	100
4	202	20	628,576	3,112	156.0	12,258,184	20	140
5	130	25	233,780	1,798	71.9	8,777,812	38	100
6	60	26	73,593	1,227	47.2	1,759,013	24	40
7	135	15	302,549	2,241	150.0	2,759,063	9	99
8	186	25	303,393	1,631	65.2	9,260,979	31	86
9	157	40	1,100,000	7,000	175.3	Unknown	—	195
10	135	30	333,706	2,472	82.4	5,080,554	15	80
11	1,010	30	3,830,000	3,790	126.3	Unknown	—	224
12	168	30	565,934	3,369	112.0	10,356,037	18	90
13	180	40	462,500	2,560	64.2	Unknown	—	216
14	44	25	62,389	1,418	56.6	733,691	12	82
15	128	30	246,021	1,922	65.0	2,026,126	8	66
16	130	30	482,000	3,588	123.6	11,102,847	23	135
17	208	22	392,213	1,886	86.0	4,127,646	11	106
18	40	25	185,497	4,637	185.5	2,427,132	13	118
19	100	12	116,208	1,162	96.9	1,324,400	10	93
20	34	28	150,877	4,438	158.3	6,038,414	40	103
21	220	40	1,125,608	5,110	121.8	19,600,000	17	249
Total and Averages	3,465	27.2	11,008,464	2,846	105.0	107,843,583	19.6	123

(After Smith and Worrel, Ref. 17)

Table 10-15
Flood Life vs. Ultimate Waterflood Recovery
(Months vs. Per cent)

Curve No.	First Response	10%	20%	30%	40%	50%	60%	70%	80%	90%	100%
1	4	23.0	35.0	48.0	58.4	65.6	72.0	75.6	87.0	100.5	139.0
2	8	20.0	27.5	34.0	40.1	47.3	55.2	65.5	79.9	98.0	119.0
3	3	8.3	13.3	18.4	23.3	28.4	33.5	40.1	47.4	63.0	100.0
4	6	12.5	18.9	25.0	31.6	38.6	46.2	55.0	65.9	83.0	140.0
5	4	15.3	20.8	23.9	27.2	32.0	28.2	45.8	54.2	68.4	100.0
6	4	8.2	10.8	13.3	15.7	18.3	21.0	24.8	28.5	32.0	40.0
7	3	10.6	15.0	19.5	23.8	28.2	32.5	38.7	45.6	58.6	99.0
8	7	11.2	16.8	22.0	27.1	33.3	40.9	47.5	53.8	64.2	86.0
9	6	7.6	9.2	10.8	12.3	14.0	16.6	21.7	26.8	49.5	195.0
10	11	11.0	13.3	15.9	18.3	20.8	24.8	28.9	33.0	44.0	80.0
11	6	13.4	20.4	25.8	31.1	37.0	43.1	52.7	64.8	95.2	224.0
12	6	8.8	11.3	13.9	16.8	19.9	23.0	26.0	37.4	54.9	90.0
13	4	16.3	23.0	29.0	35.0	42.1	50.2	62.3	82.9	121.5	216.0
14	31	33.0	37.4	42.0	46.4	50.5	54.6	59.3	65.3	72.3	82.0
15	8	11.2	15.0	20.1	25.3	30.0	35.0	40.0	45.0	51.3	66.0
16	5	12.7	17.7	21.5	25.2	30.2	35.7	43.0	54.0	81.2	135.0
17	7	19.3	25.1	30.7	35.2	39.9	45.6	52.4	60.8	72.8	106.0
18	2	11.7	17.0	22.9	27.0	38.0	52.5	62.2	71.4	88.5	118.0
19	2	15.4	23.1	29.5	33.9	38.4	44.5	52.0	62.5	75.4	93.0
20	6	10.5	15.2	19.9	24.0	28.4	33.5	41.0	51.1	67.5	103.0
21	2	31.8	40.6	47.8	55.2	64.0	75.3	89.6	111.9	169.0	249.0
Avg., Mos.	6.4	14.85	20.30	25.42	30.14	35.47	41.61	48.29	58.53	76.70	122.86
Avg., Yrs.	0.53	1.24	1.69	2.12	2.51	2.96	3.47	4.02	4.88	6.39	10.2

(After Smith and Worrel, Ref. 17)

Chapter 11

GAS RESERVOIRS

Non-associated gas reservoirs are those which do not change state in the reservoir during depletion. A typical multi-component pressure-temperature phase diagram is shown in Figure 11-1. Point C_1 is the *cricondentherm*, the maximum temperature at which two phases can exist in equilibrium, and any reservoir whose initial conditions of temperature and pressure lie to the right of line AC_1B will be referred to as a non-associated gas reservoir, or, as they will be henceforth designated, a gas reservoir.

Production from the reservoir occurs by a reduction in pressure, with the reservoir temperature changing little, if any. Therefore, the gas is removed from the reservoir isothermally. However, once the gas has entered the well bore and flows to the surface, the temperature, as well as the pressure, is reduced. Thus, in order to define the surface recovery, the surface temperature and pressure must also be plotted on the phase diagram of Figure 11-1. If the surface temperature and pressure are those shown as P_2T_2 in Figure 11-1, then the recovery at the surface will also be 100% vapor. However, if surface temperature and pressure are equivalent to that shown at P_3T_3, then the recovery at the surface will be 80% vapor (dry gas) and 20% liquid. It is emphasized that this liquid cannot begin forming until the temperature has been lowered, and as has been mentioned, the temperature is not lowered until the gas is in the well bore and on the way to the surface. Hence, liquid is never formed in the reservoir.

Hydrocarbons in the liquid state are normally more valuable than those in the gaseous state, and Figure 11-1 indicates possibilities for obtaining liquid recovery from this "dry gas reservoir." If the temperature can be lowered to some point such as T_3, then liquid can be recovered. The low-temperature separation plants, which are so prevalent in many areas, are designed to take advantage of the phenomenon shown in Figure 11-1. Since the molecular composition of no two gas reservoirs will be alike, when studying the economics of low-temperature separation, a pilot test and/or K valve calculations, should be made to determine the actual liquid recovery to be expected.

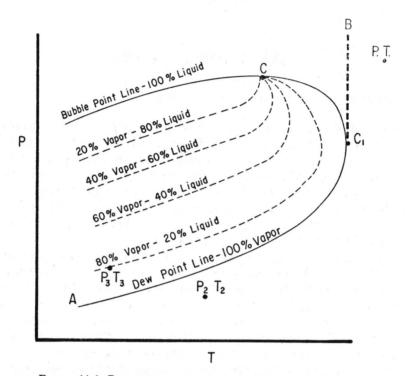

FIGURE 11-1. Pressure-temperature phase diagram, gas reservoir.

Gas Reservoir Material Balance

A material balance on a gas reservoir, although not commonly used, has several very useful purposes. It can be used for estimating the size of the gas reservoir, the ultimate recovery to be expected, the rate of gas production, and the effects of water encroachment in the reservoir.

A material balance on a closed gas reservoir, i.e. no water influx, can be developed as follows:

SCF gas originally = SCF gas produced + SCF gas remaining

$$\frac{G}{B_{gi}} = V_g + \frac{G}{B_g} \tag{11-1}$$

where:

SCF = Standard cubic feet

G = Reservoir gas space, barrels

B_{gi} = Gas conversion factor, bbls/SCF at original reservoir temperature and pressure.

B_g = Gas conversion factor, bbls/SCF at any later pressure and temperature.

V_g = Cumulative gas produced, SCF.

Equation (11-1) can be rearranged to solve for G, the amount of the original gas in place in barrels, as follows:

$$G \left(\frac{1}{B_{gi}} - \frac{1}{B_g} \right) = V_g \qquad (11\text{-}2)$$

$$G \left(\frac{1}{B_g} \right) \left(\frac{B_g}{B_{gi}} - 1 \right) = V_g \qquad (11\text{-}3)$$

$$G = \frac{V_g \, B_g}{\left(\dfrac{B_g}{B_{gi}} - 1 \right)} \qquad (11\text{-}4)$$

The gas conversion factor, B_g is identical to the gas conversion factor used in the oil reservoir material balance calculations, and is derived as follows: From the perfect gas laws,

$$\frac{P_1 V_1}{Z_1 T_1} = \frac{P_s V_s}{Z_s T_s} \qquad (11\text{-}5)$$

where the subscript 1 refers to conditions at a specific time, and the subscript s, refers to standard conditions. By definition, B_g is equal to the volume in barrels, at reservoir temperature and pressure, occupied by one standard cubic foot of gas. Therefore, if V_s is equal to one, then the V_1 shown in Equation (11-5) is equal to B_g, after conversion to barrel units. The calculation of B_g is accomplished by use of the following equation:

$$B_g = \frac{P_s V_s Z_1 T_1}{P_1 Z_s T_s \times 5.62} \qquad (11\text{-}6)$$

As the quantities at standard conditions are known, Equation (11-6) can be simplified as follows:

$$B_g = \frac{14.7 \times 1.0 \times Z_1 \times T_1}{P_1 \times 1.0 \times 520 \times 5.62} \qquad (11\text{-}7)$$

$$= 0.00504 \, \frac{Z_1 T_1}{P_1} \qquad (11\text{-}8)$$

The size of a gas reservoir can be calculated directly from Equation (11-4). However, as in all material balance calculations the accuracy of this method is directly dependent upon the data used in the equation, and in general, the accuracy of the method increases as cumulative gas production increases.

The amount of gas in place originally, in Standard Cubic Feet, can be determined by the following equation:

$$\text{Gas in place, SCF} = G(1/B_{gi}) \qquad (11\text{-}9)$$

Gas reservoirs may be subjected to a water drive in the same manner as oil reservoirs. A material balance can also be developed to consider water influx into the reservoir. The basis for development of the equation will be the same as that used in development of the material balance with no water influx:

$$\text{SCF gas originally} = \text{SCF gas produced} + \text{SCF gas remaining} \qquad (11\text{-}10)$$

However,

SCF gas remaining =

$$\frac{\text{Original Reservoir Volume} - \text{Remaining Liquid Volume}}{B_g} \qquad (11\text{-}11)$$

Combining Equations (11-10) and (11-11), and using the proper symbols yields:

$$V_g = \frac{G}{B_{gi}} - \left[\frac{G - (W_e - W_p B_w)}{B_g}\right] \qquad (11\text{-}12)$$

where:

W_e = Gross water influx into reservoir, reservoir barrels.
W_p = Water production, stock tank barrels.

Equation (11-12) contains two unknowns, G, and W_e. Therefore where a gas reservoir has a water drive, the material balance equation cannot be used alone to calculate gas in place. When good geologic data are available the magnitude of water influx can be calculated from Equation (11-12) by rearranging the equation to solve for W_e:

$$\frac{W_e - W_p B_w}{B_g} = -\frac{G}{B_{gi}} + \frac{G}{B_g} + V_g \qquad (11\text{-}13)$$

$$W_e - W_p B_w = -G\left(\frac{B_g}{B_{gi}} - 1\right) + V_g B_g \qquad (11\text{-}14)$$

$$W_e = -G\left(\frac{B_g}{B_{gi}} - 1\right) + V_g B_g + W_p B_w \qquad (11\text{-}15)$$

Equation (11-15) can be very useful in determining the recovery to be obtained as a result of water drive, and also to determine the rate of change of the gas-water contact for planning completion and recompletion practices, water disposal practices, and for solving other operating problems.

The material balance equation can be used to advantage to determine (1) amount of gas originally in place, (2) the pressure-production history of the reservoir, (3) the recoverable gas, (4) and the size of the reservoir.

The determination of (1) above has already been presented. However, the amount of gas originally in place can also be calculated by using the well-known gas laws:

$$\frac{P_i V_i}{Z_i T_i} = \frac{P_s V_s}{Z_s T_s} \qquad (11\text{-}16)$$

$$V_s = \frac{P_i V_i Z_s T_s}{P_s Z_i T_i} \qquad (11\text{-}17)$$

where the subscripts i and s refer to original conditions and standard conditions respectively.

The pressure production history of a gas reservoir can be predicted by using the material balance equation shown in Equation (11-1):

$$\frac{G}{B_{gi}} = V_g + \frac{G}{B_g} \qquad (11\text{-}1)$$

rearranging:

$$V_g = \frac{G}{B_{gi}} - \frac{G}{B_g} \qquad (11\text{-}18)$$

combining Equations (11-8) and (11-18) yields:

$$V_g = \frac{G}{0.00504\dfrac{Z_i T_i}{P_i}} - \frac{G}{0.00504\dfrac{ZT}{P}} \qquad (11\text{-}19)$$

$$= \frac{G\left(\dfrac{P_i}{Z_i}\right)}{0.00504\,T_i} - \frac{G\left(\dfrac{P}{Z}\right)}{0.00504\,T} \qquad (11\text{-}20)$$

multiplying both sides of Equation (11-20) by 0.00504 T_i yields:

$$V_g(0.00504\,T_i) = G\left(\frac{P_i}{Z_i}\right) - G\left(\frac{P}{Z}\right)\frac{T_i}{T} \qquad (11\text{-}21)$$

however, reservoir temperature does not change, therefore $T_i = T$. Solving Equation (11-21) for $\dfrac{P}{Z}$:

$$\frac{P}{Z} = \frac{P_i}{Z_i} - V_g\left(\frac{0.00504\ T_i}{G}\right) \tag{11-22}$$

Equation (11-22) is of the form $y = mx + b$, which plots as a straight line on coordinate graph paper. Thus a plot of $\dfrac{P}{Z}$ vs V_g should yield a straight line.

Equation (11-22) is very useful for graphically determining the amount of gas to be produced at any pressure. The utility of the equation can be illustrated by an example problem:

Example Problem 11-1

The following information on a closed gas reservoir is available:

Reservoir temperature, $T_i = 175°$ F.
$$= 175° + 460° = 635°\ \text{Absolute}$$
Original Reservoir Pressure, $P_i = 3,000$ psia
Specific gravity of gas $= 0.60$

After producing 400,000,000 SCF, the reservoir pressure is 2,000 psia.

Determine: (1) Amount of gas originally in place.
(2) Amount of gas which will have been produced after reservoir pressure has been reduced to 1,000 psia.
(3) Cumulative gas recovery, if abandonment pressure is 300 psia.
(4) Recovery efficiency.

(1) $G = \dfrac{V_g B_g}{\left(\dfrac{B_g}{B_{gi}} - 1\right)}$ \hfill (11-4)

$$B_{gi} = 0.00504\ \frac{Z_i T_i}{P_i} = \frac{0.00504 \times 0.88 \times 635}{3000} = 0.000940$$

$$B_{g\,2000} = 0.00504\ \frac{ZT}{P} = \frac{0.00504 \times 0.89 \times 635}{2000} = 0.001425$$

$$G = \frac{400 \times 10^6 \times 0.001425}{\left(\dfrac{0.001425}{0.000940} - 1\right)} = 1.10 \times 10^6\ \text{Bbls. of reservoir space}$$

$$\text{Gas in place, SCF} = \frac{G}{B_{gi}} = \frac{1.10 \times 10^6}{0.000940} = 1.17 \times 10^9 \text{ SCF}$$

(2) $B_{g\,1000} = 0.00504\dfrac{ZT}{P} = \dfrac{0.00504 \times 0.92 \times 635}{1000} = 0.00295$

$$V_g = \frac{G}{B_g}\left(\frac{B_g}{B_{gi}} - 1\right) = \frac{1.10 \times 10^6 \left(\dfrac{0.00295}{0.00094} - 1\right)}{0.00295}$$

$= 798 \times 10^6$ SCF, cum. production when reservoir pressure is 1000 psia.

(3) $B_{g\,300} = 0.00504\dfrac{ZT}{P} = \dfrac{0.00504 \times 0.97 \times 635}{300} = 0.01034$

$$V_g = \frac{1.10 \times 10^6 \left(\dfrac{0.01034}{0.00094} - 1\right)}{0.01034} = 1.063 \times 10^9 \text{ SCF},$$

cum. production to abandonment pressure.

(4) Recovery Efficiency $= \dfrac{\text{Cum. Prod. to Abandonment}}{\text{Original Gas in Place}} \times 100$

$$= \frac{1.063 \times 10^9}{1.170 \times 10^9} \times 100 = 90.8\%.$$

A plot of $\dfrac{P}{Z}$ vs V_g is shown in Figure 11-2. As previously discussed, this plot is a straight line on coordinate graph paper, and after a reasonable amount of gas has been produced (at least 20% of the reserve), this straight-line plot will provide a satisfactory procedure for estimating recoverable gas. The calculated points from Parts (2) and (3) of Example 11-1 are shown on the graph.

Size of a Gas Reservoir

The material balance equation can be used in conjunction with the volumetric equation to determine the approximate number of acres occupied by the reservoir. This technique is particularly advantageous when a well has been drilled into a new gas reservoir and it is desired to know the size of the reservoir in order to determine whether additional wells can, or should, be drilled. This technique has the same limitation as any other application of the material balance, i.e., the accuracy increases as more production

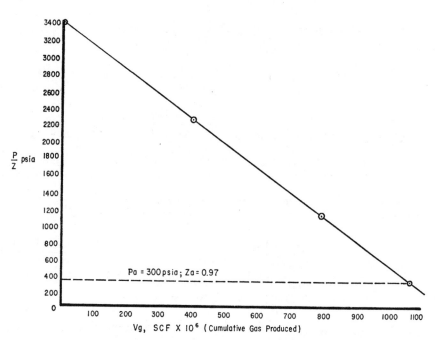

$\frac{P}{Z}$ psia

Pa = 300 psia ; Za = 0.97

Vg, SCF X 10⁶ (Cumulative Gas Produced)

FIGURE 11-2. Pressure-production graph, gas reservoir.

data become available. The equations used to determine the size of the reservoir are:

$$G = \frac{V_g B_g}{\left(\dfrac{B_g}{B_{gi}} - 1\right)} \tag{11-4}$$

and

$$G = 7758 \, Ah\phi \, (1 - S_{wi}) \tag{11-23}$$

where:

A = Areal extent of reservoir, acres.
h = Thickness of reservoir, feet.
ϕ = Porosity of reservoir, fraction.
S_{wi} = Connate water saturation, fraction.
7758 = Conversion factor, barrels per acre-foot.

After one well has been drilled, the assumption must be made that reasonable values of porosity, connate water saturation, and reservoir thickness are available. Equations (11-4) and (11-23) can be combined to solve for A:

$$7758 \, Ah\phi \, (1 - S_{wi}) = \frac{V_g B_g}{\left(\dfrac{B_g}{B_{gi}} - 1\right)} \qquad (11\text{-}24)$$

$$A = \frac{V_g B_g}{7758 \, h\phi \, (1 - S_{wi})\left(\dfrac{B_g}{B_{gi}} - 1\right)} \qquad (11\text{-}25)$$

The only unknown in Equation (11-25) is A, the areal extent of the reservoir. Equation (11-25) must be used only with a full realization of its weaknesses.

Example Problem 11-2

Determine the areal extent of the reservoir described in Example 11-1. One well has been drilled, and from this one well the following data were determined:

$$h = 10 \text{ feet}$$
$$\phi = 0.10$$
$$S_{wi} = 0.35$$

At the time the calculation is made, reservoir pressure has declined to 2,000 psia and 400,000,000 SCF of gas has been produced.

Equation 11-25) is used to determine the answer:

$$A = \frac{V_g B_g}{7758 \, h\phi \, (1 - S_{wi})\left(\dfrac{B_g}{B_{gi}} - 1\right)} \qquad (11\text{-}25)$$

$$= \frac{400 \times 10^6 \times 0.001425}{7758 \times 10 \times 0.10 \times (1 - 0.35)\left(\dfrac{0.001425}{0.00094} - 1\right)}$$

$$= 219 \text{ acres.}$$

Therefore, in all probability, another well would not be justified.

The principal utility of an equation such as this would be in its application soon after a new gas reservoir was discovered, to determine whether additional wells should be drilled. Where only one well has been drilled, good values for average reservoir thickness, porosity, and connate water saturation may not be available because of the limited amount of data. However, probably more important are the limitations imposed by the material balance equation. The factor $\left(\dfrac{B_g}{B_{gi}} - 1\right)$ is a very small number early in the life of the reservoir, and small errors in the numbers which make up this factor can lead to large errors in the final answer. For example, consider the reservoir used in Example 11-2. The pressure-production history of this reservoir is shown in Figure 11-2. In Example 11-2 a substantial amount of gas had been produced before the method was used to determine the size of the reservoir. Another calculation will now be made using data from early in the life of the reservoir to illustrate the magnitude of the error which may be involved.

Example Problem 11-3

When reservoir pressure has declined to 2,800 psia, the applicable Z factor will be 0.87; and $\frac{p}{Z} = 2,800/0.87 = 3,220$. From Figure 11.2, when $p/Z = 3,220$, $V_g = 60,000,000$ SCF. The areal extent of the reservoir, calculated by Equation (11-25) is:

$$B_{g\,2800} = \frac{0.00504 \times 0.87 \times 635}{2800} = 0.000993$$

$$A = \frac{60 \times 10^6 \times 0.000993}{7758 \times 10 \times 0.10 \times (1 - 0.35)\left(\dfrac{0.000993}{0.000940} - 1\right)}$$

$$= 219 \text{ acres}$$

which is the same answer obtained by the calculation in Example 11-2. Next, assume that an error in the pressure measurement was made, and that when 60,000,000 SCF of gas had been produced, the observed reservoir pressure was 2,900 psia, rather than 2,800 psia. The apparent areal extent of the reservoir will now be calculated, using this erroneous pressure data:

$$B_{g\,2900} = \frac{0.00504 \times 0.87 \times 635}{2900} = 0.000960$$

$$A = \frac{60 \times 10^6 \times 0.000960}{7758 \times 10 \times 0.10 \times (1 - 0.35)\left(\dfrac{0.000960}{0.000940} - 1\right)}$$

$$= 543 \text{ acres.}$$

Thus, an error of 3.5% in the measurement of reservoir pressure has caused an error of 248% in the calculated areal extent of the reservoir.

Calculations for Water Drive Gas Reservoirs

Most of the calculations presented have assumed that no water influx was occurring. It is well known that active water drives exist for gas reservoirs as well as for oil reservoirs; in fact, there are reservoirs along the Texas Gulf Coast where gas reserves become depleted without any appreciable drop in reservoir pressure due to the existence of a very active water drive.

Several methods are available for estimating the rate of water influx into a reservoir. The most common of these are:
1. Determining the gas-water contact in wells drilled after substantial quantities of gas have been produced. The gas-water contact may be determined by logs, drill-stem tests, or by temporary completions.
2. Using the material balance equation at several different times.
3. Using individual well production data.

The material balance equation can be used in some cases with a reasonable degree of accuracy to determine water influx. A similar technique has been proposed for use with the oil reservoir material balance equation. Referring again to Equation (11-4):

$$G = \frac{V_g B_g}{\left(\dfrac{B_g}{B_{gi}} - 1\right)} \qquad (11\text{-}4)$$

it is obvious that G, the amount of gas originally in place expressed must be a constant, and, regardless of the amount of gas, V_g, which has been produced, the value of G, calculated from Equation (11-4) will always be the same if the correct data have been used. Therefore, a plot of G vs. V_g must be a horizontal line, as shown in Figure 11-3. However, if Equation (11-4) is used to calculate G in a reservoir where there is water influx, the calculated value of G will continue to increase as V_g increases. This is because an incorrect material balance equation is being used and instead of calculating G, the amount of gas originally in place, the actual calculation is $G + f(W)$, where $f(W)$ is some function of water influx. This can be illustrated by using the material balance for a gas reservoir with water influx:

$$W_e = -G\left(\frac{B_g}{B_{gi}} - 1\right) + V_g B_g + W_p B_w \qquad (11\text{-}15)$$

rearranging, and solving for G:

$$G = \frac{V_g B_g - (W_e - W_p B_w)}{\left(\dfrac{B_g}{B_{gi}} - 1\right)} \qquad (11\text{-}26)$$

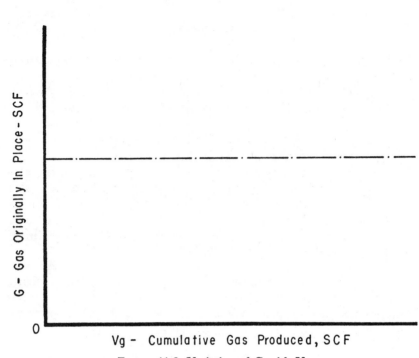

FIGURE 11-3. Variation of G with V_g.

If there actually is some water influx into the reservoir, instead of plotting G on the ordinate, the plot should properly be $G + \dfrac{W_e - W_p B_w}{\left(\dfrac{B_g}{B_{gi}} - 1\right)}$ as shown by rearranging Equation (11-26):

$$G + \frac{W_e - W_p B_w}{\left(\dfrac{B_g}{B_{gi}} - 1\right)} = \frac{V_g B_g}{\left(\dfrac{B_g}{B_{gi}} - 1\right)} \qquad (11\text{-}27)$$

$$G + C = \frac{V_g B_g}{\left(\dfrac{B_g}{B_{gi}} - 1\right)} \qquad (11\text{-}28)$$

where:

$$C = \frac{W_e - W_p B_w}{\left(\dfrac{B_g}{B_{gi}} - 1\right)} \qquad (11\text{-}29)$$

A plot of $G + C$ vs. V_g is shown in Figure 11-4. The ordinate will continue to increase because W_e, in the term C will continue to increase with time. However, at the time when the cumulative

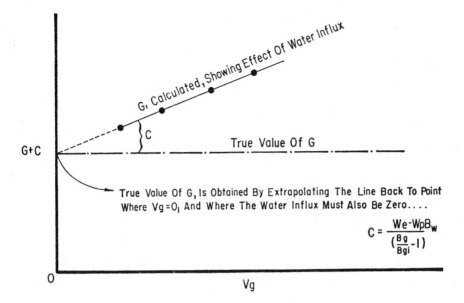

FIGURE 11-4. Calculations showing effect of water influx into a gas reservoir.

gas production is zero, there will be no water influx and the term C will also be zero. If several points of the plot $G + C$ vs. V_g can be extrapolated back to the point where V_g equals zero, a true value of G can be determined. This technique can often be reliably used in water drive reservoirs. However, this technique uses the material balance equation and is therefore subject to the limitations of the material balance equation. In particular, it is not unusual for data points calculated early in the producing life of the reservoir to be erratic, and greater weight should be placed on the reliability of the later data points.

This method is not only useful for determining the amount of gas originally in place, but it can be used to predict the magnitude of future water encroachment into the reservoir. Very often a plot such as that shown in Figure 11-4 using past production data will reveal a more or less constant water influx per unit of gas production. This constant water influx can then be used in further reservoir calculations involving future production. The value of C can be determined at any time by subtracting the true value of G (the horizontal line in Figure 11-4) from the value of $G + C$. Once C is known, W_e can also be determined by rearranging Equation (11-29):

$$W_e = C\left(\frac{B_g}{B_{gi}} - 1\right) \tag{11-30}$$

Water influx can also be estimated from individual well production data, as outlined in Chapter 6, *Water Drive Reservoirs*. The reliability of this method is increased as the number of structurally low wells increases. Therefore, it usually has more application in oil reservoirs, where the well spacing is more dense, than in gas reservoirs. However, if the basic data are available, the method should prove useful in gas reservoirs also.

Effect of Producing Rate on Ultimate Recovery

Closed gas reservoirs, having no water drive, are depleted by expansion. Therefore ultimate recovery is independent of producing rate.

It should be noted that gas is actually sold in terms of weight. Since gas is measured and sold in standard cubic feet, or standard cubic meters, the specification of standard pressure and temperature results in an actual weight of gas. In a closed gas reservoir the initial gas saturation is never reduced, only the number of pounds of gas occupying the pore spaces is reduced. Therefore, it is important to reduce the abandonment pressure to the lowest possible level. In closed gas reservoirs, it is not uncommon to recover as much as 90 percent of the initial gas in place.

For those gas reservoirs having a water drive, recovery may be rate dependent. There are two possible influences which producing rate may have on ultimate recovery. First, in an active water drive reservoir, the abandonment pressure may be quite high, sometimes only a few psi below initial pressure. In such a case the number of pounds of gas remaining in the pore spaces at abandonment will be relatively great. However, the initial gas saturation is reduced by the encroaching water. Therefore, the high abandonment pressure is somewhat offset by the reduction in initial gas saturation. If the reservoir can be produced at a rate greater than the rate of water influx rate, without water coning, then a high producing rate could result in maximum recovery, by taking advantage of a combination of reduced abandonment pressure and reduction in initial gas saturation. Second, the water coning problems may be very severe in gas reservoirs, in which case it will be necessary to restrict withdrawal rates to reduce the magnitude of this problem.

Normally, recovery from water drive gas reservoir is substantially less than recovery from closed gas reservoirs. As a rule of thumb, recovery from a water drive reservoir will be approximately

50 to 60 percent of the initial gas in place. The structural location of producing wells and the degree of water coning are important considerations in determining ultimate recovery. A set of circumstances could exist—such as the location of wells very high on the structure with very little coning tendencies—where water drive recovery would be greater than depletion drive recovery. Abandonment pressure is a major factor in determining recovery efficiency, and permeability is usually the most important factor in determining the magnitude of the abandonment pressure. Reservoirs with low permeability will have higher abandonment pressures than reservoirs with high permeability. A certain minimum flow rate must be sustained, and a higher permeability will permit this minimum flow rate at a lower pressure.

Example Problem 11-4

Using the reservoir data shown in Examples 11-2 and 11-3 calculate:

(1) Recovery efficiency if abandonment pressure is 500 psia.
(2) Recovery efficiency at 500 psia abandonment pressure if an active water drive reduces the final gas saturation to 35%.

(1) $B_{g\,500} = \dfrac{0.00504 \times 0.96 \times 635}{500} = 0.00615$

$$V_g = \frac{G}{B_g}\left(\frac{B_g}{B_{gi}} - 1\right) = \frac{1.10 \times 10^6\left(\dfrac{0.00615}{0.000940} - 1\right)}{0.00615}$$

$= 991 \times 10^6$ SCF,
 cum. gas produced to 500 psia abandonment pressure

$$\text{Recovery Efficiency} = \frac{\text{Cum. Prod. to Abandonment}}{\text{Original Gas in Place}} \times 100$$

$$= \frac{991 \times 10^6}{1.170 \times 10^9} \times 100 = 84.7\%$$

(2) The reservoir originally contained 1,100,000 barrels of gas space. The connate water saturation was 35%, therefore the original gas saturation was 65%. If the water drive reduces the final gas saturation to 35%, the number of barrels of gas space remaining will be:

$$\frac{1,100,000}{(1 - S_{wi})} = \text{pore volume}$$

pore volume $\times$ residual gas saturation = Rem. gas space

$$\frac{1,100,000}{(1-0.35)} \times 0.35 = 593,000 \text{ Bbls. of gas space remaining}$$
after abandonment.

This can be converted to Standard Cubic Feet using the perfect gas laws:

$$\frac{PV}{ZT} = \frac{P_s V_s}{Z_s T_s}$$

$$V_s = \frac{PVZ_s T_s}{P_s ZT} = \frac{500 \times 593,000 \times 5.62 \times 1.0 \times 520}{14.7 \times 0.96 \times 635}$$

$$= 96.8 \times 10^6 \text{ SCF remaining at abandonment}$$

Recovery Efficiency =

$$\frac{\text{Orig. Gas in Place} - \text{Gas Rem. at Abandonment}}{\text{Original Gas in Place}} \times 100$$

$$= \frac{1.170 \times 10^9 - 96.8 \times 10^6}{1.170 \times 10^9} \times 100 = 91.8\%$$

An additional 7.1% of the gas originally in place was recovered by the active water drive.

Example 11-4 was a hypothetical situation in which two assumptions were made which are normally incorrect: (1) abandonment pressure was assumed to be the same for both cases, and (2) the water influx was assumed to have covered the entire reservoir. Abandonment pressure will invariably be higher in a water drive reservoir, and the water influx will seldom cover the entire reservoir. Example 11-14 is intended to illustrate the relatively small additional recovery as a result of reducing the gas saturation.

Value of Gas Reserves

In the final analysis the reservoir engineer must determine the worth of the gas reserve as well as determine its size.[1,2] Although a complete study of all aspects of property valuation is beyond the scope of this book, the fundamentals of gas property valuation are relatively simple, and some of these methods will be presented in an abbreviated form. Before the value of a gas reserve can be determined, such factors as lifting costs, development costs and

[1] Gruy, N. J. and Crichton, J. A., "A Critical Review of Methods Used in the Estimation of Natural Gas Reserves," *Trans.* AIME (1949) Vol. 179, p. 249.
[2] Davis, R. E. and Wege, J. M., "Valuation of Gas Reserves," *Journal of Petroleum Technology*, Sept. 1956, p. 18.

income tax must be fully evaluated. A gas property valuation work sheet provides a convenient form for appraisal work.

The following example problem will illustrate one method for determining the value of a gas reserve.

Example Problem 11-5

Determine the total value and the gas value per MCF of the following gas property:

Selling Price of Gas—0.25 per MCF
Selling Price of Liquid—$3.50 per barrel
Produced Gas-Liquid ratio—100,000 SCF/barrel
Royalty—⅛
Capital equipment investment—$225,000.00
Yearly producing rate—Shown in Table 11-1.

Table 11-1 is self-explanatory. The information just below the columnar headings indicates the development of the column. For example, column 4 shows (2 × ⅞ × $0.25). This means that the data in column 4 were obtained by multiplying column 2 by ⅞ (the working interest) and by $0.25 (the selling price of the gas). Likewise, the data in column 6 were obtained by adding columns 4 and 5. As shown in Table 11-1 the present worth of future net income is $422,300 (Σ Column 15); the payout time is 0.75 years; the profit to investment ratio is 3.06; and the unit value of the gas is 9.4 cents/MCF. Payout time, profit-to-investment ratio, and other economic aspects of valuations will be covered more thoroughly in Chapter 13.

Measurement of Gas Well Flow

The conventional back-pressure testing of gas wells to determine their theoretical productive capacity under open-flow conditions has a sound mathematical basis. This procedure involves the determination of flowing sand-face pressures at various stabilized flow rates; then plotting the square of formation pressure minus the square of flowing sand-face pressure $(p_f{}^2 - p_w{}^2)$ versus the flow rate (Q) on log-log paper. A straight line is obtained by this plot, and the calculated open-flow potential is taken at the point where the flowing sand-face pressure is zero. Typical open flow potential data are shown in Figure 11-5.

The preceding procedure for determining the open-flow potential of a gas well is almost a universal practice. Very little has ever been mentioned concerning the mathematical soundness of this

Table 11-1
Gas Property Valuation Work Sheet

(1)	(2)	(3)	(4)	(5)	(6)	(7)
Year	Gas Prod. MCF	Liquid Recovery[1] Bbls.	Gross Income from Gas to Working Int. (2) × 7/8 × $0.25	Gross Income from Liquid to Working Int. (3) × 7/8 × $3.50	Total Gross Income to Working Int. (4) + (5)	Lifting Costs[2] $
1959	1,500,000	15,000	$328,000	$ 45,900	$ 373,900	$ 75,000
1960	1,500,000	15,000	328,000	45,900	373,900	75,000
1961	1,000,000	10,000	219,000	30,600	249,600	50,000
1962	500,000	5,000	109,000	15,300	124,300	25,000
	4,500,000	45,000	$984,000	$137,700	$1,121,700	$225,000

	(8)	(9)	(10)	(11)	(12)
Year	Depreciation on Capital Equipment[3] $	Net Income to Working Interest (6) — (7) — (8)	Depletion Allowance[4] $	Net Income for Tax Purposes $	U. S. Income Tax[5] (11) × 0.52
1959	$ 75,000	$223,900	$90,300	$133,600	$69,500
1960	75,000	223,900	90,300	133,600	69,500
1961	50,000	149,600	60,200	89,400	46,500
1962	25,000	74,300	30,000	44,300	23,000
	$225,000	$671,700			

	(13)	(14)	(15)	(16)	(17)
Year	Net Income After Taxes (9) — (12)	Discount Factor 6%	Present Worth of Net Income (13) × (14)	Total Generated Net Revenue (8) + (13)	Present Worth of Generated Net Revenue (14) × (16)
1959	$154,400	0.9713	$149,500	$229,400	$222,500
1960	154,400	0.9163	141,000	229,400	210,000
1961	103,100	0.8644	90,000	153,100	132,000
1962	51,300	0.8155	41,800	76,300	62,200
	$463,200		$422,300	$688,200	$626,700

$$\text{Payout Time} = \frac{\$225,000}{\$229,000} = 0.75 \text{ years}$$

$$\text{Profit to Investment Ratio} = \frac{\Sigma \text{ Col.16}}{\text{Investment}} = \frac{\$688,200}{\$225,000} = 3.06$$

$$\text{Value of Gas per MCF} = \frac{\Sigma \text{ Col.15}}{\Sigma \text{ Col. 2}} = \frac{\$ 422,300}{4,500,000 \text{ MCF}} = \$0.094 \text{ per MCF}$$

[1]Gas-liquid ratio = 100,000 SCF /Bbl.

[2]Assumed $0.05 per MCF

[3]$225,000 capital investment. Depreciated on basis of remaining reserve:

$$\frac{\$225,000}{4,500,000 \text{ MCF}} = \$0.05 \text{ per MCF produced}$$

[4]27½% of gross income (Col. 6), but not to exceed 50% of Net Income (Col. 9).
[5]Assumed U. S. Corporation tax at the rate of 52%.

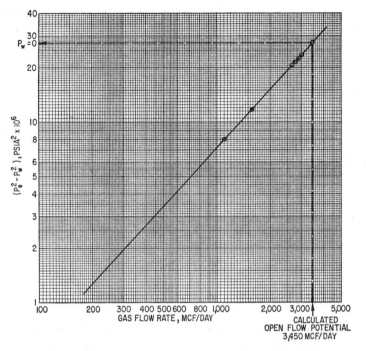

FIGURE 11-5. Open flow potential, example problem 11-6.

procedure, although, as will be shown, the basis of the procedure is mathematically sound. The entire method can be developed with the Darcy flow equation as a basis.

Beginning with the basic Darcy radial flow equation modified for compressible fluid flow:

$$q_m = \frac{2\pi kh(p_t - p_w)}{\mu_g \ln r_e/r_w}$$ (11-31)

where:

q_m = reservoir flow rate, cc/second
k = permeability, darcys
h = reservoir thickness, centimeters
p_t = reservoir pressure, atmospheres
p_w = flowing sand face pressure, atmospheres
μ_g = reservoir gas viscosity, centipoise
r_e = radius of drainage, centimeters
r_w = well bore radius, centimeters

Converting the reservoir flow rate to surface flow at standard conditions of temperature and pressure using the perfect gas laws:

$$\frac{q_m p_m}{Z_m T_m} = \frac{q_s p_s}{Z_s T_s}$$

rearranging:

$$q_s = \frac{q_m p_m Z_s T_s}{p_s Z_m T_m} \tag{11-32}$$

where:

q_s = flow rate at standard conditions, cc/second

p_m = average pressure $\dfrac{(p_f + p_w)}{2}$, atmospheres

Z_m = gas compressibility factor at standard conditions

T_s = standard temperature, degrees Rankine

p_s = standard pressure, atmospheres

Z_m = gas compressibility factor at mean flowing pressure

T_m = reservoir temperature, degrees Rankine.

Combining Equations (11-31) and (11-32) and adding a conversion factor C, to convert flow from cc/second to standard cubic feet/day, results in the following equation:

$$Q = \frac{C 2\pi k h Z_s T_s p_m (p_f - p_w)}{p_s Z_m T_m \mu_g \ln r_e/r_w} \tag{11-33}$$

where:

Q = flow rate, standard cubic feet/day

however:

$$p_m = \frac{p_f + p_w}{2}$$

substituting this value of p_m into Equation (11-33) and simplifying:

$$Q = \frac{C \pi k h Z_s T_s}{p_s Z_m T_m \mu_g \ln r_e/r_w} (p_f{}^2 - p_w{}^2)$$

Taking the logarithm of both sides:

$$\log Q = \log \frac{C \pi k h Z_s T_s}{p_s Z_m T_m \mu_g \ln r_e/r_w} + \log (p_f{}^2 - p_w{}^2) \tag{11-34}$$

Equation (11-34) will plot a straight line on log-log paper. A more general form of Equation (11-34) is as follows:

$$\log Q = \log \frac{C_\pi khZ_sT_s}{p_sZ_mT_m\mu_g\ln r_e/r_w} + n \log (p_t^2 - p_w^2) \qquad (11\text{-}35)$$

where:

n = slope of the line.

In this equation, n = 1, and therefore the line should have a 45 degree slope. The deviation of this line from a 45 degree angle in most cases indicates errors in some of the measured values.

The preceding development contains two erroneous assumptions in the derivation: (1) Z_m is not a constant, but varies with pressure changes, and (2) μ_g is not a constant, and it also varies with pressure changes. However, the magnitude of the error involved as a result of these two erroneous assumptions is probably not large in most cases.

Relating Future Producing Rates to Time

In order to relate future producing rates to time the following data are required:

1. p/Z versus Cumulative Gas Production.

2. Back pressure test data or isochronal test data.

If the p/Z vs. Cumulative Gas Production data are not available, then some reasonable estimate needs to be developed. This is relatively simple for a closed gas reservoir (no water influx) because the plot is a straight line, and two points on this line can usually be determined. The first point which can usually be determined is the initial pressure, at which point the cumulative gas production is zero. The second point which can usually be determined is the total gas initially in place, which would be equal to the total gas produced to zero pressure. This type of graph is shown in Figure 11-2.

A typical back pressure graph is shown in Figure 11-5. Theoretically, a plot of $(p_t^2 - p_w^2)$ vs. Q on log-log paper should plot a straight line, with a slope of one,

where:

p_t = Reservoir pressure (shut-in-bottom hole pressure) psia

p_w = Flowing sand face pressure, psia

Q = Flow rate, MCF/Day

At any given time the reservoir pressure, p_t, is a constant, and the data for Figure 11-5 can be developed by first measuring the shut-in bottom hole pressure after the well has been shut in for some period. Next the well is opened and flow is stabilized through a small choke. The flow rate becomes stabilized when the flow rate and surface flowing pressure remain constant for some period of time. After flow has stabilized, accurate measurements of flow rate and flowing bottom hole pressure are made. This provides the information for plotting one point on Figure 11-5. The flowing bottom hole pressure measurement can be obtained by either direct measurement with a subsurface pressure gauge or by measuring the flowing surface pressure and using published methods to calculate the flowing bottom-hole pressure. The use of a subsurface pressure gauge to measure the flowing bottom-hole pressures will provide more reliable data than calculated numbers. However, a subsurface pressure instrument is seldom used because of the hazards involved in leaving the instrument in the hole during the flow test periods and also because of the additional cost.

The other three points of Figure 11-5 are obtained in the same way as the first point was obtained, except that higher flow rates are used. The higher flow rates will result in lower values of p_w.

After the four points have been plotted, the line is extrapolated to the value of $p_t{}^2$. This is the point where $p_w = 0$, and this is the point of the highest possible flow rate for the well. This rate, shown on Figure 11-5, is referred to as the calculated open flow potential. It is a theoretical flow rate because it is impossible to reduce the bottom hole flowing pressure to zero.

Back pressure tests are used extensively to determine the productivity of gas wells. The exact procedures used to obtain the data vary from one place to another, but the principle of measurement is the same. In some areas surface pressure data, instead of bottom-hole data, are used in the back pressure plot. This results in some deviation from the theory on which the plot was based, but it usually results in acceptable data at less cost. In the past many gas well allowables have been set at one-fourth of the calculated open flow potential.

One of the principal disadvantages of the back pressure method of testing gas wells is that often the time required to obtain a stabilized flow rate is so long that, for practical reasons, it is not feasible to obtain stabilized flow rates. The isochronal test was developed to overcome this problem. An isochronal test, as the name implies, is a series of back pressure tests, each taken at some equal time interval. Figure 11-6 is a plot of an isochronal test. As shown by this figure, the isochronal test is essentially the same thing as

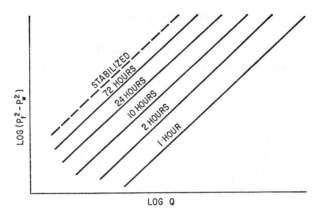

FIGURE 11-6. Isochronal text.

the conventional back pressure test, except that more data are required. The stabilized line, shown in Figure 11-6, is the desired data, and examination of this figure shows that the space between the time plots decreases as the time increases.

A step-by-step procedure for relating gas producing rate to time can be outlined as follows:

1. Draw a graph of p/Z versus Cumulative Gas Production.

2. Plot back pressure test data or isochronal test data.

3. Arbitrarily select a value of p, and from the decline curve, read the cumulative gas produced (note that p_t and p are identical). Use small pressure increments to increase the accuracy of the calculations.

4. At the selected value of p, determine the calculated open flow potential. If the contract producing rate does not exceed the allowable producing rate (usually $\frac{1}{4}$ of the open flow potential), then use the contract rate for this time interval. If the contract producing rate exceeds the allowable producing rate, then the allowable producing rate must be used for the interval.

5. Obtain the time required to produce the gas during the first interval by:

$$\text{time} = \frac{\text{Gas produced during interval}}{Q_{\text{average}}}$$

6. Repeat steps 2 through 5 for consecutively lower values of p until the abandonment pressure is reached.

Example Problem 11-6 illustrates this method.

Example Problem 11-6

A gas well in the Vern Field of Southwest Texas, E. Jones No. 1, has just been completed. An open flow potential test has been taken. Results of this test are plotted in Figure 11-5. The following data are available.

$$\begin{array}{ll}
\text{Depth} & = 10,800 \text{ feet} \\
p_i & = 5,240 \text{ psia} \\
T_f & = 281° \text{ F} \\
\text{Gas Gravity} & = 0.78 \\
\text{Porosity} & = 12\% \\
S_{wi} & = 15\%
\end{array}$$

1. Calculate the volume of initial gas in-place. Isopachous maps show that the well will drain 159,617 acre-feet.

2. Calculate the future deliverability of the well (Gas producing rate vs. Time). The contract producing rate is 1376 MCF/Day, but the allowable producing rate cannot exceed one-fourth of the calculated open flow potential at any time. The minimum well bore flowing pressure will be 1,000 psia.

Answer:

1. $$V_i = \text{Initial Gas in-place} = \frac{7758 \, A \, h \, \phi \, (1 - S_{wi})}{B_{gi}}$$

$$B_{gi} = 0.00504 \frac{T \, Z_i}{p_i}$$

$$B_{gi} = 0.00504 \frac{(460 + 281) \, (1.043)}{5240} = 0.000743 \text{ bbls/SCF}$$

$$V_i = \frac{7758 \times 159,617 \times 0.12 \times (1 - 0.15)}{0.000743}$$

$$V_i = 17,000,000,000 \text{ SCF} = 17,000 \text{ MMCF}.$$

2. Step 1:

Plot p/Z vs. Cum. Gas Produced. Since no gas has been produced, only two points are known:

a. $= p_i = 5240 ; V_g = 0.$
b. $= \text{When } p = 0 ; V_g = 17,000 \text{ MMCF}.$

This plot is shown in Figure 11-7

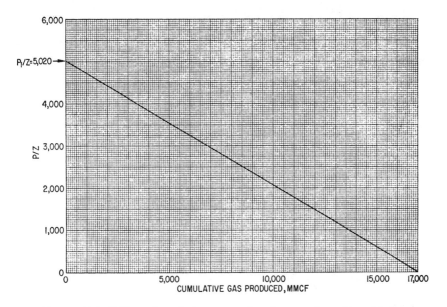

Figure 11-7. P/Z vs. Cumulative gas produced, example problem 11-6.

Step 2:

From Figure 11-7:

if $p_1 = 5240$ then $p/Z = 5020$; and $V_1 = 0$ MCF
if $p_2 = 4951$ then $p/Z = 4902$; and $V_2 = 434,520$ MCF

From Figure 11-5:

$$Q_{o1} = 3450 \text{ MCF/day}$$

$$Q_{o2} = 2999.99 \text{ MCF/day}$$

$$Q_{o(avg)} = \frac{3450 + 2999.99}{2} = 3225 \text{ MCF/day}$$

where:

Q_o = Calculated open flow potential

$$\Delta T = \frac{(434,520 - 0) \text{ MCF}}{(365 \text{ days/yr}) \dfrac{3225}{4} \text{ MCF/day}} = 1.47 \text{ years}$$

Step 3:

Repeating procedure used in Step 2, using 4,851 psia as the next pressure step.

$$\text{At 4951 psia, } V_{g2} = 434{,}520 \text{ MCF}$$
$$\text{At 4851 psia, } V_{g3} = 664{,}050 \text{ MCF}$$
$$\text{At 4951 psia, } Q_{o2} = 2999.99$$
$$\text{At 4851 psia, } Q_{o3} = 2880.03$$

$$Q_{o(avg)} = \frac{2999.99 + 2880.03}{2} = 2940 \text{ MCF/day}$$

$$\Delta T = \frac{(644{,}050 - 434{,}520) \text{ MCF}}{(365 \text{ days/year})\dfrac{2940}{4} \text{ MCF/day}}$$

$$\Delta T = 0.85 \text{ year}$$
$$\Sigma T = 1.47 + 0.85 = 2.32 \text{ years}$$

Step 4:

$$\text{At 4851 psia, } V_{g3} = 664{,}050 \text{ MCF}$$
$$\text{At 4751 psia, } V_{g4} = 896{,}390 \text{ MCF}$$
$$\text{At 4851 psia, } Q_{o3} = 2880.03 \text{ MCF/day}$$
$$\text{At 4751 psia, } Q_{o4} = 2762.51 \text{ MCF/day}$$

$$Q_{o(avg)} = \frac{2880.03 + 2762.51}{2} = 2821.20 \text{ MCF/day}$$

$$\Delta T = \frac{(896{,}390 - 664{,}050) \text{ MCF}}{(365 \text{ days/year})\left(\dfrac{2821.20}{4} \text{ MCF/day}\right)} = 0.90 \text{ years}$$

$$\Sigma T = 0.90 + 2.32 = 3.22 \text{ years}$$

Step 5:

$$\text{At 4751 psia, } V_{g4} = 896{,}390 \text{ MCF}$$
$$\text{At 4651 psia, } V_{g5} = 1131{,}590 \text{ MCF}$$
$$\text{At 4751 psia, } Q_{o1} = 2762.51 \text{ MCF/day}$$
$$\text{At 4651 psia, } Q_{o2} = 2647.45 \text{ MCF/day}$$

$$Q_{o(avg)} = \frac{(2762.51 + 2647.45) \text{ MCF/day}}{2} = 2705.0 \text{ MCF/day}$$

$$\Delta T = \frac{(1131{,}590 - 896{,}390) \text{ MCF}}{(365 \text{ days/year})\left(\dfrac{2705.0}{4} \text{ MCF/day}\right)} = 0.95 \text{ years}$$

$\Sigma \, T = 3.22 + 0.95 = 4.17$ years

Note: Additional pressure steps are taken until the pressure is depleted. Table 11-2 shows the completed computer output for this calculation.

Table 11-2
Well Sheet Calculated Deliverabilities

P Psia	Z	CM MMCF	QC MCF/Day	QO MCF/Day	QO/4 MCF/Day	Q* MCF/Day	DT Years	T Years
5240.00	1.04	0	1375.98	3450.00	862.50	862.50	0	0
4951.00	1.01	434.52	1375.98	2999.99	749.99	749.999	1.47	1.47
4851.00	1.00	664.05	1375.98	2880.03	720.00	720.008	.85	2.32
4751.00	.99	896.39	1375.98	2762.51	690.62	690.629	.9u	3.22
4651.0u	.99	1131.59	1375.98	2647.45	661.86	661.862	.95	4.17
4551.u0	.98	1369.69	1375.98	2534.83	633.70	633.707	1.00	5.17
4451.00	.97	161u.76	1375.98	2424.65	6u6.16	606.164	1.06	6.23
4351.00	.97	1854.85	1375.98	2316.93	579.23	579.233	1.12	7.35
4251.00	.96	2102.02	1375.98	2211.65	552.91	552.913	1.19	8.54
4151.00	.96	2352.32	1375.98	2108.82	527.2u	527.206	1.26	9.80
400u.00	.95	2736.36	1375.98	1958.19	489.54	489.547	2.06	11.86
3900.00	.94	3013.39	1375.98	1861.50	465.37	465.376	1.58	13.44
3800.00	.94	3293.24	1375.98	1767.26	441.81	441.817	1.69	15.13
3700.00	.93	3575.96	1375.98	1675.47	418.86	418.869	1.80	16.93
3600.00	.93	3861.59	1375.98	1586.13	396.53	396.533	1.91	18.84
3500.00	.92	4150.17	1375.98	1499.24	374.81	374.810	2.05	20.89
3400.00	.92	4444.37	1375.98	1414.79	353.69	353.698	2.21	23.10
3300.00	.91	4741.52	1375.98	1332.79	333.19	333.198	2.37	25.47
3200.00	.91	5041.66	1375.98	1253.24	313.31	313.310	2.54	28.01
3100.u0	.90	5344.84	1375.98	1176.13	294.03	294.034	2.73	30.74
3000.00	.90	5651.09	1375.98	1101.48	275.37	275.370	2.94	33.68

where:

CM = Cumulative gas produced, MMCF   DT = Delta time, years
QC = Contract producing rate, MCF/day   T = Cumulative time, years
QO = Open flow potential, MCF/day
Q* = Actual producing rate, MCF/day

Material Balance Equation as a Straight Line

The gas reservoir material balance can be rearranged to plot as a straight line. The procedure is similar to that described in Chapter 6, "Water Drive Reservoirs."

For a closed gas reservoir, Equation (11-4) is rearranged as follows:

$$V_g = G \left(\frac{1}{B_{gi}} - \frac{1}{B_g} \right) \tag{11-31}$$

A plot of V_g vs $\left(\dfrac{1}{B_{gi}} - \dfrac{1}{B_g} \right)$ should be a straight line on ordinary Cartesian coordinate graph paper, with a slope of G, and having an intercept at O, O (origin). Thus, the production data could be plotted to determine the initial gas in place, G. This plot would have the usual limitations of the material balance equation early in the producing life of the reservoir.

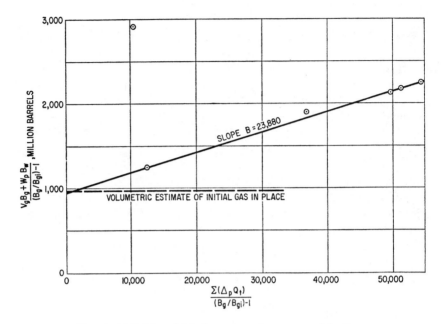

FIGURE 11-8. Material balance equation as a straight line.

For a water drive gas reservoir the material balance equation can be combined with the unsteady state water influx equation, and the resulting equation can be plotted as a straight line to provide some very useful information. Combining Equation (6-27):

$$W_e = B \, \Sigma \, \Delta_p \times Q_{(t)} \qquad\qquad (6\text{-}27)$$

with Equation (11-26):

$$G = \frac{V_g \, B_g - (W_e - W_p \, B_w)}{\left(\dfrac{B_g}{B_{gi}} - 1\right)} \qquad\qquad (11\text{-}26)$$

and rearranging as follows:

$$\frac{V_g \, B_g + W_p \, B_w}{\dfrac{B_g}{B_{gi}} - 1} = G + B\left[\frac{\Sigma \, \Delta_p \, Q_{(t)}}{\left(\dfrac{B_g}{B_{gi}} - 1\right)}\right] \qquad (11\text{-}32)$$

Equation (11-32) is a straight line when $\dfrac{V_g \, B_g + W_p \, B_w}{\left(\dfrac{B_g}{B_{gi}} - 1\right)}$ is plotted on the ordinate and $\dfrac{\Sigma\,\Delta_p\,Q_{(t)}}{\left(\dfrac{B_g}{B_{gi}}-1\right)}$ is plotted on the abscissa. This line

will have a slope equal to B, the water influx constant, and will intercept the y-axis at G, the initial gas size, in units of reservoir barrels. Figure 11-8 shows this technique used on a water drive gas
reservoir in Canada.[3] As shown in Figure 11-8, the initial gas in
place calculated by the volumetric equation is in good agreement
with that determined by the straight line plot of the material balance equation. Both the material balance equation and the unsteady
state water influx equation are very sensitive to small errors in
pressure early in the producing life of a reservoir. As shown in
Figure 11-8, the first data point does not fit the straight line relationship assumed by the later points, but lies well above the line.
This point is presumed to be in error and is disregarded in the plot.

[3] Cole, Frank W., "Methods of Calculating Oil and Gas Reserves," Ontario Petroleum Institute, Volume 3, 1966.

Chapter 12

GAS-CONDENSATE RESERVOIRS

With the advent of deeper drilling, high-pressure gas reservoirs have been discovered with properties materially different from those of the "dry" gas reservoirs previously encountered. The composition of the reservoir fluid is still predominately methane, although the relative amounts of the heavier hydrocarbons are considerably increased. These reservoir fluids are commonly called *gas-condensate* fluids and the reservoirs are referred to as *gas-condensate* reservoirs. Table 12-1 compares the composition of typical fluids from "dry" gas reservoirs with fluids from gas-condensate reservoirs.

Figure 12-1 shows a pressure-temperature diagram for a typical gas-condensate fluid. The initial reservoir state is shown at point R_i, and the state of the reservoir at abandonment is shown at point R_a. The dashed line connecting R_i and R_a shows the state of the reservoir at any pressure between initial and abandonment conditions. The point S on the diagram in Figure 12-1 represents

Table 12-1
Composition of Typical Reservoir Fluids

Component	"Dry" Gas Reservoir Mol %	Gas-Condensate Reservoir Mol %
C_1	96.00	85.00
C_2	2.00	5.00
C_3	0.60	2.00
C_4	0.30	1.50
C_5	0.20	0.80
C_6	0.10	0.60
C_{7+}	0.80	5.10
	$\Sigma = 100.00$	$\Sigma = 100.00$

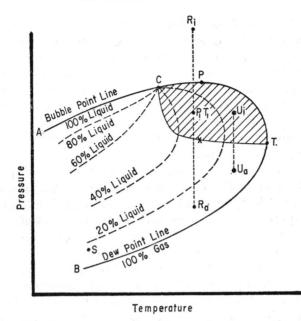

FIGURE 12-1. Pressure-temperature diagram for a gas-condensate fluid.

the surface pressure and temperature to which the reservoir fluid is subjected.

There are several characteristic features of gas-condensate reservoirs. The reservoir fluid at original pressure and temperature is a single-phase fluid, and is usually referred to as a gas. As long as the fluid is in a single-phase, the gas laws can be used to predict behavior of the fluid, if the applicable gas deviation factors, Z, can be determined. Gas-condensate reservoir fluids exhibit a phenomenon known as *retrograde condensation.*

Retrograde condensation is said to occur when liquid is condensed from the reservoir fluid (which is a gas) upon reduction of pressure and temperature. If the formation of liquid occurs isothermally (at constant temperature) with a reduction of pressure, the phenomenon is then often referred to as *isothermal* retrograde condensation.

Retrograde condensation is illustrated in Figure 12-1. At initial reservoir conditions, R_i, the reservoir fluid is a gas. As fluid is first withdrawn from the reservoir, the temperature and pressure on the fluid as it passes up the well bore will be reduced until it finally approaches the surface temperature and pressure, designated by S on the diagram. Once the phase boundary, designated by line ACPTB, has been crossed, liquid begins forming, the final relative volumes of liquid and gas being dependent on the location of S with respect to the PT diagram. As long as there is no liquid accumulation in the reservoir, there is no loss of product, since the liquid which forms in the well bore and tubing will flow to the surface and be recovered. However, as reservoir fluid is withdrawn, the pressure in the entire reservoir will be reduced. Since reservoir temperature does not change, the reduction in reservoir pressure is an isothermal process and is designated on Figure 12-1 as the dotted line $R_i R_a$. When the reservoir pressure declines to the point where the phase boundary is crossed, liquid will be condensed from the reservoir fluid and a two-phase fluid saturation will exist in the reservoir. When reservoir pressure has declined to P_1, as shown on Figure 12-1, the reservoir fluids will be approximately 70% gas and 30% liquid. As this liquid saturation can never be reduced to zero, some valuable hydrocarbons will have been lost. When reservoir pressure is reduced further (line $R_i R_a$) some of these condensed liquids will revaporize until at abandonment (conditions R_a) the reservoir fluids will be approximately 10% liquid and 90% gas. However, Figure 12-1 is a laboratory-derived phase diagram, and actual field experience indicates that only a small fraction of the liquid will be returned to the vapor state upon further reduction in pressure because once the liquid has been formed, the surface forces will tend to retain it in the liquid phase. As the liquefiable portion of the reservoir fluids are usually the most valuable components of the reservoir fluid, the loss of part of these fluids could substantially reduce the ultimate income from the property. In a dry gas reservoir it is not unusual to recover more than 85% of the initial gas in place. In gas-condensate reservoirs, although 85% of the dry gas can be recovered by pressure depletion, it is not unusual to lose as much as 50% to 60% of the liquefiable hydrocarbons due to retrograde condensation. It is the job of the reservoir engineer to devise means of preventing this loss where economically feasible. Before considering methods of increasing the liquid recovery from a gas-condensate reservoir, several basic ideas concerning the behavior of gas-condensate fluids will be reviewed.

The region of retrograde condensation is the shaded area shown in Figure 12-1. An interesting type of reservoir is shown as U_i on Figure 12-1. This reservoir lies within the phase envelope, which means it is a two-phase reservoir, i.e., an oil reservoir with a gas cap. However, it also lies within the region of retrograde condensation. Therefore, it is an oil reservoir with an initial gas cap, and the gas cap exhibits the phenomenon of retrograde condensation. This type reservoir is not uncommon. The Katy reservoir near Houston, Texas, which has been discussed in various petroleum industry publications, is this type reservoir.

Referring again to Figure 12-1, line AC, is the *bubble point* line above which the fluid is 100% liquid, and below which the fluid contains some gas. Line CPTB is the *dew point* line below which the fluid is 100% gas, and above which the fluid contains some liquid. The *critical point,* C, is the point where the bubble-point and dew-point lines meet. The point P, shown on the dew-point line, is the *cricondenbar* which is the maximum pressure under which the fluid can exist as two phases (liquid and gas) in equilibrium.

The cricondenbar can be located on either the dew-point line or the bubble point line. The point T, located on the dew-point line, is called the *cricondentherm* and is defined as the maximum temperature under which the fluid can exist as two phases (liquid and gas) in equilibrium.

Isothermal retrograde condensation can occur only at temperatures between the critical point, C, and the cricondentherm T. If the reservoir temperature is greater than the cricondentherm, then the reservoir fluid will be a "dry" gas. The term "dry" gas is used in a relative sense, as it is quite possible that the surface conditions of temperature and pressure will be such that there will be some condensation of liquids from the reservoir fluid after the fluid leaves the reservoir. But because the reservoir temperature does not change, there will be no condensation in the reservoir as long as the reservoir temperature is greater than the cricondentherm.

Weight Percent, Volume Percent, and Mol Percent

When studying gas-condensate reservoirs, frequent reference is made to the terms weight percent, volume percent, and mol percent, when the composition of the fluids are being described. Weight percent and volume percent require no discussion as their meanings are clear. The term mol percent (or more properly, mole percent) is the percentage of molecules of one specific type in the system. If a gas contains two moles of methane, CH_2, one mole of ethane, C_2H_6, and one mole of propane, C_3H_8, then the mole percentage of each of these components is:

Component	Mol %
CH_4	50
C_2H_6	25
C_3H_8	25
Total	100

Volume percent and mol percent are identical. It is often necessary, or desirable, to convert from weight percent to mol percent, or volume percent. The number of moles of a component can be determined by dividing the weight of a particular component by its molecular weight. The conversion from weight fraction to mol fraction is illustrated by the following:

Example Problem 12-1

(1)	(2)	(3)	(4)	(5)
			Moles	Mole
	Wt.	Molecular	Per Lb.	Fraction
Component	Fraction	Wt.	(2) $\div$ (3)	(4) $\div \Sigma$(4)
CH_4	0.50	16	0.0312	0.69
C_2H_6	0.25	30	0.0083	0.18
C_3H_8	0.25	44	0.0057	0.13
	1.00		0.0452	1.00

The reverse of the above procedure would be used when converting from mole fraction to weight fraction.

Vapor-Liquid Equilibrium Ratios

Fixing the temperature and the pressure will also fix the relative amounts of vapor phase and liquid phase for a fluid of given composition. Expressed in equation form, this statement reduces to:

$$K_i = Y_i/X_i \qquad (12\text{-}1)$$

where:

K = vapor-liquid equilibrium constant
Y = mole fraction in vapor phase
X = mole fraction in liquid phase
i = subscript designating a specific component.

The numerical value of the vapor-liquid equilibrium ratio, or the *equilibrium constant*, as this number will be referred to henceforth, is dependent on pressure, temperature, and composition of the fluid. Various investigators have determined the ranges of the K values for many different fluid compositions under wide ranges of both temperature and pressure. These K values have a very practical application in the solution of many petroleum engineering problems, for if the K values for a given reservoir fluid are known, the relative amounts of liquid and vapor phases at any temperature and pressure can be calculated. For example, this is invaluable in the determination of optimum separator pressure for a reservoir producing volatile crude oil. The principal problem in the application of K values to petroleum reservoir problems, is that every reservoir fluid is different. It would be necessary to physically measure the K values for each reservoir fluid in order to determine the absolutely correct values. Fortunately, the compositions of many reservoir fluids are sufficiently close, and there has been such a relatively large number of K value measurements, that in most cases, reasonable K values can be selected from the published literature.

Use of K Values

The following relationships are derived on the basis of one mole of the fluid. For this case, the following equation holds true:

$$n_1 + n_2 + n_3 + \ldots n_i = 1 \qquad (12\text{-}2)$$

where:

n_1 = number of moles of component 1 in the mixture

n_2 = number of moles of component 2 in the mixture

n_3 = number of moles of component 3 in the mixture

n_i = number of moles of component i in the mixture.

Also:

$$N_l + N_v = 1 \qquad (12\text{-}3)$$

where:

N_l = number of moles of the fluid in the liquid phase

N_v = number of moles of the fluid in the vapor phase.

From Equation (12-3), it is seen that the number of moles in the liquid phase is:

$$N_l = n_{l1} + n_{l2} + n_{l3} + \ldots n_{li} \qquad (12\text{-}4)$$

where:

n_l = number of moles in the liquid phase of the various components.

The mole fraction of a component in the liquid phase is:

$$X_i = \frac{n_{li}}{N_l} \qquad (12\text{-}5)$$

Because that part of a component in the fluid which is not liquid will be in the vapor phase, the mole fraction of a component in the vapor phase is:

$$Y_i = \frac{n_{vi}}{N_v} = \frac{n_i - n_{1i}}{1 - N_1} \qquad (12\text{-}6)$$

Combining Equations (12-1), (12-5), and (12-6) results in a useful equation for calculating molal volumes in the liquid or vapor phases:

$$K_1 = Y_i/X_i = \frac{\dfrac{n_i - n_{1i}}{1 - N_1}}{n_{1i}/N_1} = \frac{(n_i - n_{1i})\, N_1}{(1 - N_1)\, n_{1i}} \qquad (12\text{-}7)$$

Rearranging Equation (12-7) to solve for n_{1i}, the number of moles of component, i, in the liquid phase:

$$n_{1i} = \frac{n_i\, N_1}{K_i\, (1 - N_1) + N_1} \qquad (12\text{-}8)$$

Similarly, the number of moles of any component, i, in the vapor phase can be calculated by:

$$n_{vi} = \frac{n_i}{(1/K_i)\left(\dfrac{N_1}{1 - N_1}\right) + 1} \qquad (12\text{-}9)$$

Equations (12-5) and (12-8) can be combined to solve directly for X_i as follows:

$$X_i = \frac{n_i}{K_i\, (1 - N_1) + N_1} \qquad (12\text{-}10)$$

Equations (12-8), (12-9) and (12-10) involve a trial and error solution, since both N_1 and n_{1i} are unknowns. However, it is known that the sum of the moles of the various components in the liquid phase must be equal to the total number of moles in the liquid phase. Equation (12-4) expressed this relationship in mathematical form. Therefore in order to solve Equation (12-10), a value of N_1 must be assumed. If for the assumed value of N_1, the $\Sigma\, X_i \neq 1.00$, then the procedure must be repeated until a value of N_1 is selected where $\Sigma\, X_i = 1.00$.

Predicting Reservoir Performance

Prediction of the future performance of a gas-condensate reservoir is desirable in order to establish the optimum reservoir operating plan. Theoretically, several operating programs are possible:

1. Pressure depletion without any form of pressure maintenance or gas return. For reservoirs which have active natural water drives, this may be a very efficient and economical method of operation.

2. The produced fluid can be passed through a gasoline plant where liquids are recovered and the dry gas is returned to the reservoir. This is a form of pressure maintenance and is referred to as *cycling*. The purpose of cycling is to maintain reservoir pressure above the phase boundary in order to prevent condensation of liquids in the reservoir. This process will be discussed at length later in the chapter.

3. The reservoir can be produced by pressure depletion to the economic limit at which time gas return operations can be initiated with the objective of sweeping the accumulated liquids from the reservoir. This sweeping process is a combination of physical displacement and absorption. As the dry gas moves through the reservoir it will contact the reservoir liquid and will become enriched by the liquid. In actual practice this last recovery method is seldom used for two reasons:

   a. The recovery by *absorption* is usually relatively small, and, as a rule it will not, by itself, economically support the large investment required.

   b. The remaining liquid saturation will be relatively small; and therefore the gas relative permeability will be extremely high as compared with the liquid relative permeability. Thus, physical displacement of liquid by the gas will be small. One factor which somewhat offsets the adverse relative permeability relationships is that the dry gas and the reservoir liquid, although not truly miscible, certainly approach miscibility. This trend toward miscibility would improve somewhat the adverse relative permeability relationships.

The decision as to the method of producing the reservoir must be based solely on economics. The operator of the property is primarily interested in obtaining the largest *present-value* net income from the property. If, for some reason, there existed an exceptionally good market for gas immediately, while future prospects for good contracts did not appear as attractive, the operator might be willing to sacrifice some loss in ultimate recovery in order to obtain the favorable contract. One of the disadvantages of cycling is that the dry gas is not available for sale until the recoverable liquids have been stripped from the reservoir fluid and the "blowdown" period has begun. On the other hand, the demand for gas has been increasing so fast, that it is often desirable to postpone the sale of gas for a few years in order to take advantage of rapidly increasing gas prices.

Because the decision as to the method of producing the reservoir is primarily economic, the need for determining the recovery of both liquids and gas from the reservoir under the various methods of operation is readily apparent. In order to predict the recovery under various possible producing methods, the following data are needed:

1. Geologic data concerning the size of the reservoir, its porosity, permeability and interstitial water saturation. The variation in permeability throughout the reservoir, especially vertical permeability variation, is very important where cycling is being considered.

2. The composition of the original reservoir material, density of the fluid, and the original pressure and temperature of the fluid.

3. The composition of the produced gas at various reservoir pressures, and the amount of liquid condensed in the reservoir at these pressures. From this information the surface recovery and subsurface losses due to pressure reduction can be computed.

4. The amount of recoverable liquid which can be achieved by utilizing various combinations of surface separation equipment.

Number 1 above can be obtained during the development of the reservoir and by core analysis methods. The remainder of the information can be obtained by taking a representative sample of reservoir fluid and then duplicating the depletion history of the reservoir in the laboratory. This method, or variations of it, are commonly used in the analysis of gas-condensate reservoirs.

Sampling Procedures

Obtaining a representative sample of the reservoir fluid is considerably more difficult for a gas-condensate fluid than for a conventional black-oil reservoir. The principal reason for this difficulty is that liquid may condense from the reservoir fluid during the sampling process, and if representative proportions of both liquid and gas are not recovered then an erroneous composition will be calculated. Because of the possibility of erroneous compositions and also because of the limited volumes obtainable, subsurface sampling is seldom used in gas-condensate reservoirs. Instead, surface sampling techniques are used, and samples are obtained only after long stabilized flow periods. During this stabilized flow period, volumes of liquid and gas produced in the surface separation facilities are accurately measured, and the fluid samples are then recombined in these proportions.

Condensate Yield

The reservoir engineer usually prepares the basic data and engineering calculations on which decisions concerning future operating methods are based. As mentioned previously, the total recovery of both liquid and gas, from various methods of operation, with the present value of the net income to be generated by each of these different operating methods are the most important results of the engineering study. The gas recovery can be reliably estimated from conventional gas law calculations as outlined in Chapter 11. The condensate yield, however, will vary under different operating programs, and it is the principal variable which affects ultimate net income. Two basic methods for determining the condensate yield appear to have merit, although many variations of these two methods have also been used successfully.

The first method to be discussed utilizes laboratory PVT data. A representative sample of the original reservoir fluid is charged to a PVT cell. The composition of the original reservoir fluid is determined, and then a pressure depletion process (at constant volume) is initiated. The dew point is determined, as this is a very important point in the entire process. Pressure depletion is accomplished by withdrawing a portion of the reservoir gas. The gas withdrawn is carefully analyzed, and by the use of appropriate equilibrium constants (K factors) this gas can be converted to liquid and gas recovery at the field separation conditions of temperature and pressure. This procedure is continued until the abandonment pressure has been reached, at which time the gas and the accumulated liquid remaining in the PVT cell are analyzed. A material balance comparing the original composition to that of the produced fluid plus remaining fluid will serve as a test of the accuracy of the measurements. The liquid accumulated in the PVT cell will be considered as lost if cycling or other recovery methods are not initiated. It should be noted that, because of liquid condensation that comes as pressure decreases, the composition of the produced gas is constantly changing. This procedure has one distinct disadvantage. The initial sample is small, and the volumes of gas withdrawn at each pressure increment are still smaller. Therefore, the possible errors involved in analyzing these extremely small fractions and projecting these values to an entire reservoir, are quite large. However, similar procedures have been reportedly used with reasonable success, and more detailed discussions of the method are available in literature.[1,2,3,4]

Probably the best method yet devised for the determination of liquid recovery from gas-condensate reservoirs is the use of portable well-testing equipment where reservoir pressures and temperatures, and field separation conditions can actually be simulated in the field and data gathered during actual flow of large volumes of reservoir fluids. The United States Bureau of Mines has used this type of equipment extensively. Similar equipment has been described in the literature.[5]

With this equipment a volume chamber (or separator) is used to simulate the reservoir. This chamber is heated to reservoir temperature and the fluids in it are maintained at reservoir pressure. The reservoir fluid is flowed from the volume tank to a second separator which is operated at the field pressure and temperature separation conditions. During the test this second separator can be operated at several different pressures to actually determine the optimum field separation conditions. Figure 12-2 shows a diagram of a portable apparatus for gas-condensate testing. This general type of portable testing equipment has many advantages over conventional laboratory analysis methods, the principal one being that in the field testing equipment, the volumes of

[1] Curtis, R. C., and Brinkley, T. W., "Calculation of Natural Condensate Recovery," A.P.I., *Drilling and Production Practice,* 1949, p. 166.

[2] Allen, F. H., and Roe, R. P., "Performance Characteristics of a Volumetric Condensate Reservoir, *Trans.* AIME, 1949, Vol. 189, p. 83.

[3] Brinkley, T. W., "Calculation of Rate and Ultimate Recovery from a Gas Condensate Reservoir," paper 1028-G, Proceedings AIME Production and Reservoir Engineering Conference, Tulsa, Okla., March 20-21, 1958.

[4] Berryman, J. E., "The Predicted Performance of a Gas-Condensate System," *Trans.* AIME, 1957, Vol. 210, p. 102.

[5] Hoffman, A. E., Crump, J. S., and Hocott, C. R., "Equilibrium Constants for a Gas-Condensate System," *Trans.* AIME, 1953, Vol. 198, p. 1.

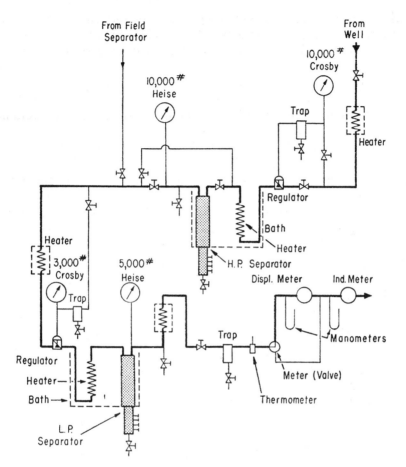

FIGURE 12-2. Flow diagram, portable apparatus for gas-condensate testing.

samples used are many times that of the samples used in laboratory analysis.

Cycling

A cycling operation requires the installation of a gasoline plant, where the produced gas is stripped of its liquid content, the dry gas remaining is compressed and returned to the producing formation. As mentioned previously, the principal disadvantage of cycling operations is that the reservoir gas is not available for sale until the cycling operation becomes uneconomic. The only income during the cycling period is that realized from sale of the liquids. However, in many cases, this income is quite large.

A thorough study of the reservoir is desirable before initiating a cycling program, because of the large investment in plant facilities which will be required. The dry gas can be expected to displace all of the reservoir gas with which it comes in contact, as the two fluids will be miscible at reservoir temperature and pressure. However, due to reservoir inhomogeneities, a part of the reservoir will probably never be contacted by the displacing gas. Since the economics of the cycling operation are directly related to the removal of the "wet" gas from the reservoir, it is essential for the engineer to determine that fraction of the reservoir which will be contacted by the "dry" gas. The use of models to study the various parameters involved is usually the most satisfactory method of obtaining the desired answers. The influence of the following factors is important in the overall economic analysis.

1. Effect of permeability variations
2. Location of injection wells
3. Location of producing wells
4. Well spacing.

The cycling operation becomes uneconomic when the value of the liquids recovered from the produced gas is less than the cost of running the plant and injection facilities.

Flash Vaporization, Example Calculations

The object of this problem is to calculate the amount and composition of the gas and liquid exiting from the separator and the stock tank under the following conditions.

The composition of the stream entering the separator is shown in Table 12-2:

Table 12-2
Composition of Fluid Entering Separator

Comp.	Mole %
C_1	86.10
C_2	6.70
C_3	2.61
i-C_4	0.50
n-C_4	0.85
i-C_5	0.26
n-C_5	0.29
C_6	0.39
C_{7+}	2.30

The operating temperature of the stock tank and separator is 80° F. The operating pressure of the separator is 50 psia and the operating pressure of the stock tank is 14.5 psia. The specific gravity of the C_{7+} component is 0.730.

Calculation Procedure

I. Determination of Convergence Pressure

In order to determine the convergence pressure, the composition of the separator exit liquid stream must be known. It has been found that the K values of a fixed-composition system will converge toward a common value of unity at some high pressure. This pressure is defined as the convergence pressure. However, at this point in the problem the exit stream composition is unknown. Therefore, an approximation of the convergence pressure is obtained by assuming that the exit liquid stream composition is equal to the entering stream composition except that methane (or the lightest component) is neglected. Before the convergence pressure can be approximated, the weight average critical temperature (T_c) must be obtained. For this calculation refer to Example Calculation 12-2, Table 12-3. Having obtained T_c refer to page 172 of the 1957 edition of the Natural Gasoline Supply Men's Association manual (NGSMA). Now connect, with a straight line, the critical points of the hydrocarbons in the range of T_c. Then take

Table 12-3

Calculation of T_c and Approximation of Convergence Pressure
(Example Calculation 12-2)

Component	Moles	Mol. Weight	Weight (2) × (3)	T_c, °F	Weight × T_c (4) × (5)
C_1	86.10	16.0	omit	lightest	component
C_2	6.70	30.1	201.7	90.1	18173.2
C_3	2.61	44.1	115.1	206.3	23745.1
iC_4	0.50	58.1	29.1	275.0	8002.5
nC_4	0.85	58.1	49.4	305.6	15096.6
iC_5	0.26	72.1	18.7	370.0	6919.0
nC_5	0.29	72.1	20.9	385.9	8065.3
C_6	0.39	86.2	33.6	454.5	15271.2
C_{7+}	2.30	137.0*	315.1	590.0	185909.0
			$\Sigma = 783.6$		$\Sigma = 281181.9$

* From 1957 NGSMA, page 135.

Weight average Critical Temperature:

$$T_c = \frac{\Sigma \, \text{Weight} \times T_c}{\Sigma \, \text{Weight}} = \frac{281,181.9}{783.6} = 358.8° \text{ F.}$$

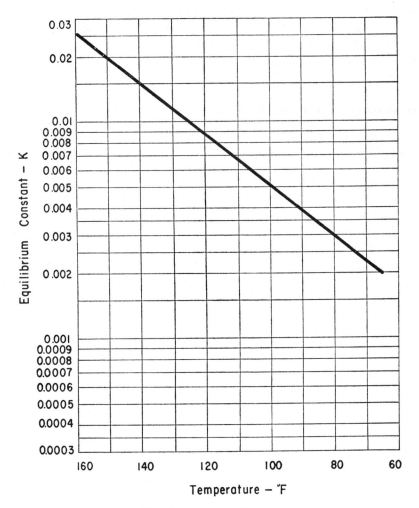

FIGURE 12-3. K values for C_{7+} component.

the intersection of this line and the T_c line and draw a critical locus through this point and the critical for methane. At the intersection of this locus and the operating temperature (80° F. in this example) read the convergence pressure. In this example a convergence pressure of 2300 psia was read; but since the K value charts do not have this convergence pressure the next higher pressure (3000) was used for the determination of the K values for all of the components except the C_{7+}.

In special cases the convergence pressure can be more accurately approximated on the first attempt by taking T_c as the critical temperature of the C_{7+}. This method works best when the operating pressure of the separator is low and the mole fraction of the C_{7+} is relatively high—such as in this example problem. Often the specific gravity of the C_{7+} is not available. If this is the case, then T_c is usually taken as half way between heptane and octane.

II. Estimation of the Equilibrium Constants (K) for the C_{7+}

Knowing the specific gravity and molecular weight (page 134 NGSMA manual) of the heptane plus component, the average boiling temperature, critical temperature, and the characterization factor can be obtained. With this information and the chart on page 155 of NGSMA, the K values at 160° and 100° F are read as 0.0255 and 0.0051 respectively. By plotting Log K versus temperature and performing a straight line extrapolation, the K value for the heptane plus at 80° F is obtained as 0.00295. (Refer to Figure 12-3.)

If the specific gravity of the heptane plus is unavailable then a K value which is an average between heptane and octane is usually assumed.

III. Calculation of the Composition of the Separator
   Exit Liquid Stream

The equations used in this portion of the solution of this problem can be derived as shown in Figure 12-4. By an overall material balance on the separator the following equation is obtained:

$$N = N_v + N_l \tag{12-11}$$

And by a component material balance:

$$Z_i N = X_i N_l + Y_i N_v \tag{12-12}$$

K_i was previously defined as $\dfrac{Y_i}{X_i}$ $\tag{12-1}$

Since X_i and Y_i are the mole fractions of the i th. component in the liquid and vapor streams respectively, the summation of $X_i = 1$ and the summation of $Y_i = 1$.

where:

   Z_i = the mole fraction of the i th. component in the entering stream

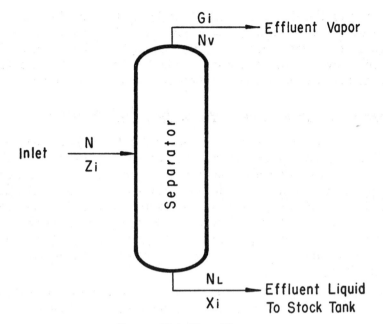

FIGURE 12-4. Flow Diagram

N = the number of moles in the entering stream
N_l = the number of moles in the effluent liquid stream
N_v = the number of moles in the effluent vapor stream.

Rearrangement of Equations (12-12) and (12-1) yields:

$$X_i = \frac{Z_i N}{K_i N_v + N_l} \qquad (12\text{-}13)$$

A 100 lb-mole basis is taken for the inlet stream; therefore N equals 100. The solution of this portion of the problem is trial and error using Equation (12-13) and the summation of $X_i = 1$. First, a value for N_v is assumed and X_i for each component is calculated from Equation (12-13). If the correct value of N_v was assumed then the summation of $X_i = 1$. However, if the summation of X_i is greater than *one*, the next value of N_v should be assumed smaller. When the summation of X_i starts approaching unity, the next value to assume for N_v can be obtained by plotting N_v, assumed, versus the summation of X_i and reading the N_v, assumed, at the intersection between the line connecting the N_v points and the summation of X_i equals one line. After X_i has been obtained with the desired accuracy then Y_i can be calculated from Equation

Table 12-4
Example Separator Calculations[1] (Example 12-3)

(1) Component	(2) Z_i	(3) $Z_i N$ (2) × 100	(4) K_i	(5) Trial 1 Assume: $N_v = 90, N_L = 10$ $K_i N_v + N_L$	(6) X_i (3) ÷ (5)
C_1	0.8610	86.10	52.0[2]	4690.0	0.01836[3]
C_2	0.0670	6.70	9.4	856.0	0.00783
C_3	0.0261	2.61	2.62	245.8	0.01062
iC_4	0.0050	0.50	1.00	100.0	0.00500
nC_4	0.0085	0.85	0.75	77.5	0.01097
iC_5	0.0026	0.26	0.305	37.45	0.00694
nC_5	0.0029	0.29	0.241	31.69	0.00915
C_6	0.0039	0.39	0.070	16.30	0.02393
C_{7+}	0.0230	2.30	0.00295[3]	10.266	0.22404
					Σ = 0.31684

(7) Trial 2 Assume: $N_v = 97.7, N_L = 2.3$ $K_i N_v + N_L$	(8) X_i	(9) Trial 3 Assume: $N_v = 97.699, N_L = 2.301$ $K_i N_v + N_L$	(10) X_i	(11) Y_i ($Y_i = K_i X_i$) (4) × (10)
5082.7	0.01694	5082.65	0.01694	0.88088
920.68	0.00728	920.67	0.00728	0.06843
258.27	0.01011	258.27	0.01011	0.02649
100.00	0.00500	100.00	0.00500	0.00500
75.575	0.01125	75.575	0.01125	0.00844
32.099	0.00810	32.0992	0.00810	0.00247
25.846	0.01122	25.8465	0.01122	0.00270
9.139	0.04267	9.13993	0.04267	0.00299
2.5882	0.88865	2.58921	0.88830	0.00262
	Σ = 1.00122		Σ = 1.00087	Σ = 1.00002

[1] Operating Conditions:

    Temp. = 80° F

    Press. = 50 psia

    N = 100 lb.-mole (basis)

[2] K values obtained from 1957 NGSMA, p. 155

[3] K value obtained from Figure 12-3

SCF Gas from Separator: $N_v = 97.699$

$$SCF = \text{No. of moles} \times \frac{379 \text{ ft.}^3 \text{ at } 60° \text{ F and } 14.7 \text{ psia}}{\text{mole}}$$

$$= 97.699 \times 379 = 27,028 \text{ SCF/100 lb.-moles inlet to separator}$$

(12-1). It should be noted that when the K values are large as in the case of the stock tank, the accuracy of the X_i's must be very good for the summation of Y_i to equal *one*. (Refer to Table 12-4.)

Table 12-5
Checking Convergence Pressure

(1) Component	(2) Mol. Fraction	(3) Moles (1) $\times$ N$_L$	(4) Mol. Weight	(5) Weight	(6) T$_c$	(7) T$_c$ $\times$ Weight (4) $\times$ (5)
C$_1$	omit lightest component					
C$_2$	0.00728	0.01675	30.1	0.50418	90.1	45.43
C$_3$	0.01011	0.02326	44.1	1.02577	206.3	211.62
iC$_4$	0.00500	0.01151	58.1	0.66873	275.0	183.90
nC$_4$	0.01125	0.02589	58.1	1.50421	305.6	459.69
iC$_5$	0.00810	0.01864	72.1	1.34394	370.0	497.26
nC$_5$	0.01122	0.02582	72.1	1.86162	385.9	718.40
C$_6$	0.04267	0.09818	86.2	8.46312	454.5	3846.49
C$_{7+}$	0.88830	2.04399	137.0	280.02663	590.0	165215.71
				$\Sigma = 295.39820$		$\Sigma = 171178.50$

Weighted Average T$_c$:

$$T_c = \frac{\Sigma \text{ Weight} \times T_c}{\Sigma \text{ Weight}} = \frac{171,178.5}{295.3982} = 579.5° \text{ F.}$$

Note: Convergence pressure is 3500 psia. Use K values for 4000 psia convergence pressure. For 50 psia and 80° F. the K values at 3000 psia and 4000 psia are equal. Therefore, it is not necessary to recalculate for the 4000 psia convergence pressure.

IV. Check Convergence Pressure

Using the procedure previously outlined and the composition (X$_i$) determined in Part III of the calculation procedure, the convergence pressure is reapproximated. If the K values at the reapproximated convergence pressure are different from the K values used in Part III, then X$_i$ must be recalculated using the new K values. This procedure should continue until the convergence pressure does not change. In this example problem the K values at the reapproximated pressure (4000) were not different from the values at a convergence pressure of 3000. This is because the K value charts at low operating pressures are relatively insensitive to convergence pressures. (Refer to Table 12-5.)

V. Example Calculations

Example calculations showing the conversion of N$_l$ and N$_v$ to bbls/100 lb-moles inlet and SCF/100 lb-moles inlet respectively are shown in Table 12-6. These data are converted to producing gas-oil ratio in Table 12-7.

Table 12-6
Example Stock Tank Calculations[1]

(1) Component	(2) Z_i[2]	(3) Z_iN[3]	(4) K_i	(5) Trial 1 Assume: $N_v/N = 0.05$ $N_v = 0.11505$, $N_L = 2.1860$ $K_iN_v + N_L$	(6) X_i (3) ÷ (5)
C_1	0.01694	0.03898	175.0	22.31975	0.00175
C_2	0.00728	0.01675	34.0	6.09770	0.00275
C_3	0.01011	0.02326	8.7	3.18694	0.00730
iC_4	0.00500	0.01151	3.32	2.56797	0.00448
nC_4	0.01125	0.02589	2.38	2.45982	0.01053
iC_5	0.00810	0.01864	0.89	2.28840	0.00815
nC_5	0.01122	0.02582	0.71	2.26769	0.01139
C_6	0.04267	0.09818	0.21	2.21016	0.04442
C_{7+}	0.88830	2.04398	0.00885[4]	2.18702	0.93460
					$\Sigma = 1.02537$

(7) Trial 2 Assume: $N_v/N = 0.015$ $N_v = 0.03452$, $N_L = 2.26648$ $K_iN_v + N_L$	(8) X_i (3) ÷ (7)	(9) $K_iN_v + N_L$	(10) Trial 3 Assume: $\dfrac{N_v}{N} = 0.0172$ $N_v = 0.0406$, $N_L = 2.2604$ X_i (3) ÷ (9)	(11) Y_i ($Y_i = K_iX_i$) (4) × (10)
8.30748	0.00469	9.3654	0.00416	0.72800
3.44016	0.00487	3.6408	0.00460	0.15640
2.56680	0.00906	2.61362	0.00890	0.07743
2.38109	0.00483	2.39519	0.00481	0.01597
2.34864	0.01102	2.35713	0.01098	0.02613
2.29720	0.00811	2.29653	0.00812	0.00723
2.29099	0.01127	2.28923	0.01128	0.00801
2.27373	0.04318	2.26893	0.04327	0.00909
2.26679	0.90171	2.26076	0.90411	0.00800
	$\Sigma = 0.99874$		$\Sigma = 1.00023$	$\Sigma = 1.03625$

[1] Operating Conditions:
    Temp. $= 80°$ F
    Press. $= 14.7$ psia

[2] Z_i terms for the stock tank are the X_i terms leaving the separator (Table 12-4)

[3] $N = 2.301$ lb.-moles effluent from separator (N_L from Table 12-4)

[4] K value obtained from Figure 12-5, where Temp. $= 80°$ F.

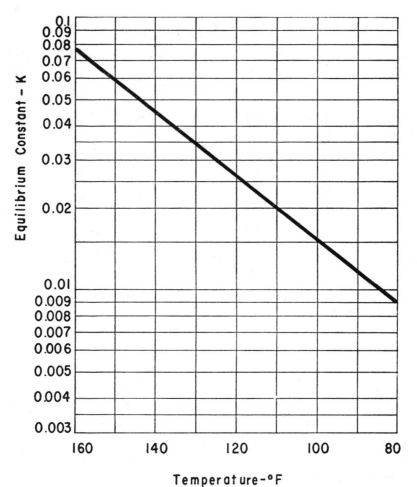

FIGURE 12-5. K values for C_{7+} component.

Liquid-Gas Ratio History

Figure 12-6 shows the liquid-gas ratio history of a typical gas-condensate reservoir. In this reservoir the initial reservoir pressure was 4,500 psi and dew point pressure was 3,240 psi. As the figure shows, from initial pressure down to dew point pressure there is no change in the separator liquid-gas ratio because there is no change in state of the fluids in the reservoir. However, below dew point pressure some of the heavier (i.e. higher molecular weight) hydrocarbons begin to condense in the reservoir. Since there is no liquid hydrocarbon saturation in the reservoir, these condensed hydro-

Table 12-7
Gas-Oil Ratio Calculations

(1) Component	(2) Mol Fraction X_i	(3) $X_i \times N_L$ (2) $\times$ 2.2604	(4) Mol. Wt.	(5) Weight (4) $\times$ (3)	(6) Sp. Gr.	(7) Pounds/ Sp. Gr. (5) ÷ (6)
C_1	0.00416	0.0094	16.0	0.15	0.30	0.50
C_2	0.00460	0.0104	30.1	0.313	0.374	0.837
C_3	0.00890	0.0201	44.1	0.886	0.0577	1.745
iC_4	0.00481	0.0109	58.1	0.663	0.5631	1.124
nC_4	0.01098	0.0248	58.1	1.441	0.5844	2.466
iC_5	0.00812	0.0184	72.1	1.327	0.6248	2.124
nC_5	0.01128	0.0255	72.1	1.839	0.6312	2.913
C_6	0.04327	0.0978	86.2	8.430	0.6640	12.696
C_{7+}	0.90411	2.0437	137.0	279.987	0.730	383.544
						$\Sigma = 407.949$

Gas from stock tanks: $N_v = 0.0406$ moles/100 lb. moles inlet to separator.

SCF Gas/100 lb. moles inlet to separator $= (0.0406)$ $(379$ SCF/mole$) =$
15.39 SCF per 100 moles inlet to separator

Liquid into stock tanks: Bbls/100 lb. moles inlet to separator $=$

$$\frac{407.949}{62.4 \frac{\#}{ft.^3} \times 5.61 \ ft.^3/bbl} = 1.165 \ bbls/per \ 100 \ lb.\text{-moles inlet to separator}$$

Producing Gas-Oil Ratio:

$$Prod. \ GOR = \frac{GOR \ from \ Separator \ (from \ Table \ 12\text{-}4)}{Liquid \ into \ Separator}$$

$$= \frac{37,028}{1.165} = 31,784 \ SCF/ST \ Bbl.$$

Note: The gas from the stock tanks is not included in the producing GOR as
this gas will probably escape through the vent lines.

carbons will not flow until an equilibrium hydrocarbon liquid saturation has been developed. The exact magnitude of the equilibrium
liquid hydrocarbon saturation will depend on relative permeability
considerations, such as wettability and pore configuration. In any
event, it will be relatively large, possibly as much as 20 to 30 percent.

As a result of this liquid condensation in the reservoir, the separator liquid-gas ratio will decrease below the dew point pressure,
and will continue to decrease until reservoir pressure declines below
the region of retrograde condensation. This pressure is marked x
on the vertical dotted line of Figure 12-6. Below this pressure, the
liquid in the reservoir should begin to revaporize, with a resulting

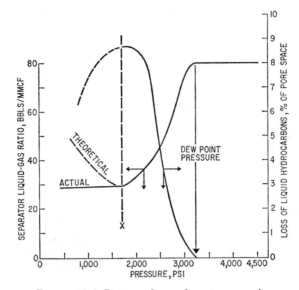

FIGURE 12-6. Retrograde condensate reservoir.

increase in separator liquid-gas ratio, as shown by the dashed line in Figure 12-6. However, as previously explained, once the liquids have formed in the reservoir, their surface forces will tend to keep them in the liquid phase, and the actual separator liquid-gas ratio will remain essentially constant during the remaining life of the reservoir.

The loss of liquid hydrocarbons, expressed as percent of pore space, is also shown in Figure 12-6. In this particular fluid, the maximum liquid hydrocarbon saturation is approximately 9 percent, which is probably below the equilibrium liquid hydrocarbon saturation.

Chapter 13

ECONOMICS

Reservoir studies are actually one type of engineering evaluation. Thus all the elements of an evaluation are also applicable to the economic considerations of a reservoir study.

As has been stated many times previously, the oil producer is in business to make money, and therefore the engineers and other employees of an oil producing company should confine their activities to projects which, either directly or indirectly, can be expected to yield an operating profit.

The income from oil and gas production is usually received monthly, and the income from a particular property may continue for many years, either at a declining rate or at a constant rate followed by a declining rate. In order to properly interpret the relative merits of different reservoir operating programs, the engineer must determine the relative values of the income from the various possible operating programs.

A fundamental concept in economic analyses is the value of money. It is readily apparent that one dollar received ten years from now is not as valuable as one dollar received today. The dollar received today could be put to work (loaned at interest, used as capital in a business, etc.) and at the end of ten years it would have generated more money and the original dollar would then be worth considerably more. This reasoning led to the development of the "present worth" concept in determining the actual value of money due sometime in the future.

Many methods have been used in analyzing the economic aspects of investments. Probably no one method is entirely suitable for the innumerable variations in investment situations. An investment can be viewed from several different standpoints. For example, which investment would be more attractive, one which yields the greatest *dollar* or the greatest *percent* return? If the funds available for investment are limited and all available funds can be used in an investment, then the investment yielding the greatest *per-*

centage return would be more attractive. On the other hand, if the funds available for investment are quite large, and if all the funds are not required for a particular investment and some of the funds will lie unused, the investment yielding the largest *dollar* return would probably be preferred.

Another typical investment problem is deciding whether to select a short-term investment yielding a relatively high return, or a long-term investment yielding a more moderate return. Here, again, the situation of the particular investor would in a large measure, determine which of the two investments was the more attractive. If the future investment prospects did not appear good, or if the overhead costs as a result of having to reinvest capital for short-term investments were high, then the long-term investment yielding a more moderate return might be preferred.

Evaluating the element of risk is another factor which is an important aspect of investment selection. None of the methods commonly used in evaluating investments include the element of risk. The types of risk are so varied that it would be physically impossible to include the risk factor along with the other factors pertinent to the economic analysis. However, the fact that the element of risk cannot be included with the other economic aspects of the problem does not preclude a thorough analysis and discussion of the various elements of risk involved in the particular problem under study. Then the company management can compare the merits of the investment with the degree of risk involved to determine whether the proposal is a suitable investment. For example, if the purchase of an oil property is being considered, a one-well lease has a higher element of risk involved than a multi-well lease. If the well on a one-well lease were destroyed, the income from the property would completely cease, while the destruction of one well on a multi-well lease would cause only a partial reduction in income.

The preceding examples illustrate the fact that each investment opportunity must be investigated in the light of circumstances peculiar to the particular investor involved. Several methods of comparing investment possibilities have been evolved which have particular merit in oil and gas operations. These methods are:

1. present worth
2. profit-to-investment ratio
3. payout time
4. rate of return

1. Present Worth

As previously discussed, the concept of present worth attempts to determine the actual present-day value of future income. This is accomplished by applying suitable *discount factors* to the future income. These discount factors can be evaluated as follows:

The interest earned on money can be determined by multiplying the Principal invested by the Interest Rate, or expressed in mathematical form:

$$I = P \times r \qquad (13\text{-}1)$$

where:

I = Interest earned, dollars

P = Principal invested, dollars

r = Interest rate during the interest period, fraction.

Interest on money is paid at stipulated intervals, and Equation (13-1) actually determines the interest generated during any one period, where the principal amount is P. Since oil income is of a periodic nature it is necessary to examine the effects of the present-worth concept on this income.

A. At the end of the first period the amount of capital on hand would be equal to the principal at the beginning of the first period plus the interest earned during the period. Expressed in equation form, this is:

$$A = P + I \qquad (13\text{-}2)$$

where:

A = Amount of capital at the end of the period, dollars.

Combining Equations (13-1) and (13-2) results in:

$$A = P + Pr = P(1 + r) \qquad (13\text{-}3)$$

B. At the end of the second period the interest earned can still be expressed by Equation (13-1); however, the principal has now been increased by the interest earned during the first period. Therefore, the interest earned during the second period can be calculated by the following equation:

$$I_2 = [P(1 + r)]r \qquad (13\text{-}4)$$

The term within the brackets of Equation (13-4) can be recognized as the amount of capital on hand at the end of the first period, as calculated by Equation (13-3). The amount of capital on hand at the end of the period can still be represented by $A = P + I$, or:

$$A = \underset{\text{(Principal)}}{P(1 + r)} + \underset{\text{(Interest)}}{P(1 + r)r} \qquad (13\text{-}5)$$

or:

$$A = [P(1 + r)][1 + r] \qquad (13\text{-}6)$$

which reduces to:

$$A = P(1 + r)^2 \qquad (13\text{-}7)$$

Equation (13-7) shows the new principal amount available at the end of the second interest conversion period.

C. At the end of the third period:

$$I = P_3r = [P(1 + r)^2]r \qquad (13\text{-}8)$$

where:

P_3 = Principal amount available at the beginning of the third period, dollars.

Since: $A = P + I$, then:

$$A = P(1 + r)^2 + P(1 + r)^2r \qquad (13\text{-}9)$$

After factoring $P(1 + r)^2$ from the right-hand side of Equation (13-8), the result is:

$$A = [P(1 + r)^2][1 + r] \qquad (13\text{-}10)$$

which can be simplified to:

$$A = P(1 + r)^3 \qquad (13\text{-}11)$$

Examination of the equations developed for the first three periods leads to the development of a general equation for determining the amount of money generated:

$$A = P(1 + r)^n \qquad (13\text{-}12)$$

where:

n = Number of periods of interest conversion.

Equation (13-12) can be rearranged into a more convenient form as follows:

$$P = \frac{A}{(1 + r)^n} \qquad (13\text{-}13)$$

If an amount of money A, will be available at some future date, the present value, or present worth, of that money can be determined by solving for P in Equation (13-13). Or, viewing the situation from another standpoint, the capital amount P, if put to work at interest, would be increased to the amount A, after n periods.

The "discount factor" which has been referred to previously is the reciprocal of the denominator in Equation (13-13), or:

$$\text{Discount Factor} = F = \frac{1}{(1 + r)^n} \qquad (13\text{-}14)$$

To determine the present worth of an amount due sometime in the future the following equation can be used:

$$P = F \times A \qquad (13\text{-}15)$$

where F, the discount factor, is determined from Equation (13-14).

Interest rates are usually quoted on a yearly basis. For example, if a lender charges an interest rate of 6 percent on the money he lends, he generally means that his interest rate is *6 percent per year*. Equations (13-1) through (13-14) were developed using an interest factor which was the "interest rate for the period." These equations can be modified to use the annual interest rate, since:

$$r = \frac{i}{p} \qquad (13\text{-}16)$$

where: i = annual interest rate, fraction

p = number of interest conversion periods per year.

Thus, Equation (13-12), after combining with Equation (13-16) becomes:

$$A = P\left(1 + \frac{i}{p}\right)^n \qquad (13\text{-}17)$$

and Equation (13-13) becomes:

$$P = \frac{A}{\left(1 + \frac{i}{p}\right)^n} \qquad (13\text{-}18)$$

Likewise, the discount factor, F, now reduces to:

$$F = \frac{1}{\left(1 + \frac{i}{p}\right)^n} \qquad (13\text{-}19)$$

Example Problem 13-1

Calculate the present value of $1,000 to be received one year from date. The interest rate is **6 percent** per annum, simple interest.

Answer: In this case there is **only** one interest conversion period, and since this is simple interest there is only one interest conversion per year. Therefore $n = 1$ and $P = 1$. The first part of the problem is to calculate the discount factor.

$$F = \frac{1}{\left(1 + \dfrac{i}{p}\right)^n} = \frac{1}{\left(1 + \dfrac{.06}{1}\right)^1} = 0.943$$

then $P = F \times A = 0.943 \times \$1,000$
$$P = \$943.00$$

A separate discount factor must be computed for each period. This is best illustrated by a typical problem.

Example Problem 13-2

Calculate the present value of $1,000 to be received in two installments of $500 each. First payment is due in 6 months and the final payment is due in 12 months. Interest rate is 6 percent per annum.

Answer: Since payments are to be received twice each year, $p = 2$. As there are two payments, two different discount factors will have to be calculated.

$$F_1 = \frac{1}{\left(1 + \dfrac{i}{p}\right)^n} = \frac{1}{\left(1 + \dfrac{0.06}{2}\right)^1} = 0.971$$

$$P_1 = F_1 \times A_1 = 0.971 \times \$500 = \$485.50$$

$$F_2 = \frac{1}{\left(1 + \dfrac{i}{p}\right)^n} = \frac{1}{\left(1 + \dfrac{0.06}{2}\right)^2} = 0.943$$

$$P_2 = F_2 \times A_2 = 0.943 \times \$500 = \$471.50$$

Total present worth $= P_1 + P_2$
$$= \$485.50 + 471.50$$
$$= \$957.00$$

Since oil and gas income is normally received monthly, the interest conversion periods are also monthly, and there are 12

Table 13-1
Discount Factor ... 6% Per Period Interest Rate

Period	Discount Factor	Period	Discount Factor	Period	Discount Factor
1	0.9434	21	0.2942	41	0.0918
2	0.8900	22	0.2775	42	0.0865
3	0.8396	23	0.2618	43	0.0816
4	0.7921	24	0.2470	44	0.0770
5	0.7473	25	0.2330	45	0.0727
6	0.7050	26	0.2198	46	0.0685
7	0.6651	27	0.2074	47	0.0646
8	0.6274	28	0.1956	48	0.0610
9	0.5919	29	0.1846	49	0.0575
10	0.5584	30	0.1741	50	0.0543
11	0.5268	31	0.1643	51	0.0512
12	0.4970	32	0.1550	52	0.0483
13	0.4688	33	0.1462	53	0.0456
14	0.4423	34	0.1379	54	0.0430
15	0.4173	35	0.1301	55	0.0406
16	0.3936	36	0.1227	56	0.0383
17	0.3714	37	0.1158	57	0.0361
18	0.3503	38	0.1092	58	0.0341
19	0.3305	39	0.1031	59	0.0321
20	0.3118	40	0.0972	60	0.0303

interest conversion periods per year. Table 13-1 shows for 60 periods the discount factor for an interest rate of 6 percent per period.

Quite often it becomes necessary to calculate the present value of monthly oil or gas income which will last for many years, in which case the number of individual calculations becomes very large. In order to save time and simplify the calculations the income is determined by years and the assumption is made that this income is received once each year, in the middle of the year. The correct formula for the discount factor where this simplifying assumption is used is:

$$F = \frac{1}{\left(1 + \dfrac{i}{p}\right)^{\frac{2n-1}{2}}} \tag{13-20}$$

For the first interest conversion, $n = 1$, and the exponent in Equation (13-20) is equal to 0.5, which is correct because the conversion takes place at the mid-point of the first year. The second interest

Table 13-2

Discount Factors for Various Interest Rates. Money to be Received
at the Mid-Point of the Year.

Year	Discount Factors for Various Interest Rates				
	6%	10%	20%	30%	40%
1	.972	.954	.913	.878	.846
2	.915	.867	.762	.675	.603
3	.865	.789	.634	.519	.432
4	.813	.718	.528	.399	.308
5	.770	.652	.440	.307	.220
6	.727	.594	.367	.236	.158
7	.685	.538	.306	.182	.112
8	.647	.490	.255	.140	.081
9	.610	.446	.213	.108	.057
10	.575	.405	.177	.083	.041
15	.430	.252	.071	.022	.008
20	.321	.156	.029	.006	.001
25	.241	.098	.011	.002	—

conversion takes place one year later, or one and one-half years from the beginning. The exponent is now $1.5 \left[\dfrac{(2)\ (2) - 1}{2} = 1.5 \right]$.

Table 13-2 shows discount factors computed by this method, where it is arbitrarily assumed that the interest is received once each year at the mid-point of the year.

Equations (13-14) and (13-20) will plot as a straight line if logarithm F is plotted on the ordinate and n is plotted on ordinary cartesian coordinates on the abscissa. This semi-log plot of discount factor versus the number of the period may be quite useful where a large number of calculations at varying interest rates may be required.

There is a definite lack of agreement as to the proper interest rate to be used in developing a discount factor. One school of thought adheres to the concept that the interest rate used should be that for which money can be borrowed, and therefore represents only the cost of using money. Another concept is that the interest rate used in determination of discount factor should be the interest rate actually earned by the capital of the organization. For example, many major oil companies earn approximately 12 percent on their entire capital. Many smaller organizations, with less capital with which to do business must earn 15 to 25 percent on their money.

Either of the two preceding methods can be safely used provided the company management, who will be using the information, understands which interest rate was used. However, the rate which reflects the cost of money (such as borrowing from a bank) is normally the preferred rate.

Large discount factors, i.e. large interest rates, are sometimes used in an attempt to reduce the element of risk or to increase the conservative nature of the report. This is clearly an unjustified use of the discount factor, and its use for these purposes is not justified. The discount factor should be used solely to indicate the value of money.

2. Profit-to-Investment Ratio

This is a simple factor which nevertheless is an excellent measure of the investment potential of a particular project. Reduced to a formula, the profit-to-investment ratio is:

$$PIR = \frac{\text{Cumulative net income} - \text{original investment}}{\text{Original Investment}}$$

(13-21)

where:

PIR = Profit to Investment Ratio

Example Problem 13-3

Determine the profit-to-investment ratio for a repressuring plant, where the cost of the plant will be $200,000 and the additional net profit as a result of the plant installation will be $100,000 per year for 12 years.

Answer:

$$PIR = \frac{(\$100,000 \times 12) - \$200,000}{\$200,000} = 5$$

It should be noted that a discount factor is not applied to the net income when determining the profit to investment ratio.

3. Payout Time

The use of payout time for comparing investments is probably the most commonly used yardstick. Payout time is defined as the number of years (or months) required to pay out the original investment from the net income from the investment.

Example Problem 13-4

Determine the payout time for a secondary recovery project where the initial cost of the project is $350,000. Net income from the property is expected to be $100,000 per year for the first two years, after which the net income will be reduced at the rate of 10 percent per year.

Answer: The yearly income from the property is as follows:

Year	Net Income	Cumulative Net Income
1	$100,000	$100,000
2	100,000	200,000
3	90,000	290,000
4	81,000	371,000

From the preceding table it can be seen that after three years the property will not yet have paid for itself, but after four years it will have more than paid for itself. After three years the cumulative net income will be $290,000. Therefore, only $60,000 will be remaining before payout. During the fourth year the net income is expected to be $81,000. The fraction of the fourth year required to payout the $60,000 will be:

$$\frac{\$60,000}{\$81,000} = 0.74$$

Thus the payout time will be three years plus 0.74 years, or 3.74 years.

The payout method of comparing investments is simple, straightforward, and usually is a reliable guide. It should be noted that this method does not take into consideration the present value of money invested. The principal limitation of the payout method is that no consideration is given to the ultimate life of the prospect. A property having a payout time of 4 years and an ultimate life of 20 years would probably be more desirable than a property having a payout time of 3 years but with an ultimate life of only 4 years.

4. Rate of Return

A yardstick which has received considerable attention in recent years is the rate-of-return method. This method reduces the future income from a property to a present worth value. It has the additional advantage of taking into consideration the entire earnings of a particular prospect. The rate of return is actually that interest rate which will yield a total present value of future income which is exactly equal to the initial investment. Expressed in mathematical form this is:

$$\Sigma_0^n \, FA = II \qquad\qquad (13\text{-}21)$$

where:

II = Initial investment, dollars.

Unless certain simplifying assumptions are made, rate of return calculations involve a trial-and-error solution. A short example calculation will be used to illustrate one method of calculating rate of return.

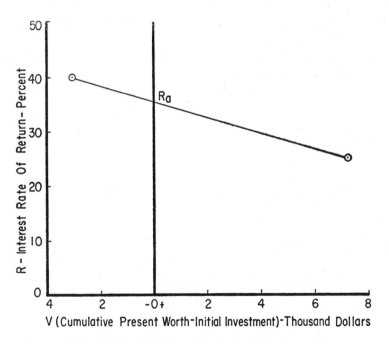

FIGURE 13-1. Graphical solution of determination of rate of return.

Example Problem 13-5

Determine the interest rate of return for a potential investment requiring $40,000 initial investment and yielding $20,000 per year net income, payable at the end of each year, for a period of four years.

Answer: Since this is a trial-and-error solution, select two values of interest rate, one which is larger than the actual rate, and one which is smaller than the actual rate. With the actual rate bracketed, mathematical calculations will yield a solution to the problem.

A plot of R, interest rate of return, vs. V, the difference between cumulative present worth and initial investment, is made as shown in Figure 13-1.

The two interest rates chosen are shown as R_1 and R_2. Since this is a straight line over a short range the slope of the line remains constant and the following mathematical relationships hold true.

$$\text{slope} = \frac{R_1 - R_a}{V_1 - V_a} = \frac{R_1 - R_2}{V_1 - V_2} \qquad (13\text{-}23)$$

where:

R_1 = Assumed value of rate of return which is higher than the actual value, percent

R_2 = Assumed value of rate of return which is less than the actual value, percent

R_a = Actual value of rate of return, percent

V_1 = Cumulative present worth of R_1 rate of return minus initial investment, dollars

V_2 = Cumulative present worth at R_2 rate of return minus initial investment, dollars

V_a = Cumulative present worth at the actual rate of return, R_a, minus the initial investment. By definition V_a must be zero.

It should be noted that this plot is not actually a straight line, but it usually does not deviate much from a straight line if the two interest rates are not greatly different. If in doubt about the answer derived from the plot, the answer can always be tested by direct calculation to determine whether or not it is correct.

Rearranging Equation (13-23) and solving for R_a:

$$R_a = R_1 - \frac{(V_1 - V_a)\,(R_1 - R_2)}{V_1 - V_2} \qquad (13\text{-}24)$$

However, since $V_a = 0$, Equation (13-24) reduces to:

$$R_a = R_1 - \frac{V_1(R_1 - R_2)}{V_1 - V_2} \qquad (13\text{-}25)$$

The following table shows the complete calculations for a rate-of-return determination:

| Year | Income | $R_1 = 40\%$ | | $R_2 = 25\%$ | |
		Discount Factor	Present Worth	Discount Factor	Present Worth
1	$20,000	0.714	$14,280	0.800	$16,000
2	20,000	0.510	10,200	0.640	12,800
3	20,000	0.364	7,280	0.512	10,240
4	20,000	0.260	5,200	0.408	8,160
			Total $36,960		$47,200

$$V_1 = 36,960 - 40,000 = -\$3,040$$

$$V_2 = 47,200 - 40,000 = \quad \$7,200$$

$$R_a = R_1 - \frac{V_1(R_1 - R_2)}{V_1 - V_2}$$

$$= 40 - \frac{(-3,040)\ (40 - 25)}{-3040 - 7200} = 40 - 4.5 = 35.5\%$$

which agrees with the graphical answer obtained in **Figure 13-1**.

The use of rate-of-return calculations as a guide in investment selection involves two serious limitations: (1) Because of the high interest rates sometimes used, the value of future income becomes insignificant after only a few years. The example problem shows this quite clearly. This approach may be especially fallacious for a large company which will be in business for many years. Income due in 10 or 20 years, although having little effect on rate-of-return calculations, is certainly very important to such a company, (2) The rate-of-return calculations presuppose that all income from the prospect will be reinvested at the same interest rate of return. When a prospect yielding a relatively high rate of return on a short-term investment is compared to a prospect yielding a more moderate rate of return on a long-term investment, erroneous conclusions as to the better investment will often be reached.

One method which has been used to overcome the disadvantage in comparing investments of unequal life is to extend the comparative period of the shorter-term investment to the same length of time as the longer-term investment, using the company's average annual rate-of-return on past investments for the extended period of the shorter-term investment. For example, if two investments are being considered, one of which will last 20 years, and the other will last 10 years, the rate of return will first be determined for the two investments. The shorter-term investment will next be continued for another 10 years using the company's past average annual rate of return for computing the discount factor for the last ten years. Some decision must be made regarding the income during the last ten years. In the case of constant income, this same income can be continued, but in the case of a declining income it may be more desirable to continue reducing the income. The cumulative present worth of the extended shorter-term investment is now used as the initial investment, and a single average rate of return is computed for the new assumed initial investment and the longer term. This new average rate of return is then compared with the rate of return for the longer-term investment to aid in selecting the better investment.

An example problem will be used to illustrate the method.

Example Problem 13-6

Two potential investments are being studied to determine which is the better. A review of previous company investments shows that the average rate of return on all investments has been 15%. One of the potential investments will require an initial investment of $23,300, and will last two years, producing an income of $20,000 per year. The other potential investment will require an initial investment of $40,000, and will last four years. This latter investment is identical to the one worked in Example 13-5, and, as has been shown in the previous example will yield a rate of return of 35.5%.

Answer: The first step is to determine the rate of return for the short term investment. As this is a trial-and-error solution, a rate of return of 45% will be assumed.

Year	Income	R = 45% Discount Factor	Present Worth
1	$20,000	.690	$13,800
2	20,000	.475	9,500
			Total $23,300

Since the first estimate yielded the correct answer, it is unnecessary to continue with the trial and error procedure as before.

In order to properly compare the short-term investment with the long-term investment, the short-term investment will now be continued for two additional years with a rate of return of 15%. Since the income was constant for the first two years, it will be continued in the same amount for the next two years. The following table shows the procedure for developing the present worth of the extended investment:

Year	Income	Discount Factor		Present Worth
		45%	15%	
1	$20,000	.690		$13,800
2	20,000	.475		9,500
3	20,000		.657	13,140
4	20,000		.572	11,440

Total $47,880

The cumulative present worth of $47,880 will now be used to determine an average rate of return on the extended investment. Two interest rates, 40% and 25%, will be assumed in order to calculate the proper rate of return. This is accomplished in the following table:

Year	Income	Discount Factor $R = 40\%$	Present Worth	Discount Factor $R = 25\%$	Present Worth
1	$20,000	0.714	$14,280	0.800	$16,000
2	20,000	0.510	10,200	0.640	12,800
3	20,000	0.364	7,280	0.512	10,240
4	20,000	0.260	5,200	0.408	8,160
			Total $36,960		$47,200

$$V_1 = \$36,960 - \$47,880 = -\$10,920$$

$$V_2 = \$47,200 - \$47,880 = -\$680$$

$$R_a = R_1 - \frac{V_1(R_1 - R_2)}{V_1 - V_2}$$

$$= 40 - \frac{(-\$10,920)\ (40 - 25)}{(-\$10,920) - (-\$680)} = 40 - 16 = 24\%$$

Thus, if the short-term investment is continued for two additional years at the company's average rate of return, the overall rate of return on the investment is now reduced from 45% to 24%, which materially alters the investment picture.

It is not suggested that the preceding analysis be used in analyzing all investment situations. For example, where a short-term investment yielding a relatively high return is available and if it is anticipated that at the end of the short term, other good investments, also yielding relatively high returns, will be available, then the procedure used in the preceding example might lead to erroneous conclusions. Another factor of importance in many companies is the cost of acquisition of the investment. Where acquisition costs are high, the longer term investments are preferred in order to reduce these acquisition costs. In the final analysis all of the factors previously mentioned should be analyzed to determine their effects on the company's particular investment situation.

Rate of return calculations should not be used as the sole guide to investment selection. The other three factors discussed, present worth, profit-to-investment ratio, and payout time should also be considered in the overall analysis of investment opportunities.

At the present time, federal income taxes have a pronounced effect on potential investments in the oil industry, and no investment should be recommended without determining the effect of income tax on the investment. In fact the income tax aspects of the investment may be most important single aspect of the entire proposal. Different components of the petroleum industry may have different tax rates, each with their own peculiar advantages and disadvantages. For example, statutory depletion can be applied in lease income, but it cannot be applied to income from gasoline plants. Thus the location of lease or plant extraction equipment may be important from a tax standpoint. In Chapter 11, *Gas Reservoirs*, Table 11-1 showed a Gas Property Valuation Work Sheet, where the effects of depletion, depreciation, and income tax were illustrated in an example problem.

Methods of Justifying Expenditures

Expenditures can normally be justified only if they realize a profit or increase the safety of certain operations where human lives may be in danger. This last factor is more or less intangible and each situation must be examined on its own merits; therefore it will not be discussed further.

Capital outlays, in order to be justified, must show a net profit which is at least acceptable to the company's minimum profit requirements. In addition to the standard methods of justifying expenditures, such as increased oil recovery from pressure maintenance projects, or additional oil recovery from secondary recovery projects, several other methods peculiar to reservoir engineering problems can be used as a justification for expenditures of capital.

As mentioned in previous chapters, control of a gas cap is requisite to efficient operation of a petroleum reservoir. A shrinking gas cap will cause the loss of substantial oil which might otherwise be recovered. Normally there is little or no oil saturation in the gas cap, and if oil moves into the original gas zone there will necessarily be some residual oil saturation remaining in this portion of the gas cap at abandonment. The magnitude of this loss may be quite large, depending upon the area of the gas-oil contact, the rate of gas cap shrinkage, and the relative permeability characteristics of the reservoir. The difference between the original volume of the gas cap and the volume occupied by the gas cap at any subsequent time is a measure of the volume of oil which has migrated into the gas cap.

Shrinking Gas Cap

If the size of the original gas cap in barrels is denoted by G, then the expansion of the original free gas resulting from reducing the pressure from p_i to p is:

$$\text{Expansion of Original Gas Cap} = G\left(\frac{B_g}{B_{gi}} - 1\right) \quad (13\text{-}26)$$

If the gas cap is shrinking, then the volume of produced gas must be larger than the gas cap expansion. All of the oil which moves into the gas cap will not be lost as this oil will also be subject to the various driving mechanisms. There was originally no oil saturation in the gas cap; therefore the oil which will be lost is the residual oil saturation remaining at abandonment. If the cumulative volume of gas cap gas produced, in standard cubic feet is denoted by g, then for a shrinking gas cap, the volume of gas cap shrinkage is equal to:

$$\text{Gas cap shrinkage, bbl.} = g\,B_g - G\left(\frac{B_g}{B_{gi}} - 1\right) \quad (13\text{-}27)$$

Also, from the well-known volumetric equation it can be shown that:

$$g\,B_g - G\left(\frac{B_g}{B_{gi}} - 1\right) = 7758\,Ah\,\phi\,S_g \quad (13\text{-}28)$$

where:

A = Average cross-sectional area of the gas-oil contact, acres.
h = Average change in depth of the gas-oil contact, feet.
ϕ = porosity, fraction
S_g = Reduction in gas saturation in the volume where shrinkage is taking place, fraction.

However:

$$S_g = 1 - S_{wi} - S_{gr} \qquad (13\text{-}29)$$

where:

S_{gr} = Gas saturation in the zone after gas cap shrinkage occurs, fraction.

Combining quations (13-28) and (13-29) results in:

$$g\,B_g - G\left(\frac{B_g}{B_{gi}} - 1\right) = 7758\ Ah\phi\ (1 - S_{wi} - S_{gr}) \qquad (13\text{-}30)$$

The volume of oil lost as a result of oil migration to the gas cap can also be calculated from the volumetric equation as follows:

$$\text{Oil lost, barrels} = 7758\ Ah\ \phi\ S_{org}/B_{oa} \qquad (13\text{-}31)$$

where:

S_{org} = Residual oil saturation in the zone of shrinkage after abandonment, fraction.
B_{oa} = Formation volume factor at abandonment.

As the $7758\ Ah\phi$ cannot often be determined directly, Equations (13-30) and 13-31) can be combined as follows:

$$\text{Oil lost, barrels} = \frac{\left[g\,B_g - G\left(\frac{B_g}{B_{gi}} - 1\right)\right](S_{org})}{(1 - S_{wi} - S_{gr})\,B_{oa}} \qquad (13\text{-}32)$$

The residual oil saturation remaining in the gas zone can be determined by knowing the relative permeability characteristics of the reservoir and the mechanism by which this oil in the gas cap will be produced. There are four principal methods or combinations of methods by which this oil can be produced:

1. Depletion drive
2. Future expansion of the gas cap
3. Water drive
4. Gravity drainage

A knowledge of the producing mechanism is essential as there will be a wide variation in the residual oil saturation left by the different driving mechanisms.

Control of the gas cap size is very often a reliable guide to the efficiency of reservoir operation. A shrinking gas cap can be controlled by either shutting in wells which are producing large quantities of gas cap gas or by returning gas (or in some cases water) to the gas cap portion of the reservoir. In many cases, the shrinkage cannot be completely eliminated by shutting in wells producing excessive quantities of gas cap gas, as there is a practical limit to the number of wells which can be shut in. The return of fluids, either gas or water, to the gas cap may be the only practical method of eliminating or reducing gas cap shrinkage. The amount of oil lost by the shrinking gas cap can very well be the engineer's most important economic justification for the installation of gas-return facilities. Normally, there must be some economic justification for this relatively large investment.

The terms in Equation (13-32) are familiar material balance terms. If there have been any material balance calculations performed for a reservoir, these terms will be readily available. Even though no material balance work has been performed, the data for the terms in the equations are normally not difficult to obtain.

Expanding Gas Cap

In order to recover the maximum amount of oil, the most efficient oil-expulsion mechanism available must be utilized. If a water-drive is present this will normally be the most efficient oil-recovery mechanism. Where an active water-drive is present, good reservoir engineering practice dictates that the gas cap shall remain stationary. If there is no water drive, then an expanding gas cap will probably be the most efficient oil-recovery mechanism available. The reservoir in this case should be operated to take maximum advantage of the expanding gas, minimizing as much as possible the recovery of oil by the depletion drive process.

A reservoir produced with an active water drive in such a manner that the gas cap is also expanding may result in the loss of substantial oil which could have been recovered with the proper control and operation of the reservoir. The amount of oil which will be lost because of this expanding gas cap is determined by the volume of net gas cap expansion and the difference between the displacement efficiencies of gas and water. If the relative permeability relationships are such that the displacement of oil by gas is as efficient as the displacement of oil by water, then of course no oil will be lost by reason of an expanding gas cap.

If the gas cap is expanding, the net gas cap expansion is equal to the expansion of the original gas cap minus the gas cap gas production, or expressed mathematically:

$$\text{Net gas cap expansion, bbls.} = G\left(\frac{B_g}{B_{gi}} - 1\right) - g\,B_g$$

$$(13\text{-}33)$$

The net gas cap expansion represents the gas invasion into the original oil zone. Using the volumetric equation, this is:

$$G\left(\frac{B_g}{B_{gi}} - 1\right) - g\,B_g = 7758\,Ah\,\phi\,S_{go} \qquad (13\text{-}34)$$

where:

S_{go} = Gas saturation in the oil zone, fraction.

The gas saturation in the oil zone can also be calculated by:

$$S_{go} = 1 - S_{wi} - S_{og} \qquad (13\text{-}35)$$

where:

S_{og} = residual oil saturation resulting from expanding gas, fraction.

Combining Equations (13-34) and (13-35):

$$G\left(\frac{B_g}{B_{gi}} - 1\right) - g\,B_g = 7758\,Ah\phi\,(1 - S_{wi} - S_{og}) \qquad (13\text{-}36)$$

The oil remaining in the expanded gas zone at abandonment is equal to:

$$V_{og} = \frac{7758\,Ah\phi\,S_{og}}{B_{oa}} \qquad (13\text{-}37)$$

where:

V_{og} = oil remaining after gas cap expansion, barrels
S_{og} = residual oil saturation in the gas-invaded zone, fraction.

If the oil from this same zone had been produced by a water drive the oil remaining at abandonment would have been:

$$V_{ow} = \frac{7758 \, Ah\phi \, S_{ow}}{B_{oa}} \qquad (13\text{-}38)$$

where:

V_{ow} = oil remaining by water drive, barrels
S_{ow} = residual oil saturation after water drive, fraction.

The oil lost as a result of using the less efficient gas drive is:

$$\text{oil lost, barrels} = V_{og} - V_{ow} \qquad (13\text{-}39)$$

Combining Equations (13-37) and (13-38), and (13-39) results in:

$$\text{Oil lost, barrels} = \frac{7758 \, Ah\phi}{B_{oa}} (S_{og} - S_{ow}) \qquad (13\text{-}40)$$

Since the term $Ah\phi$ in Equation (13-40) may be difficult to evaluate, it can be determined indirectly by using another equation. Combining Equations (13-36) and (13-40):

$$\text{Oil lost, bbls.} = \frac{\left[G \left(\frac{B_g}{B_{gi}} - 1 \right) - g \, B_g \right] (S_{og} - S_{ow})}{(1 - S_{wi} - S_{og}) \, B_{oa}} \qquad (13\text{-}41)$$

Equation (13-41) assumes that the expanding gas will reduce the oil saturation in the original oil zone to below the economic limit. Normally it would not be economical to continue producing the reservoir until the encroaching water sweeps that portion of the oil zone initially swept by gas.

An expanding gas cap can be controlled by:

1. Increasing gas cap withdrawals to such an extent that the net gas cap expansion is zero.
2. Regulating the reservoir fluid withdrawal rates to such an extent that the reservoir pressure decrease is zero.
3. Returning water to the formation for pressure maintenance.

Although the first method will physically control the expanding gas cap, it normally would not constitute good reservoir engineering practice as this would cause a more rapid decline in reservoir pressure. Therefore, the latter two methods are preferred. The simplest, least expensive method for controlling gas cap expansion is by regulating reservoir fluid withdrawals to such an extent that the encroaching water can move into the oil zone at the same rate that the oil is withdrawn.

Each reservoir engineering problem will have characteristic features which can be used as an economic justification for any proposed expenditures. The economic aspects of each of these features should be adequately described as the principal justification for the expenditure of money is the ultimate profit which will be realized as a result of the expenditure.

Appendix

STANDARD LETTER SYMBOLS

Quantities in Alphabetical Order

		Dimensions
absolute permeability	k	L^2
acceleration of gravity	g	L/t^2
area	A	L^2
atmospheric pressure	p_a	m/Lt^2
average or mean value of a quantity x	$\bar{x}$	$[x]$
average pressure	$\bar{p}$	m/Lt^2
bottom-hole pressure, flowing	p_{wf}	m/Lt^2
bottom-hole pressure, general	p_w	m/Lt^2
bottom-hole pressure, static	p_{ws}	m/Lt^2
bubble-point (saturation) pressure	p_b	m/Lt^2
bulk volume	V_b	L^3
capillary pressure	P_c	m/Lt^2
casing pressure, flowing	p_{cf}	m/Lt^2
casing pressure, static	p_{cs}	m/Lt^2
coefficient, diffusion	D	L^2/t
coefficient, thermal cubic expansion	β beta	$1/T$
common logarithm, base 10	log	
component, mole fraction of, in liquid phase	x	
component, mole fraction of, in mixture	z	
component, mole fraction of, in vapor phase	y	
compressibility	c	Lt^2/m
compressibility factor or deviation factor for gas ($z = pV/nRT$)	z	
compressibility, formation (rock)	c_f	Lt^2/m
compressibility, gas	c_g	Lt^2/m
compressibility, oil	c_o	Lt^2/m
compressibility, water	c_w	Lt^2/m
concentration	C	various
critical gas saturation	S_{gc}	
critical pressure	p_c	m/Lt^2

critical temperature	T_c	T
critical water saturation	S_{wc}	
cubic expansion coefficient, thermal	β beta	$1/T$
cumulative gas influx (encroachment)	G_e	L^3
cumulative gas injected	G_i	L^3
cumulative gas produced	G_p	L^3
cumulative gas-oil ratio	R_p	
cumulative oil influx (encroachment)	N_e	L^3
cumulative oil produced	N_p	L^3
cumulative water influx (encroachment)	W_e	L^3
cumulative water injected	W_i	L^3
cumulative water produced	W_p	L^3
density	ρ rho	m/L^3
density, gas	ρ_g rho	m/L^3
density, oil	ρ_o rho	m/L^3
density, water	ρ_w rho	m/L^3
depth	D	L
deviation factor (compressibility factor) for gas ($z = pV/nRT$)	z	
dew-point pressure	p_d	m/Lt^2
difference ($x_2 - x_1$ or $x_1 - x_2$)	Δx	$[x]$
diffusion coefficient	D	L^2/t
diffusivity, hydraulic ($k/\varphi c\mu$ or $\lambda/\varphi c$)	η eta	L^2/t
dimensionless pressure	p_D	
dimensionless production rate	q_D	
dimensionless quantity proportional to x	x_D	
dimensionless radial distance	r_D	
dimensionless time	t_D	
distance, radial	r	L
distance, radial, dimensionless	r_D	
effective permeability to gas	k_g	L^2
effective permeability to oil	k_o	L^2
effective permeability to water	k_w	L^2
encroachment or influx, gas, cumulative	G_e	L^3
encroachment or influx, gas, during an interval	ΔG_e	L^3
encroachment or influx, oil, cumulative	N_e	L^3
encroachment or influx, oil, during an interval	ΔN_e	L^3
encroachment or influx rate	e	L^3/t
encroachment or influx rate, gas	e_g	L^3/t
encroachment or influx rate, oil	e_o	L^3/t
encroachment or influx rate, water	e_w	L^3/t

encroachment or influx, water, cumulative	W_e	L^3
encroachment or influx, water, during an interval	ΔW_e	L^3
equilibrium ratio (y/x)	K	
expansion coefficient, thermal cubic	β beta	$1/T$
external boundary pressure	p_e	m/Lt^2
external boundary radius	r_e	L
flow rate per unit area (volumetric velocity)	u	L/t
flowing pressure, bottom-hole	p_{wf}	m/Lt^2
flowing pressure, casing	p_{cf}	m/Lt^2
flowing pressure, tubing	p_{tf}	m/Lt^2
flux or flow rate, per unit area (volumetric velocity)	u	L/t
formation (rock) compressibility	c_f	Lt^2/m
formation volume factor	B	
formation volume factor, gas	B_g	
formation volume factor, oil	B_o	
formation volume factor, total (two-phase)	B_t	
formation volume factor, water	B_w	
fraction (such as the fraction of a flow stream consisting of a particular phase)	f	
front or interface pressure	p_f	m/Lt^2
gas compressibility	c_g	Lt^2/m
gas constant, universal (per mole)	R	mL^2/t^2T
gas density	ρ_g rho	m/L^3
gas deviation factor (compressibility factor, $z = pV/nRT$)	z	
gas, effective permeability to	k_g	L^2
gas formation volume factor	B_g	
gas in place in reservoir, total initial	G	L^3
gas influx (encroachment), cumulative	G_e	L^3
gas influx (encroachment) during an interval	ΔG_e	L^3
gas influx (encroachment) rate	e_g	L^3/t
gas injected, cumulative	G_i	L^3
gas injected during an interval	ΔG_i	L^3
gas injection rate	i_g	L^3/t
gas mobility	λ_g lambda	L^3t/m
gas produced, cumulative	G_p	L^3
gas produced during an interval	ΔG_p	L^3
gas production rate	q_g	L^3/t
gas, relative permeability to	k_{rg}	

gas saturation	S_g	
gas saturation, critical	S_{gc}	
gas saturation, residual	S_{gr}	
gas solubility in oil (solution gas-oil ratio)	R_s	
gas solubility in water	R_{sw}	
gas viscosity	μ mu	m/Lt
gas-oil ratio, cumulative	R_p	
gas-oil ratio, producing	R	
gas-oil ratio, solution (gas solubility in oil)	R_s	
gravity, acceleration of	g	L/t^2
gross pay thickness	H	L
hydraulic diffusivity ($k/\varphi c\mu$ or $\lambda/\varphi c$)	η eta	L^2/t
index, injectivity	I	L^4t/m
index, productivity	J	L^4t/m
index, specific injectivity	I_s	L^3t/m
index, specific productivity	J_s	L^3t/m
influx (encroachment), cumulative, gas	G_e	L^3
influx (encroachment), cumulative, oil	N_e	L^3
influx (encroachment), cumulative, water	W_e	L^3
influx (encroachment) during an interval, gas	ΔG_e	L^3
influx (encroachment) during an interval, oil	ΔN_e	L^3
influx (encroachment) during an interval, water	ΔW_e	L^3
influx (encroachment) rate	e	L^3/t
influx (encroachment) rate, gas	e_g	L^3/t
influx (encroachment) rate, oil	e_o	L^3/t
influx (encroachment) rate, water	e_w	L^3/t
initial pressure	p_i	m/Lt^2
injected gas, cumulative	G_i	L^3
injected gas during an interval	ΔG_i	L^3
injected water, cumulative	W_i	L^3
injected water during an interval	ΔW_i	L^3
injection rate	i	L^3/t
injection rate, gas	i_g	L^3/t
injection rate, water	i_w	L^3/t
injectivity index	I	L^4t/m
injectivity index, specific	I_s	L^3t/m
in-place gas in reservoir, total initial	G	L^3
in-place oil in reservoir, initial	N	L^3
in-place water in reservoir, initial	W	L^3
interfacial or surface tension	σ sigma	m/t^2

kinematic viscosity	v nu	L^2/t
length	L	L
liquid (oil) formation volume factor	B_o	
liquid phase, mole fraction of component in	x	
liquid phase, moles of	L	
logarithm, common, base 10	log	
logarithm, natural, base e	ln	
mass	m	m
mean or average pressure	$\bar{p}$	m/Lt^2
mean or average value of a quantity x	$\bar{x}$	$[x]$
mixture, mole fraction of component in	z	
mobility (k/μ)	λ lambda	L^3t/m
mobility, gas	λ_g lambda	L^3t/m
mobility, oil	λ_o lambda	L^3t/m
mobility, ratio (λ_1/λ_2)	M	
mobility, water	λ_w lambda	L^3t/m
molal volume (volume per mole)	V_M	L^3
mole fraction of a component in liquid phase	x	
mole fraction of a component in mixture	z	
mole fraction of a component in vapor phase	y	
molecular weight	M	m
moles of liquid phase	L	
moles of vapor phase	V	
moles, total	n	
natural, logarithm, base e	ln	
net pay thickness	h	L
oil compressibility	c_o	Lt^2/m
oil density	ρ_o rho	m/L^3
oil, effective permeability to	k_o	L^2
oil formation volume factor	B_o	
oil in place in reservoir, initial	N	L^3
oil influx (encroachment), cumulative	N_e	L^3
oil influx (encroachment) during an interval	ΔN_e	L^3
oil influx (encroachment) rate	e_o	L^3/t
oil mobility	λ_o lambda	L^3t/m
oil produced, cumulative	N_p	L^3
oil produced during an interval	ΔN_p	L^3
oil production rate	q_o	L^3/t
oil, relative permeability to	k_{ro}	
oil saturation	S_o	

oil saturation, residual	S_{or}	
oil viscosity	μ_o mu	m/Lt
pay thickness, gross	H	L
pay thickness, net	h	L
permeability, absolute	k	L^2
permeability, effective, to gas	k_g	L^2
permeability, effective, to oil	k_o	L^2
permeability, effective, to water	k_w	L^2
permeability, relative, to gas	k_{rg}	
permeability, relative, to oil	k_{ro}	
permeability, relative, to water	k_{rw}	
pore volume	V_p	L^3
porosity	φ phi	
potential	Φ phi$_{cap.}$	various
pressure	p	m/Lt^2
pressure, atmospheric	p_a	m/Lt^2
pressure, average or mean	$\bar{p}$	m/Lt^2
pressure, bottom-hole flowing	p_{wf}	m/Lt^2
pressure, bottom-hole, general	p_w	m/Lt^2
pressure, bottom-hole static	p_{ws}	m/Lt^2
pressure, bubble-point ((saturation)	p_b	m/Lt^2
pressure, capillary	P_c	m/Lt^2
pressure, casing flowing	p_{cf}	m/Lt^2
pressure, casing static	p_{cs}	m/Lt^2
pressure, critical	p_c	m/Lt^2
pressure, dew-point	p_d	m/Lt^2
pressure, dimensionless	p_D	
pressure, external boundary	p_e	m/Lt^2
pressure, flowing bottom-hole	p_{wf}	m/Lt^2
pressure, flowing casing	p_{cf}	m/Lt^2
pressure, flowing tubing	p_{tf}	m/Lt^2
pressure, front or interface	p_f	m/Lt^2
pressure, initial	p_i	m/Lt^2
pressure, reduced	p_r	
pressure, separator	p_{sp}	m/Lt^2
pressure, standard conditions	p_{sc}	m/Lt^2
pressure, static bottom-hole	p_{ws}	m/Lt^2
pressure, static casing	p_{cs}	m/Lt^2
pressure, static tubing	p_{ts}	m/Lt^2
pressure, tubing flowing	p_{tf}	m/Lt^2

pressure, tubing static	p_{ts}	m/Lt^2
produced gas, cumulative	G_p	L^3
produced gas during an interval	ΔG_p	L^3
produced oil, cumulative	N_p	L^3
produced oil during an interval	ΔN_p	L^3
produced water, cumulative	W_p	L^3
produced water during an interval	ΔW_p	L^3
producing gas-oil ratio	R	
production rate	q	L^3/t
production rate, dimensionless	q_D	
production rate, gas	q_g	L^3/t
production rate, oil	q_o	L^3/t
production rate, water	q_w	L^3/t
productivity index	J	L^4t/m
productivity index, specific	J_s	L^3t/m
radial distance	r	L
radial distance, dimensionless	r_D	
radius, external boundary	r_e	L
radius, well	r_w	L
rate, gas influx (encroachment)	e_g	L^3/t
rate, gas injection	i_g	L^3/t
rate, gas production	q_g	L^3/t
rate, influx (encroachment)	e	L^3/t
rate, injection	i	L^3/t
rate, oil influx (encroachment)	e_o	L^3/t
rate, oil production	q_o	L^3/t
rate per unit area, flow (volumetric velocity)	u	L/t
rate, production	q	L^3/t
rate, production, dimensionless	q_D	
rate, water influx (encroachment)	e_w	L^3/t
rate, water injection	i_w	L^3/t
rate, water production	q_w	L^3/t
ratio, equilibrium (y/x)	K	
ratio, gas-oil, cumulative	R_p	
ratio, gas-oil, producing	R	
ratio, gas-oil, solution (gas solubility in oil)	R_s	
ratio initial reservoir free gas volume to initial reservoir oil volume	m	
ratio, mobility (λ_1/λ_2)	M	
ratio, producing gas-oil	R	
ratio, solution gas-oil (gas solubility in oil)	R_s	

reduced pressure	p_r	
reduced temperature	T_r	
relative permeability to gas	k_{rg}	
relative permeability to oil	k_{ro}	
relative permeability to water	k_{rw}	
residual gas saturation	S_{gr}	
residual oil saturation	S_{or}	
residual water saturation	S_{wr}	
resistivity (electrical)	ρ rho	mL^3/tQ^2
rock or formation compressibility	c_f	Lt^2/m
saturation	S	
saturation, gas	S_g	
saturation, gas, critical	S_{gc}	
saturation, gas, residual	S_{gr}	
saturation, oil	S_o	
saturation, oil, residual	S_{or}	
saturation or bubble-point pressure	p_b	m/Lt^2
saturation, water	S_w	
saturation, water, critical	S_{wc}	
saturation, water, residual	S_{wr}	
separator pressure	p_{sp}	m/Lt^2
solid volume	V_s	L^3
solubility, gas in oil (solution gas-oil ratio)	R_s	
solubility, gas in water	R_{sw}	
solution gas-oil ratio (gas solubility in oil)	R_s	
specific injectivity index	I_s	L^3t/m
specific productivity index	J_s	L^3t/m
specific volume	v	L^3/m
static pressure, bottom-hole	p_{ws}	m/Lt^2
static pressure, casing	p_{cs}	m/Lt^2
static pressure, tubing	p_{ts}	m/Lt^2
stream function	Ψ psi$_{cap.}$	various
surface tension (interfacial tension)	σ sigma	m/t^2
temperature	T	T
temperature, critical	T_c	T
temperature, reduced	T_r	
temperature, standard conditions	T_{sc}	T
tension, surface (interfacial)	σ sigma	m/t^2
thermal cubic expansion coefficient	β beta	l/T
thickness, gross pay	H	L
thickness, net pay	h	L

time	t	t
time, dimensionless	t_D	
tortuosity	τ tau	
total initial gas in place in reservoir	G	L^3
total moles	n	
total (two-phase) formation volume factor	B_t	
tubing pressure, flowing	p_{tf}	m/Lt^2
tubing pressure, static	p_{ts}	m/Lt^2
two-phase or total formation volume factor	B_t	
universal gas constant (per mole)	R	mL^2/t^2T
vapor phase, mole fraction of component in	y	
vapor phase, moles of	V	
velocity	v	L/t
viscosity	μ mu	m/Lt
viscosity, gas	μ_g mu	m/Lt
viscosity, kinematic	ν nu	L^2/T
viscosity, oil	μ_o mu	m/Lt
viscosity, water	μ_w mu	m/Lt
volume	V	L^3
volume, bulk	V_b	L^3
volume per mole	V_M	L^3
volume, pore	V_p	L^3
volume, solid	V_s	L^3
volume, specific	v	L^3/m
volumetric velocity (flow rate per unit area)	u	L/t
water compressibility	c_w	Lt^2/m
water density	ρ_w rho	m/L^3
water, effective permeability to	k_w	L^2
water formation volume factor	B_w	
water in place in reservoir, initial	W	L^3
water influx (encroachment), cumulative	W_e	L^3
water influx (encroachment) during an interval	ΔW_e	L^3
water influx (encroachment) rate	e_w	L^3/t
water injected, cumulative	W_i	L^3
water injected during an interval	ΔW_i	L^3
water injection rate	i_w	$L^3/$
water mobility	λ_w lambda	L^3t/m
water produced, cumulative	W_p	L^3
water produced during an interval	ΔW_p	L^3
water production rate	q_w	L^3/t

water, relative permeability to	k_{rw}	
water saturation	S_w	
water saturation, critical	S_{wc}	
water saturation, residual	S_{wr}	
water viscosity	μ_w mu	m/Lt
well radius	r_w	L

Subscripts

atmospheric	a
bottom-hole flowing (used with pressure only)	wf
bottom-hole static (used with pressure only)	ws
bubble-point or saturation (except when used with volume)	b
bulk (used with volume only)	b
capillary (used in P_c only)	c
casing, flowing (used with pressure only)	cf
casing, static (used with pressure only)	cs
critical	c
cumulative influx (encroachment)	e
cumulative injected	i
cumulative produced	p
dew-point	d
differential separation	d
dimensionless quantity	D
encroachment or influx, cumulative	e
external boundary conditions	e
flash separation	f
flowing, bottom-hole (used with pressure only)	wf
flowing, casing (used with pressure only)	cf
flowing, tubing (used with pressure only)	tf
formation (rock)	f
front or interface	f
gas	g
gas-oil solution (used in R_s only)	s
gas-water solution (used in R_{sw} only)	sw
influx (encroachment), cumulative	e
initial value or conditions	i

injected, cumulative	i
interface or front	f
liquid	L
maximum	max
minimum	min
molal (used with volume only)	M
oil	o
pore (used with volume only)	p
produced, cumulative	p
reduced	r
relative	r
residual	r
rock or formation	f
saturation or bubble-point (except when used with volume)	b
separator conditions	sp
solid (used with volume only)	s
solution, gas-oil (used in R_s only)	s
solution, gas-water (used in R_{sw} only)	sw
specific (used with J and I)	s
standard conditions	sc
static, bottom-hole (used with pressure only)	ws
static, casing (used with pressure only)	cs
static, tubing (used with pressure only)	ts
total	t
tubing, flowing (used with pressure only)	tf
tubing, static (used with pressure only)	ts
water	w
well conditions	w

Symbols in Alphabetical Order

Dimensions

A	area	L^2
B	formation volume factor	
B_g	gas formation volume factor	
B_o	oil formation volume factor	
B_t	total (two-phase) formation volume factor	
B_w	water formation volume factor	
c	compressibility	Lt^2/m
c_f	formation (rock) compressibility	Lt^2/m
c_g	gas compressibility	Lt^2/m
c_o	oil compressibility	Lt^2/m
c_w	water compressibility	Lt^2/m
C	concentration	various
D	depth	L
D	diffusion coefficient	L^2/t
e	influx (encroachment) rate	L^3/t
e_g	gas influx (encroachment) rate	L^3/t
e_o	oil influx (encroachment) rate	L^3/t
e_w	water influx (encroachment) rate	L^3/t
f	fraction (such as the fraction of a flow stream consisting of a particular phase)	
g	acceleration of gravity	L/t^2
G	total initial gas in place in reservoir	L^3
G_e	cumulative gas influx (encroachment)	L^3
G_i	cumulative gas injected	L^3
G_p	cumulative gas produced	L^3
ΔG_e	gas influx (encroachment) during an interval	
ΔG_i	gas injected during an interval	L^3
ΔG_p	gas produced during an interval	L^3
h	net pay thickness	L
H	gross pay thickness	L
i	injection rate	L^3/t
i_g	gas injection rate	L^3/t
i_w	water injection rate	L^3/t
I	injectivity index	L^4t/m
I_s	specific injectivity index	L^3t/m
J	productivity index	L^4t/m
J_s	specific productivity index	L^3t/m
k	absolute permeability	L^2

k_g	effective permeability to gas	L^2
k_o	effective permeability to oil	L^2
k_{rg}	relative permeability to gas	
k_{ro}	relative permeability to oil	
k_{rw}	relative permeability to water	
k_w	effective permeability to water	L^2
K	equilibrium ratio (y/x)	
ln	natural logarithm base e	
log	common logarithm, base 10	
L	length	L
L	moles of liquid phase	
m	mass	m
m	ratio initial reservoir free gas volume to initial reservoir oil volume	
M	mobility ratio (λ_1/λ_2)	
M	molecular weight	m
n	total moles	
N	initial oil in place in reservoir	L^8
N_e	cumulative oil influx (encroachment)	L^8
N_p	cumulative oil produced	L^8
ΔN_e	oil influx (encroachment) during an interval	L^8
ΔN_p	oil produced during an interval	L^8
p	pressure	m/Lt^2
p_a	atmospheric pressure	m/Lt^2
p_b	bubble-point (saturation) pressure	m/Lt^2
p_c	critical pressure	m/Lt^2
p_{cf}	casing pressure, flowing	m/Lt^2
p_{cs}	casing pressure, static	m/Lt^2
p_d	dew-point pressure	m/Lt^2
p_D	dimensionless pressure	
p_e	external boundary pressure	m/Lt^2
p_f	front or interface pressure	m/Lt^2
p_i	initial pressure	m/Lt^2
p_r	reduced pressure	
p_{sc}	pressure, standard conditions	m/Lt^2
p_{sp}	separator pressure	m/Lt^2
p_{tf}	tubing pressure, flowing	m/Lt^2
p_{ts}	tubing pressure, static	m/Lt^2
p_w	bottom-hole pressure, general	m/Lt^2
p_{wf}	bottom-hole pressure, flowing	m/Lt^2

p_{ws}	bottom-hole pressure, static	m/Lt^2
$\bar{p}$	average pressure	m/Lt^2
P_c	capillary pressure	m/Lt^2
q	production rate	L^3/t
q_D	dimensionless production rate	
q_g	gas production rate	L^3/t
q_o	oil production rate	L^3/t
q_w	water production rate	L^3/t
r	radial distance	L
r_D	dimensionless radial distance	
r_e	external boundary radius	L
r_w	well radius	L
R	producing gas-oil ratio	
R	universal gas constant (per mole)	mL^2/t^2T
R_P	cumulative gas-oil ratio	
R_s	solution gas-oil ratio (gas solubility in oil)	
R_{sw}	gas solubility in water	
S	saturation	
S_g	gas saturation	
S_{gc}	critical gas saturation	
S_{gr}	residual gas saturation	
S_o	oil saturation	
S_{or}	residual oil saturation	
S_w	water saturation	
S_{wc}	critical water saturation	
S_{wr}	residual water saturation	
t	time	t
t_D	dimensionless time	
T	temperature	T
T_c	critical temperature	T
T_r	reduced temperature	
T_{sc}	temperature, standard conditions	T
u	volumetric velocity (flow rate per unit area)	L/t
v	specific volume	L^3/m
v	velocity	L/t
V	moles of vapor phase	
V	volume	L^3
V_b	bulk volume	L^3
V_M	volume per mole	L^3
V_p	pore volume	L^3
V_s	solid volume	L^3

W initial water in place in reservoir L^3

W_e cumulative water influx (encroachment) L^3

W_i cumulative water injected L^3

W_p cumulative water produced L^3

ΔW_e water influx (encroachment) during an interval L^3

ΔW_i water injected during an interval L^3

ΔW_p water produced during an interval L^3

x mole fraction of a component in liquid phase

y mole fraction of a component in vapor phase

z gas deviation factor (compressibility factor, $z = pV/nRT$)

z mole fraction of a component in mixture

Subscripts

a   atmospheric

b   bubble-point or saturation (except when used with volume)

b   bulk (used with volume only)

c   capillary (used in P_c only)

c   critical

cf   casing, flowing (used with pressure only)

cs   casing, static (used with pressure only)

d   dew-point

d   differential separation

D   dimensionless quantity

e   cumulative influx (encroachment)

e   external boundary conditions

f   flash separation

f   formation (rock)

f   front or interface

g   gas

i   cumulative injected

i   initial value or conditions

L   liquid

M   molal (used with volume only)

max   maximum

min   minimum

o   oil

p   cumulative produced

p   pore (used with volume only)

r	reduced
r	relative
r	residual
s	gas-oil solution (used in R_s only)
s	solid (used with volume only)
s	specific (used with J and I)
sc	standard conditions
sp	separator conditions
sw	gas-water solution (used in R_{sw} only)
t	total
tf	tubing, flowing (used with pressure only)
ts	tubing, static (used with pressure only)
w	water
w	well conditions
wf	bottom-hole, flowing (used with pressure only)
ws	bottom-hole, static (used with pressure only)

Greek

β	beta	thermal cubic expansion coefficient	l/T
Δ	delta$_{\text{cap.}}$	difference ($\Delta x = x_2 - x_1$ or $x_1 - x_2$)	$[x]$
η	eta	hydraulic diffusivity ($k/\varphi c\mu$ or $\lambda/\varphi c$)	L^2/t
λ	lambda	mobility (k/μ)	$L^3 t/m$
λ_g	lambda	gas mobility	$L^3 t/m$
λ_o	lambda	oil mobility	$L^3 t/m$
λ_w	lambda	water mobility	$L^3 t/m$
μ	mu	viscosity	m/Lt
μ_g	mu	gas viscosity	m/Lt
μ_o	mu	oil viscosity	m/Lt
μ_w	mu	water viscosity	m/Lt
ν	nu	kinematic viscosity	L^2/t
ρ	rho	density	m/L^3
ρ	rho	resistivity (electrical)	mL^3/tQ^2
ρ_g	rho	gas density	m/L^3
ρ_o	rho	oil density	m/L^3
ρ_w	rho	water density	m/L^3
σ	sigma	surface tension (interfacial tension)	m/t^2
τ	tau	tortuosity	
φ	phi	porosity	
Φ	phi$_{\text{cap.}}$	potential	various
Ψ	psi$_{\text{cap.}}$	stream function	various

CONVERSION FACTORS

Acre	43,560	square feet
Acre foot	7,758	barrels
Atmosphere	29.92	inches of mercury
Atmosphere	760.0	millimeters of mercury
Atmosphere	14.70	pounds per square inch
Barrel	5.6146	cubic feet
Barrel	42.0	gallons
Centimeter	0.3937	inch
Centimeter of mercury	0.1934	pound per square inch
Cubic centimeter	0.06102	cubic inch
Cubic foot	0.1781	barrel
Cubic foot	7.4805	gallons (U. S.)
Cubic inch	16.387	cubic centimeters
Foot	30.48	centimeters
Gallon (U. S.)	0.02381	barrel
Gallon (U. S.)	0.1337	cubic feet
Gallon (U. S.)	231.000	cubic inches
Inch	2.540	centimeters
Inch of Mercury	0.4912	pound per square inch
Kilogram	2.2046	pounds
Kilometer	3,281	feet
Meter	3.281	feet
Meter	39.37	inches
Mile	5,280	feet
Mile	1.609	kilometers
Square centimeter	0.1550	square inch
Square inch	6.452	square centimeters

Temperature centigrade = 5/9 (temp. Fahr. —32)
Temperature Fahrenheit = 9/5 Temp. Cent. + 32
Temperature Absolute C = Temperature °C + 273
Temperature Absolute F = Temperature °F + 460
Viscosity

    Gram weight second per square centimeter—980.665 poise
    Poise—1.00 gram per centimeter per second
    Pound weight second per square foot—478.8 poise
    Pound weight second per square inch—6.895 x 10^4 poise
    One centipoise—0.00672 lbs/ft/sec (approx)

Yard	0.9144	meter

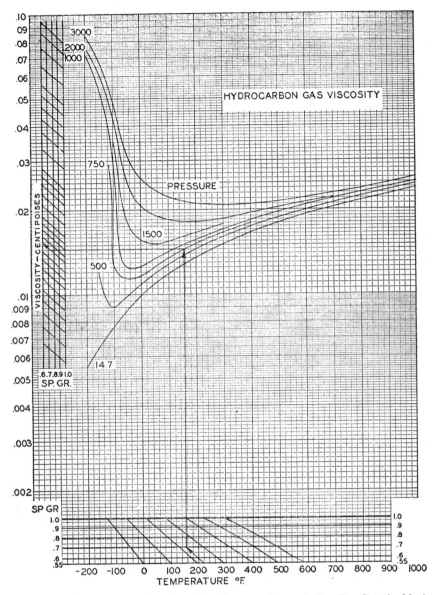

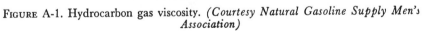

FIGURE A-1. Hydrocarbon gas viscosity. *(Courtesy Natural Gasoline Supply Men's Association)*

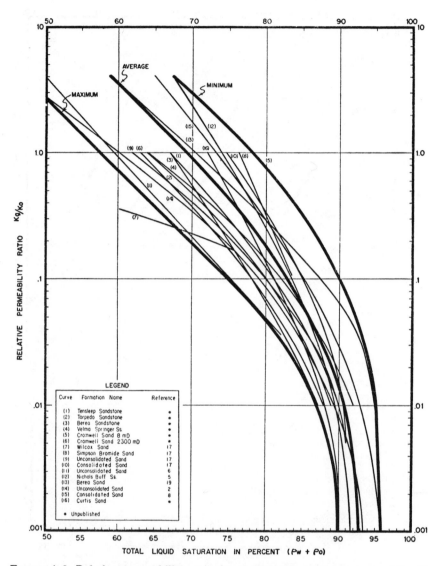

FIGURE A-2. Relative permeability ratio for sands and sandstones vs. total liquid saturation. *(After Trans., AIME, Vol. 204, p. 122)*

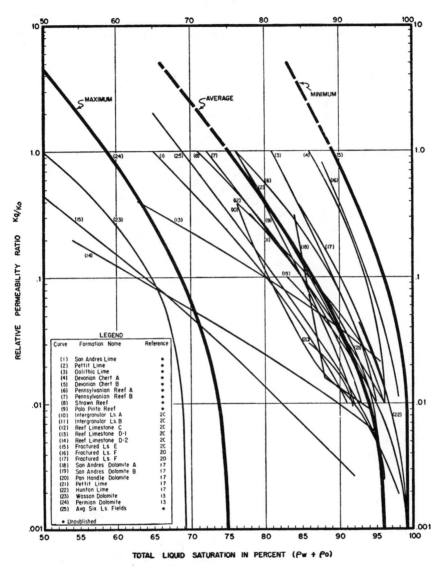

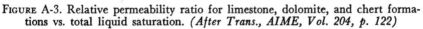

FIGURE A-3. Relative permeability ratio for limestone, dolomite, and chert formations vs. total liquid saturation. *(After Trans., AIME, Vol. 204, p. 122)*

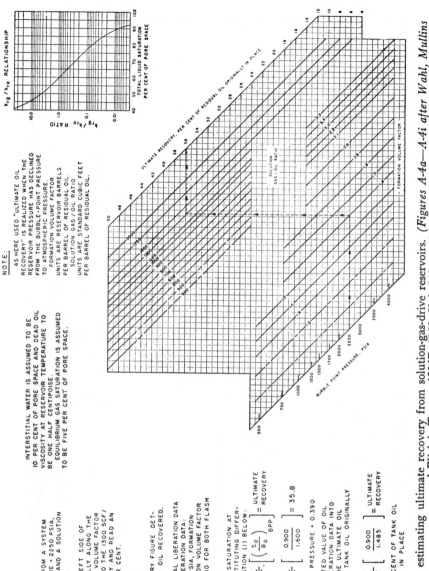

krg/kro RELATIONSHIP

ULTIMATE RECOVERY, PER CENT OF RESIDUAL OIL ORIGINALLY IN PLACE

SOLUTION GAS/OIL RATIO

FORMATION VOLUME FACTOR

BUBBLE POINT PRESSURE, PSIA

TOTAL LIQUID SATURATION
PER CENT OF PORE SPACE

NOTE:

AS HERE USED "ULTIMATE OIL RECOVERY" IS REALIZED WHEN THE RESERVOIR PRESSURE HAS DECLINED FROM THE BUBBLE-POINT PRESSURE TO ATMOSPHERIC PRESSURE.
FORMATION VOLUME FACTOR UNITS ARE RESERVOIR BARRELS PER BARREL OF RESIDUAL OIL.
SOLUTION GAS/OIL RATIO UNITS ARE STANDARD CUBIC FEET PER BARREL OF RESIDUAL OIL.

EXAMPLE I

REQUIRED: ULTIMATE RECOVERY FROM A SYSTEM HAVING A BUBBLE POINT PRESSURE = 2250 PSIA, FORMATION VOLUME FACTOR = 1.6, AND A SOLUTION GAS/OIL RATIO = 1300 SCF/BBL.

PROCEDURE: STARTING AT THE LEFT SIDE OF THE CHART, PROCEED HORIZONTALLY ALONG THE 2250 PSI LINE TO A FORMATION VOLUME FACTOR OF 1.6. NOW RISE VERTICALLY TO THE 1300 SCF/BBL LINE. THEN GO HORIZONTALLY AND READ AN ULTIMATE RECOVERY OF 35.8 PER CENT.

EXAMPLE II

REQUIRED: CONVERT THE RECOVERY FIGURE DETERMINED IN EXAMPLE I TO TANK OIL RECOVERED.

DATA REQUIREMENTS: DIFFERENTIAL LIBERATION DATA GIVEN IN EXAMPLE I. FLASH LIBERATION DATA: BUBBLE POINT PRESSURE = 2250 PSIA, FORMATION VOLUME FACTOR = 1.485, FORMATION VOLUME FACTOR AT ATMOSPHERIC PRESSURE = 1.080 FOR BOTH FLASH AND DIFFERENTIAL LIBERATION.

PROCEDURE: CALCULATE THE OIL SATURATION AT ATMOSPHERIC PRESSURE BY SUBSTITUTING DIFFERENTIAL LIBERATION DATA IN EQUATION (1) BELOW:

$$(1) \left[\left(\frac{S_o}{B_o} \right)_{BPP} - \left(\frac{S_o}{B_o} \right)_{ATMOS} \right] \left[100 \div \left[\frac{S_o}{B_o} \right]_{BPP} \right] = \text{ULTIMATE RECOVERY}$$

$$\left[\frac{0.900}{1.600} - \frac{S_o}{1.080} \right] \left[100 \div \left[\frac{0.900}{1.600} \right] \right] = 35.8$$

OIL SATURATION AT ATMOSPHERIC PRESSURE = 0.390

NEXT, SUBSTITUTE THE CALCULATED VALUE OF OIL SATURATION AND THE FLASH LIBERATION DATA INTO EQUATION (1) AND CALCULATE THE ULTIMATE OIL RECOVERY AS A PERCENTAGE OF TANK OIL ORIGINALLY IN PLACE.

$$\left[\frac{0.900}{1.485} - \frac{0.390}{1.080} \right] \left[100 \div \left[\frac{0.900}{1.485} \right] \right] = \text{ULTIMATE RECOVERY}$$

ULTIMATE RECOVERY = 40.4 PER CENT OF TANK OIL ORIGINALLY IN PLACE

INTERSTITIAL WATER IS ASSUMED TO BE 10 PER CENT OF PORE SPACE AND DEAD OIL VISCOSITY AT RESERVOIR TEMPERATURE TO BE ONE HALF CENTIPOISE. EQUILIBRIUM GAS SATURATION IS ASSUMED TO BE FIVE PER CENT OF PORE SPACE.

FIGURE A-4a. Chart for estimating ultimate recovery from solution-gas-drive reservoirs. *(Figures A-4a—A-4i after Wahl, Mullins and Elfrink, Trans., AIME, 1958, Vol. 213, p. 132)*

371

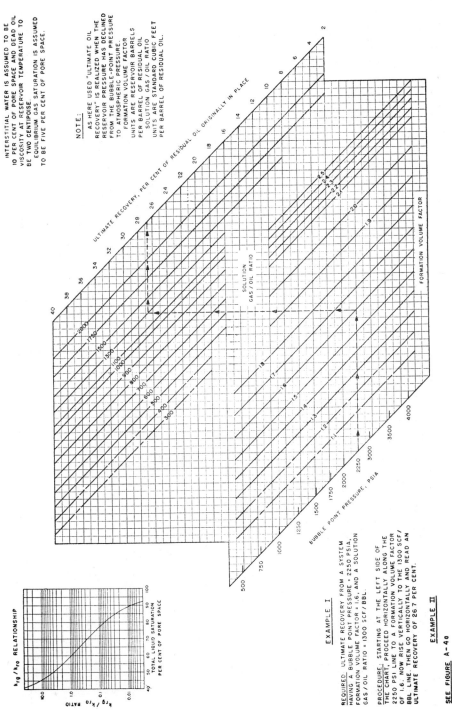

FIGURE A-4b. Chart for estimating ultimate recovery from solution-gas-drive reservoirs.

372

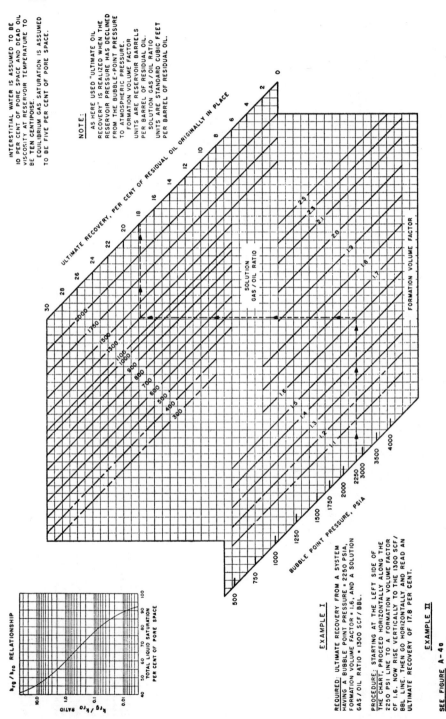

FIGURE A-4c. Chart for estimating ultimate recovery from solution-gas-drive reservoirs.

NOTE:

AS HERE USED "ULTIMATE OIL RECOVERY" IS REALIZED WHEN THE RESERVOIR PRESSURE HAS DECLINED FROM THE BUBBLE-POINT PRESSURE TO ATMOSPHERIC PRESSURE. FORMATION VOLUME FACTOR UNITS ARE RESERVOIR BARRELS PER BARREL OF RESIDUAL OIL. SOLUTION GAS/OIL RATIO UNITS ARE STANDARD CUBIC FEET PER BARREL OF RESIDUAL OIL.

INTERSTITIAL WATER IS ASSUMED TO BE 10 PER CENT OF PORE SPACE AND DEAD OIL VISCOSITY AT RESERVOIR TEMPERATURE TO BE TEN CENTIPOISE. EQUILIBRIUM GAS SATURATION IS ASSUMED TO BE FIVE PER CENT OF PORE SPACE.

EXAMPLE I

REQUIRED: ULTIMATE RECOVERY FROM A SYSTEM HAVING A BUBBLE POINT PRESSURE = 2250 PSIA, FORMATION VOLUME FACTOR = 1.6, AND A SOLUTION GAS/OIL RATIO = 1300 SCF/BBL.

PROCEDURE: STARTING AT THE LEFT SIDE OF THE CHART, PROCEED HORIZONTALLY ALONG THE 2250 PSI LINE TO A FORMATION VOLUME FACTOR OF 1.6. NOW RISE VERTICALLY TO THE 1300 SCF/BBL LINE. THEN GO HORIZONTALLY AND READ AN ULTIMATE RECOVERY OF 17.8 PER CENT.

EXAMPLE II

SEE FIGURE A-4d

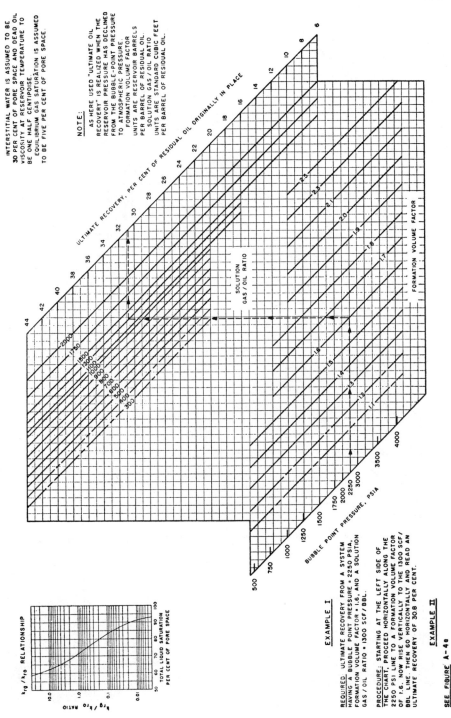

FIGURE A-4d. Chart for estimating ultimate recovery from solution-gas-drive reservoirs.

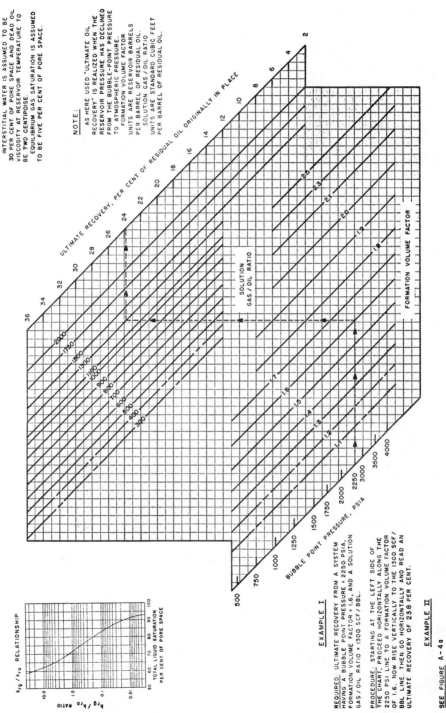

FIGURE A-4e. Chart for estimating ultimate recovery from solution-gas-drive reservoirs.

NOTE:

AS HERE USED "ULTIMATE OIL RECOVERY" IS REALIZED WHEN THE RESERVOIR PRESSURE HAS DECLINED FROM THE BUBBLE-POINT PRESSURE TO ATMOSPHERIC PRESSURE. FORMATION VOLUME FACTOR UNITS ARE RESERVOIR BARRELS PER BARREL OF RESIDUAL OIL. SOLUTION GAS/OIL RATIO UNITS ARE STANDARD CUBIC FEET PER BARREL OF RESIDUAL OIL.

INTERSTITIAL WATER IS ASSUMED TO BE 30 PER CENT OF PORE SPACE AND DEAD OIL VISCOSITY AT RESERVOIR TEMPERATURE TO BE TWO CENTIPOISE. EQUILIBRIUM GAS SATURATION IS ASSUMED TO BE FIVE PER CENT OF PORE SPACE.

ULTIMATE RECOVERY, PER CENT OF RESIDUAL OIL ORIGINALLY IN PLACE

SOLUTION GAS/OIL RATIO

FORMATION VOLUME FACTOR

BUBBLE POINT PRESSURE, PSIA

k_{rg}/k_{ro} RELATIONSHIP

k_{rg}/k_{ro} RATIO

TOTAL LIQUID SATURATION PER CENT OF PORE SPACE

EXAMPLE I

REQUIRED: ULTIMATE RECOVERY FROM A SYSTEM HAVING A BUBBLE POINT PRESSURE = 2250 PSIA, FORMATION VOLUME FACTOR = 1.6, AND A SOLUTION GAS/OIL RATIO = 1300 SCF/BBL.

PROCEDURE: STARTING AT THE LEFT SIDE OF THE CHART, PROCEED HORIZONTALLY ALONG THE 2250 PSI LINE TO A FORMATION VOLUME FACTOR OF 1.6. NOW RISE VERTICALLY TO THE 1300 SCF/ BBL LINE. THEN GO HORIZONTALLY AND READ AN ULTIMATE RECOVERY OF 23.8 PER CENT.

EXAMPLE II

SEE FIGURE A-4q

375

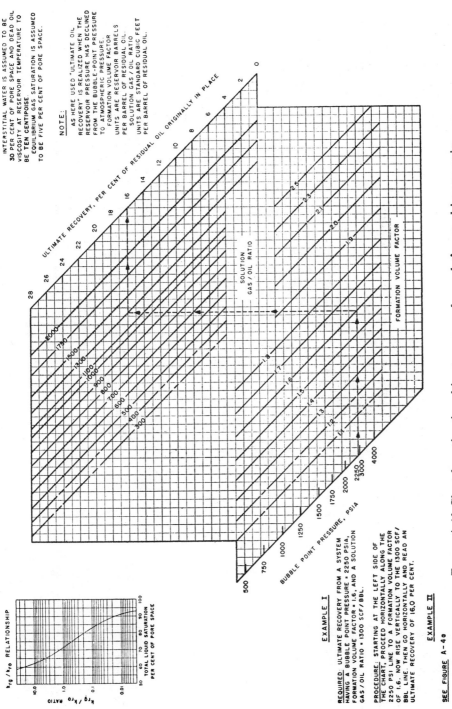

FIGURE A-4f. Chart for estimating ultimate recovery from solution-gas-drive reservoirs.

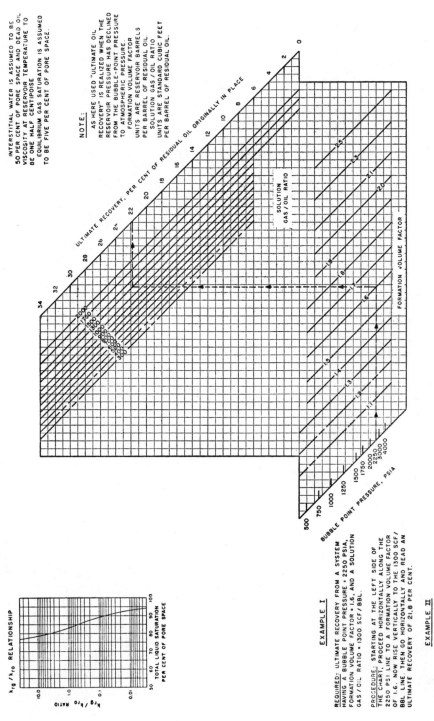

NOTE:

AS HERE USED "ULTIMATE OIL RECOVERY" IS REALIZED WHEN THE RESERVOIR PRESSURE HAS DECLINED FROM THE BUBBLE-POINT PRESSURE TO ATMOSPHERIC PRESSURE.
FORMATION VOLUME FACTOR UNITS ARE RESERVOIR BARRELS PER BARREL OF RESIDUAL OIL.
SOLUTION GAS/OIL RATIO UNITS ARE STANDARD CUBIC FEET PER BARREL OF RESIDUAL OIL.

INTERSTITIAL WATER IS ASSUMED TO BE 50 PER CENT OF PORE SPACE AND DEAD OIL VISCOSITY AT RESERVOIR TEMPERATURE TO BE ONE HALF CENTIPOISE
EQUILIBRIUM GAS SATURATION IS ASSUMED TO BE FIVE PER CENT OF PORE SPACE.

ULTIMATE RECOVERY, PER CENT OF RESIDUAL OIL ORIGINALLY IN PLACE

SOLUTION GAS/OIL RATIO

FORMATION VOLUME FACTOR

BUBBLE POINT PRESSURE, PSIA

k_{rg}/k_{ro} RELATIONSHIP

k_{rg}/k_{ro} RATIO

TOTAL LIQUID SATURATION PER CENT OF PORE SPACE

EXAMPLE I

REQUIRED: ULTIMATE RECOVERY FROM A SYSTEM HAVING A BUBBLE POINT PRESSURE = 2250 PSIA, FORMATION VOLUME FACTOR = 1.6, AND A SOLUTION GAS/OIL RATIO = 1300 SCF/BBL.

PROCEDURE: STARTING AT THE LEFT SIDE OF THE CHART, PROCEED HORIZONTALLY ALONG THE 2250 PSI LINE TO A FORMATION VOLUME FACTOR OF 1.6. NOW RISE VERTICALLY TO THE 1300 SCF/BBL LINE. THEN GO HORIZONTALLY AND READ AN ULTIMATE RECOVERY OF 21.8 PER CENT.

EXAMPLE II

SEE FIGURE A-4q

FIGURE A-4g. Chart for estimating ultimate recovery from solution-gas-drive reservoirs.

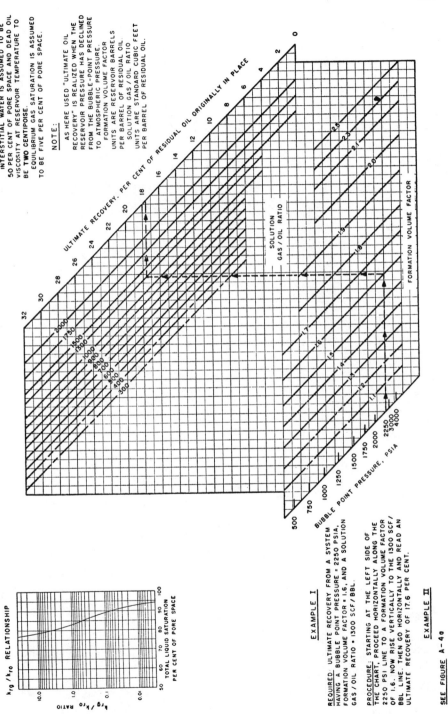

FIGURE A-4h. Chart for estimating ultimate recovery from solution-gas-drive reservoirs.

378

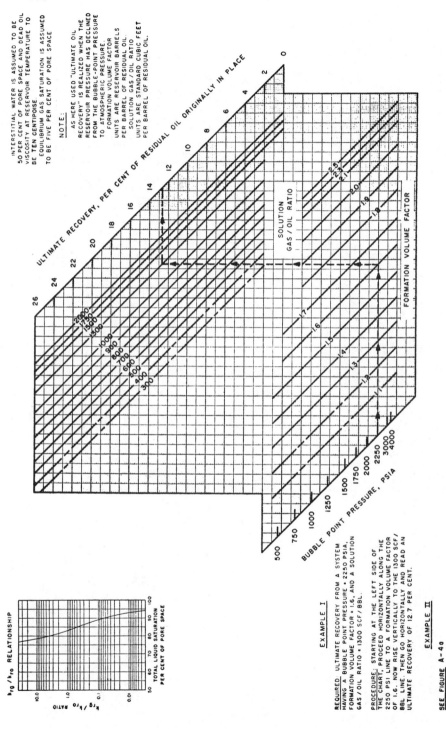

FIGURE A-4i. Chart for estimating ultimate recovery from solution-gas-drive reservoirs.

INDEX

Author

A

Allen, F. H., 314
Arps, J. J., 103
Ashby, W. H., 205
Anders, E. L., 166

B

Berry, V. J., Jr., 73
Berryman, J. E., 314
Blomberg, C. R., 205
Brinkley, T. W., 314
Buckley, S. E., 62, 104
Burchaell, E. P., 175

C

Calhoun, J. C., 263
Cassingham, R. W., 205
Caudle, B. H., 259
Cole, Frank W., 130, 227, 231,
  264, 265, 303
Cook, A. B., 73
Cooke, J. T., 203
Cowan, J. V., 128
Craze, R. C., 104
Crump, J. S., 207, 314
Curtis, R. C., 314

D-F

Dunlop, D. D., 228
Dyes, A. B., 259
Elfrink, E. B., 103
Elkins, L. F., 171, 203
Erickson, R. A., 259
French, R. W., 171

G-H

Gates, C. F., 230
Glenn, W. E., 171
Hall, H. N., 57
Hamner, E. J., 165
Havlena, D., 162
Hinds, R. F., 73
Hocott, C. R., 65, 247, 314
Holmgren, C. R., 127
Hoffman, A. E., 314
Hubbert, M. K., 164
Hurst, W., 68, 133

J-K

Jackson, M. L., 128
Jacoby, R. H., 73
Jones, M. A., 228